1979.

WILLIAM JESSOP, ENGINEER

WILLIAM JESSOP,
ENGINEER

CHARLES HADFIELD
and
A. W. SKEMPTON

with plates, maps and text illustrations

David & Charles
Newton Abbot London North Pomfret (Vt)

British Library Cataloguing in Publication Data

Hadfield, Charles
   William Jessop, engineer.
   1, Jessop, William 2. Civil engineers – England – Biography
   I. Title II. Skempton, A W
   624'.092'4   TA140.J/

ISBN 0-7153-7603-9

Set by Northern Phototypesetting Company, Bolton
and printed in Great Britain
by Redwood Burn Limited, Trowbridge and Esher
for David & Charles (Publishers) Limited
Brunel House, Newton Abbot, Devon

Published in the United States of America
by David & Charles Inc.
North Pomfret, Vermont 05053 USA

CONTENTS

LIST OF ILLUSTRATIONS

PLATES

FIGURES

PREFACE

When in 1793 the Grand Junction Canal Company engaged William Jessop as their principal engineer, they considered him as 'from his experience and abilities looked upon as the first engineer of the kingdom'. Nor did they exaggerate: from 1790 to 1806 he was indeed so. How comes it then that he is now so little known?

It is, we think, a useful rule that if a man desires his work to be well regarded after his death, he should take care to leave in reliable hands a large collection of personal papers, into which historians and seekers after doctorates can happily burrow. Jessop did not. Apart, therefore, from short essays in the *Edinburgh Encyclopaedia* and by Samuel Hughes near his own times, and by Jack Simmons and L T C Rolt in our own, no study of William Jessop's work has ever been made. In particular, he receives no more than a footnote in Smiles' otherwise comprehensive *Lives of the Engineers*.

We had to begin, therefore, by using notes taken while writing a series of books on waterway history, a yet unpublished study of London's docks, and information resulting from a circular letter to most of the country's record offices, public and university libraries. Thereafter each fact had to be separately found. We have often had in mind the tenor of Dr. Johnson's remark made in quite another context: 'It is not done well; but you are surprised to find it done at all'.

We offer *William Jessop, Engineer* as the fruit of many years of accumulative effort, and in the hope that it may prove a beginning for further Jessop studies. To that end we have deposited our copies of his letters and reports with the library of the Institution of Civil Engineers, to lie beside their Telford and Rennie collections.

Elsewhere we give thanks for the help we have been given by, literally, hundreds of kind people. Here we make only one acknowledgement, to William Jessop himself, in whose company we have lived happily for so long.

Charles Hadfield
Little Venice

Imperial College

1
FROM PLYMOUTH DOCK TO
SARAH SAWYER

William's parents were Josias Jessop and Elizabeth Foot. Though both lived in Stoke Damerel parish which included Devonport, they married just over the Devon border at Sheviock in Cornwall on 22 October 1744. The licence was issued to 'Joseph Jessop . . . Quarter Master of his Majesties Yard, and Elizabeth Foot . . . spinster'. Either 'Joseph' was a mistake for 'Josias', or he afterwards preferred the latter name. He was probably about 34 years old, she $18\frac{1}{2}$.

In 1715 Rudyerd's lighthouse on the Eddystone Rock off Plymouth had been bought by a three-man syndicate, who borrowed John Holland, a foreman-shipwright at Plymouth Dock (Devonport), from the Navy to overhaul and then maintain it. Later, Holland suggested that Josias Jessop, also a 'foreman shipwright, called a Quarter-man',[1] be put in charge of Eddystone maintenance under his supervision. Jessop took over about 1734; he kept the lighthouse operational until the great storm of December 1755, when Rudyerd's work caught fire and was destroyed.

William Jessop was born a Devon man, on 23 January 1745* at Plymouth Dock,[2] and baptised at Stoke Damerel on the 31st.[3] There were to be two younger brothers, Josias, baptised 1747, and Samuel, baptised 1749, and a sister, Mary. Thus he was rising eleven when John Smeaton, then 31, was asked early in 1756 by the Eddystone proprietors to build them a new lighthouse. He arrived in Plymouth at the end of March, met Josias, and found him 'an approved workman in his branch as a shipwright . . . a competent draughtsman and an excellent modeller'.

Later Smeaton was to say: 'Mr Jessop . . . was not a man of much invention. He had however a very clear and sound judgment in whatever his practice and experience had put him into the way of knowing.'[4] Soon they were working side by side on Smeaton's new lighthouse, Josias taking charge of the work-yard at Millbay employing twenty-six men. It was finished in October 1759.

* 12 January 1744/5 (OS).

11

William was educated at Devonport, where it was said of him:

> After making some progress in the classics, he acquired a perfect knowledge of the French language, and a considerable share of mathematical science. He early discovered a propensity to mechanical pursuits, and possessing a dexterity of working in wood and metals, he constructed with facility such articles as juvenile projects occasionally required; and his family are now in possession of a tolerably good violoncello of his workmanship when a boy.[5]

In 1759 Smeaton took William as an apprentice, to serve a 'clerkship', before becoming his draughtsman and assistant. Normally a pupil would have paid his master a premium for such an opportunity to learn, thereafter being given a small salary, but Smeaton seems to have allowed Jessop to pay the premium by deduction from his pay. Two years later Josias died, after which his widowed mother supported him. When in 1764 she could no longer do so, Robert Weston stepped in. Weston[6] had been principal shareholder in Rudyerd's lighthouse, and mover in engaging Smeaton, fixing him up with Josias, and getting the new one built. Smeaton had written to Weston in January 1764, saying: 'Billy Jessop has not had any money from me on credit, his mother has hitherto supply'd him with what he has wanted. So far he has been a very good lad and I hope will so continue; and turn out so as to do me credit, himself, and others service.'[7] Weston replied generously: 'I chuse to make myself the staff of his support',[8] and thereafter helped the boy through his clerkship.

So at 14 William had gone from his family, from Tamar's hills and the sight and sound of the sea to Austhorpe Lodge, near Leeds in Yorkshire, to begin a new life. One not, however, unfamiliar. His father's craftsmanship in things pertaining to the sea, to water, to boats, remained with William all his life, underlying the theoretical and practical engineering he learned from Smeaton. It distinguishes him from his contemporaries, for only William Chapman had a similar marine background.

John Smeaton was an unusual man. The only son of a successful lawyer, he had been born at Austhorpe Lodge in 1724. His father wanted him also to be a lawyer, but, seeing his mathematical brilliance and his passion for mechanical things, he agreed to Smeaton finding a job with an instrument-maker in London. At 26 he had his own business in marine and astronomical instruments, and before he was 29 had been elected a Fellow of the Royal Society. His interests were, however, much more in general engineering, though his capacity for instrument-making enabled him later to make the detailed models he liked to have before deciding on a new project. To widen his ideas, he visited the Low Countries in 1754, taking a special interest in harbour and dock installations, land reclamation and dyking, and in the canals he travelled over in *trekschuits*. On his return he closed his instrument business and turned to wider work, the first man to call himself a 'civil engineer' and to describe what he did as a 'profession'.

In Jessop's years as apprentice (until 1767) and assistant (until 1772), Smeaton was concerned with a great variety of work. When William came in 1759, he was just beginning the Upper Calder (later the Calder & Hebble) Navigation, upon which he was to learn some river engineering the hard way when he underestimated the fury of the Calder in flood in 1767 and 1768. From 1761 onwards he was to be surveying the Trent and canals proposed from it, and giving evidence on water supply for the Bridgewater Canal's Bill of 1762. He was also to be concerned with navigation on other rivers like the Wear, Witham, Lea and Yorkshire Ouse, canals like the Forth & Clyde, as well as harbour, drainage, bridge, and all manner of other projects.

This training taught Jessop to be a harbour, drainage and canal engineer; above all, perhaps, a river engineer. In this respect he, like Smeaton himself, followed the tradition of Thomas Steers and Thomas Yeoman, and differed from such men as John Gilbert, James Brindley, Robert Whitworth, Samuel Simcock and the Dadfords, none of whom had significant river experience.

Jessop's first known job was a plan and survey of Smeaton's own Walton estate that dates from 1766-7.[9] Later, in the spring and summer of 1770,[10] he was surveying and taking soundings for Smeaton's reports on the Ure Navigation and Ripon Canal from Swale Nab past Boroughbridge to that little city.

Also in 1770, Leeds was in turmoil as the backers of a scheme for a new canal from Leeds to Selby battled against the proprietors of the seventy-year old Aire & Calder river navigation and its lessee, Peter Birt. Accusations against the shallowness and other deficiencies of the river navigation were countered by others against the impracticability of a canal that included a ten-arched aqueduct and a quarter-mile tunnel. The situation was particularly dangerous for the river company because, across the Pennines, the equally unmodernised Mersey & Irwell Navigation had failed to defeat the Duke of Bridgewater's proposal for a bypass canal; that canal, the Bridgewater, was then being built.

Birt called in Smeaton, the local man, to advise. He was quickly followed by the Aire & Calder proprietors themselves, asking what they should do to better their waterway and so fight off the canal threat. The lower limit of their navigation was at Weeland, 12 miles from the Aire's junction with the Ouse. At Castleford it branched: one line continuing up the Aire to Leeds, where it would now join the Leeds & Liverpool Canal, authorised in 1770. The other followed the Calder to Wakefield, where it joined the Calder & Hebble, which Smeaton had rebuilt after the floods, and completed in 1770. Except for the longish Crier Cut on the Aire above Castleford, the navigation used the natural river and fifteen short lock cuts.

While Smeaton was preparing his report, the Leeds & Liverpool proprietors, in April 1771 thinking that their engineer John Longbothom had made a mistake in his surveying at the Liverpool end, asked him to resurvey this section. Too busy, he recommended Jessop, who found that Longbothom had not 'lost his level' after all.[11] It was his first known canal job.

John Smeaton's report of 28 December 1771[12] was radical. The trouble, he said, was lack of depth, the navigation not having been built for the traffic it was carrying.

Apart from considerable dredging to increase this, he proposed new cuts on the Aire at Leeds ($\frac{1}{4}$ mile, with a lock to replace the old one), Knostrop ($\frac{7}{8}$ mile with 2 locks to replace 3), Woodlesford (an extension of Crier Cut to make it $1\frac{1}{2}$ miles, with 2 new locks replacing 2 old), Methley ($\frac{3}{8}$ mile, with floodgates and a lock to replace the old one) and floodgates and a lock on the $\frac{1}{4}$ mile cut at Castleford. Below Castleford there was to be a bypass cut with floodgates from Brotherton on the north side of the river below Knottingley to join the river again above Beal and, biggest of all, either a cut from just above Haddlesey lock on the south side of the river to Gowdall above Snaith with 2 locks, or a similar one on the north side from Chapel Haddlesey to Newland above Rawcliffe. The Calder needed only minor improvements.

The proprietors accepted these proposals in principle, and sought leave to bring in a Bill, but opposition was such that they had to withdraw. Back they came to Smeaton for a survey and estimate of the north side cut he had proposed. He, being busy, asked Jessop to do it. Here, almost certainly, we have the moment when Jessop, encouraged by Smeaton, became his own man. The date was 7 July 1772,[13] his age $27\frac{1}{2}$.

So 'Mr Jessop, engineer', 'employed by the Proprietors of the Navigation', as he proudly wrote in his first printed report, did his plan,[14] survey and estimate, which reflected care to choose as far as possible poor agricultural land, do the least damage, and conform to property boundaries, all practical points in lessening opposition. He submitted it to Smeaton, who reported[15] that he agreed with his recommendations for this $7\frac{1}{2}$ mile cut. He ended with a charming piece of advice to his late assistant:

> Respecting Mr. Jessop's estimate, I beg leave to observe, that the longer I live, I every year see more into the reasons why estimates are generally exceeded in the execution, and how impossible it is, without repeated proofs from experience, to conceive how this can happen in so great a degree; I therefore do not wonder, that he has come considerably below the prices in the articles of construction, that I should esteem it necessary, he not having had an opportunity of having recourse to my estimate for the performing of the Gowdale canal, which is similar to this, but which now being put into his hands, he will be enabled to re-model his estimate according to the prices thereof.

This Haddlesey-Newland Canal was, however, early in January 1773 strongly opposed by landowners on the grounds that it would make flooding of their lands worse, not better, and during 1773 a new idea was put forward: to steal the canal promoters' best argument by building the lower bypass canal, not from Chapel Haddlesey to Newland on the Aire, but from just below West Haddlesey to Selby on the tidal Ouse itself. Jessop surveyed it, produced a plan,[16] and on 22 February 1774 for the first time 'Mr William Jessop, an Engineer' appeared before a Parliamentary Committee, with Smeaton and Gott on the river cuts (which he had helped to survey), by himself on the Selby Canal.[17] The Leeds & Selby Canal Bill failed, the Aire & Calder's succeeded, and in July Jessop was appointed engineer to execute the works. Before then, however, another opportunity had opened.

The Grand Canal of Ireland[18] to link Dublin to the Shannon had been begun in 1756 by the Commissioners of Inland Navigation, with Thomas Omer as engineer. Their ideas were large, for locks to take 175 ton barges were built: too large,* for though Dublin Corporation, interested in canal water to supply the city, had taken over

---

* If Omer was the same Thomas Omer who was appointed Master Carpenter of the Kennet Navigation in June 1740, it may explain the large locks, for the Kennet's were unusually big for the time, at first taking 80 ton, later 128 ton barges.

responsibility for construction in 1763 and Omer had been replaced by John Trail in 1768, by 1770 over £70,000 had been spent, less than 20 miles had been partly built, and none opened. Efforts were then made to get a company together to take over the work, and in 1772 one was incorporated, Trail being engaged to complete the canal from Dublin to the Liffey near Sallins. Then a difference of view arose upon where to cross the Liffey: Charles Vallancey on behalf of the Commissioners of Inland Navigation took one view, John Trail another.

Trail had suggested an outside expert should be called in, and on 6 June 1771 Redmond Morres, one of those behind the proposed company, wrote to Smeaton, at work on the Forth & Clyde Canal, to ask him to Ireland to advise. Smeaton replied that he could not spare the time. Morres then sent over Vallancey's and Trail's reports, and told Smeaton that he hoped he would be able to come in 1772.

The Grand Canal Company having been incorporated, Morres wrote again, and this time, on 19 September 1772, Smeaton agreed to go. He said, however, that because he himself could only make one visit, he would bring with him another engineer, 'a young Gentleman who has just begun Business for himself, who has served me 13 years, viz. 7 years as an Apprentice, and 6 years as an Assistant, and whom I have always found docile and intelligent.' His fee would be 'One guinea per day and 7s 6d for Maintenance besides allowance for Conveyance': the year before, to discourage his own invitation, Smeaton had asked 'Five Guineas per Day, and an allowance for chaise, coach, horse and boat hire.'[19]

The canal company were delighted, and Morres asked Smeaton to bring 'the young Gentleman' with him. Both went to Ireland in June 1773, where Smeaton was faced with twenty-seven questions relating not only to the whole line of the Grand Canal, but to connections also with the Barrow and the Boyne. On 6 October Smeaton gave some preliminary replies, saying that complete answers 'I could scarcely undertake to perform with accuracy, and upon my own knowledge, in twelve months of uninterrupted attention.'

On one point, however, the line for the central portion of the Grand Canal,

he recommended a survey to be taken of the ground ... from the Togher of Graig, in the bog of Allen, to Philipstown, as he expects that the new line will be executed with greater certainty, much sooner, and at less expense than that formerly proposed through the Bog of Allen ... it was resolved to be the opinion of the committee, that Mr Trail and Mr Jessop should be furnished with instructions to proceed immediately upon the said survey.[20]

Jessop was expected to move fast, for he was only to be employed until 1 November.[21] Smeaton did not put in final answers till 3 April 1775, when he said he had received Jessop's report upon the levels of the central section, and accepted them. Not until the 1780s did Jessop return to the Grand Canal.

While still in Ireland, Smeaton had been asked to go north and look at the Tyrone. This tub-boat coal-carrying canal had been finished, except for its three inclined planes, which would not work. Smeaton could spare no time, so Jessop went to report. Unfortunately we have no copy, only Smeaton's comments on it,[22] neither do we know just how Ducart* had built the planes in the first place.

No working canal inclined planes, ie means of moving boats from one level of canal to another other than by locks, had yet been built in the British Isles when Ducart constructed his three planes or 'hurries', with rises varying from 55ft to 70ft. The Netherlands had *ponts aux rouleaux* before 1700, and Ducart seems to have used the same idea on the Tyrone Canal, his 1 ton boats being meant to ride up and down the 1 in 5 slopes on rollers. However, trouble occurred through some rollers not turning, and others being of varying diameters, so tipping boats to one side. Smeaton suggested making a double track, and then substituting slides for rollers, at the same time doubling the length of the boats. He ended his letter to Jessop: 'I do not, however, hint these things by way of adopting the scheme, nor can I answer whether it will do or not; but ... by way of suggesting the likeliest means of getting an effectual trial of Mr. Dukart's scheme'. Otherwise, he suggested, build a horse waggonway instead of a canal.

Now comes an intriguing possibility. Chapman, writing in 1797,[23] tells us that when the planes were got to work (for their short life between 1777 and 1787) Ducart had 'a cradle or frame with four wheels, brought under his boats; upon which, over a double railway, they alternately ascended; ... he made use of a horse gin to draw his boats upon the ridge terminating the upper level'. Here we have a description in outline of almost any later canal inclined plane, except that many used caissons or tanks to float the boats, instead of cradles to carry them dry. Who thought of rails, cradles, and a horse-gin to work

---

* Usually called so: Daviso de Arcort, an architect and engineer of mixed Franco-Italian descent.

craft over the ridge from the upper pound? It is assumed to be Ducart, but it could have been Jessop.

The intriguing speculation is whether Jessop knew of the Fusina boat incline near Venice which dated from 1437, but which by the end of the sixteenth century was carrying boats on a cradle running on channelled rails and powered by a horse-gin.[24] It was illustrated by Vittorio Zonca in 1607,[25] though as double-track, as Zonca thought it ought to be, and not single-track, as it was. One could argue that Ducart, being partly Italian, was more likely to have known of Fusina. But if so, why did he use rollers on his inclines in the first place? And if not, then had Jessop seen Zonca's book, perhaps in Smeaton's library? For what Chapman describes is Fusina as Zonca had illustrated it, horse-gin and all, except that waggonway rather than channelled rails were presumably used. Did it happen, therefore, that when Jessop received Smeaton's letter, with its mention of double-tracks, waggonways, and power needed to get craft over the ridge, he suddenly remembered Zonca's picture, realised that rails, not slides, were the answer, and everything fell into place?[26] It is tantalising not to know.

In any case, it is highly probable that, as Dr Lewis has suggested,[27] Jessop told William Reynolds about the Tyrone's railed boat planes while he was surveying the Severn from 1784 onwards (see Chapter 2), and so gave him the idea behind the Ketley inclined plane,[28] first to be built in England, ancestor of many during the Canal Age that led on to Blackhill and Foxton, Ronquières and Arzviller.

In 1773, still under 30, far the youngest, and at the beginning of his professional career, William Jessop had been elected a member of the Smeatonian Society, founded in 1771 under Smeaton's leadership to bring together those from all sides of the civil engineering profession, and in 1774 became its secretary, a post he only gave up in 1792. In the Society Jessop found himself not only in the company of his old master, but of such distinguished men as Thomas Yeoman (then President), Robert Mylne, John Grundy, John Golborne, Robert Whitworth and Hugh Henshall.[29]

The Aire & Calder's Act had been passed on 14 June 1774. On 4 July the general assembly of shareholders accepted William Jessop's 'Proposal' to act as engineer to build the Selby Canal and carry out other authorised improvements. It was worded thus:

> I Understand it to be my Duty as an Engineer to make Designs for the Locks Bridges Tunnels and all other Erections necessary for compleating the Navigation, and after making the necessary

contracts with Masons Carpenters Smiths &c for their Execution I think myself bound to give due Attendance to see that the several Works are executed according to the Contracts.

I shall also think it my Duty to Mark out the Lines for the several Cuts, Banks and Back Drains and from Time to Time as I may be authorized by the Committee to make the necessary Contracts for those Works—and I do propose from Time to Time to give an Account to the Committee of the State that the Works may be in at those Times; and how the different Sets of Workmen are severally employed with such other Circumstance as may be necessary to come under their Consideration.

Without being more particular (as there may be many things necessary for me to attend to which I cannot at present Call to mind) I mean to make this Business the principal object of my attention and to give it every Degree of attendance that may be necessary to compleat it in the best manner I am able for the Advantage of the Proprietors and to my own Credit.

And I hold myself thus engaged for a Salary of £250 a year commencing this 4th Day of July 1774.

W: Jessop[30]

And so, in good clear English, William Jessop sets out the duties of an engineer engaged on waterway construction. He had done well, for he was not full-time, and £250pa was good money; John Gott, who had been 'surveyor', ie resident engineer for about thirteen years, and was now to help Jessop, was then getting £100pa.

Jessop's first task was to get the urgently wanted Selby cut started. It was to be $5\frac{1}{4}$ miles long, leaving the main channel of the Aire $\frac{3}{4}$ mile above Haddlesey lock, the lowest on the navigation, and running in gentle curves to pass Brayton to the south, and enter the Ouse just below Selby's southernmost riverside building. At the Aire end there was to be a flood-lock to prevent excess Aire water entering the canal, and a lock at Selby. Otherwise there were no major works.

He made his preparations quickly: on Tuesday 2 August the *York Courant* carried an invitation to tender for masonry, lock-gates and digging. Very soon he and Gott had chosen James Pinkerton as their contractor. And so the Pinkertons entered Jessop's life. They were to be closely linked with him for twenty years, and to become the biggest and best known firm of early canal contractors—indeed the only eighteenth-century firm to take countrywide contracts. The firm's leaders were the brothers James and John, but Robert, probably another brother, sometimes appears (a fourth, William, was later a nurseryman and seedsman at Wigan), and later Francis and George, James' sons. The Pinkertons first appear in 1768, when James Pinkerton of Cawthorne, yeoman[31] (Cawthorne is a village some 5 miles north-east of Barnsley) is appointed to build the Driffield Navigation near Hull, jointly with John Dyson. The two did the work satisfactorily, and the navigation opened in 1770. Drainage and embankment work in the East Riding followed, and in 1772 James is joined by John in an agreement for cutting the neighbouring Market Weighton Canal and making its entrance lock. They (after 1774 James alone) were still working on this when the Selby contract was taken. John was the Pinkerton whom Jessop best liked and trusted: he also became a Smeatonian, in 1777.

Jessop was in charge of building the Selby Canal, but laid out the river cuts and worked on them with Gott.[32] He was also given other jobs: to make land valuations, or, in August 1774, to measure the capacity of coal waggons on colliery railways as a basis for levying tolls—perhaps his introduction to this branch of engineering. In October 1777, too, with the Selby line nearly finished, we find Gott being given the job of keeping the construction accounts, 'except that Mr. Jessop Disburse the Money to Mr Pinkerton and settle his Accounts with him'.[33] It must have been a great day for Jessop, in his early thirties, when on 29 April 1778 the Selby Canal was opened, and 'several Vessels passed thro' to Selby, on which Occasion a large Concourse of People assembled, and the same was conducted in very great Order with firing of Cannon, Music, and ringing of bells'.[34]

In January 1779 the committee told Gott and Jessop to buy the land for Methley Cut, and in the same year Knostrop Cut was completed, and all the works authorised in 1774 accounted for, except for Woodlesford Cut, no longer needed since the Aire & Calder had bought Fleet Mills. By this time John Gott's ability had been recognised by his employers as well as by others—he became a Smeatonian in 1773. They now thought him capable of carrying on alone, and so, on 18 October 1779, the committee minuted that: 'Notice to be given to Mr. Jessop that the Undertakers will not have Occasion for his Assistance longer than the 4th Day of January next'.[35] He was to return briefly in 1792.

Even before Jessop had finished the Selby Canal, he was beginning to get other commissions, such as that of February 1776, which made him engineer to build the mile-long Mirfield Cut with two locks on the Calder & Hebble.[36] His pay was now to be $1\frac{1}{2}$ guineas a day and expenses, his contractor John Pinkerton.

In 1779, indeed, we find Jessop commenting on proposals by

MASONRY and DIGGING,

ON THE

Calder and Hebble Navigation.

MASONS

WHO would undertake the Building of a LOCK, and Two Pair of FLOOD-GATES on the RIVER CALDER, not far from *Brighouse*, may deliver in Proposals for the same on *Wednesday* the 26th of *April*, at the House of Mr. CLEGG, in *Brighouse*, to Mr. JESSOP, Engineer, who will be there on that and the two preceding Days, and will explain the Circumstances and Situation of the Work.

ALSO, about three Quarters of a Mile in length of Cutting, will, at the same Time, be contracted for, of which a proper Explanation will be given upon the Place.

APRIL 17th, 1780.

——————————————[Halifax: E. Jacob, Printer.]——————————————

Fig. 1   Jessop on the Calder & Hebble

Smeaton, a situation that must have amused the older man. Smeaton had that year surveyed the whole navigation and suggested further improvements. In December Jessop was asked to examine these.[37] As a result, he put up plans to make new cuts at Brighouse and Kirklees. These he executed in 1782 and early 1783, and went on with Samuel Hartley as resident engineer to carry out Smeaton's recommendation to replace the lock at Brooksmouth and the staircase pair at Salterhebble, planned during Brindley's short stay in 1765–6, with three new locks. Battye Cut was extended on his plan in 1785, and finally, new canals were made at Broad Cut and Cooper Bridge in 1791. Thus much work

21

on improving the Calder & Hebble, especially the upper part between Mirfield and Salterhebble, was done by Jessop: the results stood up well to the heavily increased traffic that followed the opening of the Rochdale Canal (also Jessop's) early in the new century.

The year 1777 marks the end of the first period of Jessop's life. It found him finishing the Selby Canal and the Mirfield Cut. It also saw him married, for on 3 February 1777, described in the licence as 'of Pontefract, Gentleman', he married Sarah Sawyer at Birkin Church, she being the daughter of John Sawyer[38] of Haddlesey House. She was 20 or 21, he 32. After a short time in Pontefract, they settled at Fairburn on the north side of the Aire between Ferrybridge and Castleford; their first child, John, was baptised there on 11 October 1779, their second, Josias, on 24 October 1781.[39]

In 1777 also, William received two commissions outside Yorkshire. He reported on Workington Harbour, and he was consulted on the canalisation of the Soar. With the latter invitation the second period of his life began, for it led him to the Midlands.

2
BY SOAR, TRENT AND THAMES

Loughborough Navigation

In 1776 John Smith 'the Engineer'[1] was given charge of making the Soar navigable from the Trent at Redhill to Leicester. He having begun work in rather a primitive way, and soon fallen behind schedule, in September 1777 the committee told their clerk 'to write to Mr Jessopp Engineer to desire his immediate Attendance here in order to inspect the Works already done by Mr. Smith as well as those that are intended to be done. . . .'[2] Perhaps someone on the committee had met him.

Jessop reported in December,[3] proposing a lock and weir at Redhill instead of a staunch, the deepening of cuts and making of passing places in the longer ones, and increasing the depth of the uppermost canal at Loughborough to provide a 1ft water reserve. He also gently observed: 'I believe there never was a work Executed which upon a review would not exhibit some Errors that might have been avoided. . . .'

Soon afterwards Smith was replaced by John May, and the navigation completed as Jessop had recommended.

Jessop in business

The late 1770s saw Jessop seemingly not sure whether he wanted to be solely an engineer, or also an entrepreneur in partnership with the Pinkertons. When making the Mirfield Cut with John in 1776, he must have thought the neighbourhood had possibilities, for within a few years the two had started three businesses there, lime-burning, a colliery and a dry-dock. Jessop's interest in the first two lasted till about 1791, in the last to 1800. With James and Robert Pinkerton, he also tried his hand at canal contracting, when they built a section of the broad Chester Canal between the head of Beeston Brook Lock and Nantwich, together with the basin there, early in 1779.[4]

Jessop had one more experience of partnership with a Pinkerton. In

1785 the Dudley Canal Company, intending to begin work on their Dudley Tunnel, accepted John Pinkerton's tender for making it,[5] but made him sign a bond for £4,000 that he would fulfil his engagements. This bond he and Jessop guaranteed. Pinkerton began work at the Parkhead end, then about April 1786 at the north end also. He was soon receiving progress payments of £150pw, though by August he was in trouble. Early in January 1787 payments were stopped. Agreement on abandonment of the contract was reached on 20 July: Jessop was to be released from his bond, and Pinkerton was to pay £2,000 in instalments, with Jessop as security for £500 of it. The company were to take possession at once.

The Dudley concern did not hold this failure against Jessop. In 1793, when they were fighting a tremendous battle with the Birmingham Canal for their Bill to build their No 2 line, they strengthened their team of expert witnesses with Whitworth and Jessop,[6] and were successful.

By 1783, when Jessop moved to Newark as a result of getting a job with the Trent Navigation, he must have decided that he enjoyed the world of business, even though engineering would take most of his time and energy, for he interested himself in a cotton mill there, working with men who sat on the Trent committee. By 1791 he was involved enough to attend a meeting of manufacturers in Manchester and by put on a committee, along with Arkwright and others, to press the government for protection against Indian imports.[7]

By about 1800 this sizeable business, known as Handley & Co,[8] seems to have been one of Newark's principal industries. It employed about 300 people, mainly women and children, making cotton thread for stockings. Jessop kept his interest all his life, and bequeathed it in his will to his son William. Its site can be found above the millstream at the end of Mill Lane.

Let us now return to the main stream of Jessop's life, by way of work he did on the Greasborough Canal, a tributary of the Don, from 1779 onwards, that yields us his 1783 reservoir plan.[9]

Leicester Navigation

Between 1777 and 1779, John and James Pinkerton as contractors working to John Varley as engineer had built the Erewash Canal to serve the valley collieries. Completed, coal from it crossed the Trent and passed upwards to Loughborough. A movement then arose in Leicester to extend the Soar navigation thence, and also make a branch to the collieries in Charnwood Forest.[10] Because Jessop knew the Soar, he was the obvious man to investigate it, and a meeting in June was told he would prepare a survey and estimate.[11] But though a committee was set up and a call made, impetus faded away.

We know of no other work that Jessop undertook in 1780 and 1781 outside his little Yorkshire businesses: they were years of depression as the American war dragged on. It must have been a worrying time for a young couple with an increasing family. And then, in 1782, he got his big chance: the chance that, accepted and fulfilled, made his reputation.

Trent Navigation

The River Trent was then a natural, and unsatisfactory, navigation except for two sections: a cut through Newark had been made and two locks built by local commissioners in 1772–3, and the stretch from Wilden Ferry near the Derwent confluence upwards to Burton-on-Trent had been improved on Lord Paget's initiative. The river was tidal to Gainsborough, and there seagoing ships, or those from Hull, transhipped their cargoes to river craft. These latter were small and shallow-drafted: they had to be, for the winding, shoaled river was appallingly shallow for much of the year, allowing a draft of some 18in and loads of 10–12 tons. Boats were sailed where possible; otherwise hauled by gangs of men, though some unauthorised horse-towing was tolerated.

The Trent & Mersey Canal, running from Wilden Ferry via the Potteries to join the Bridgewater Canal to the Mersey and Manchester, had been opened throughout in 1777, the Loughborough and Erewash by 1779. All three brought additional traffic to the Trent, and promised more. It was the Trent & Mersey Company that took the lead in improvement, by getting their engineer, Thomas Dadford senior, with his son Thomas, to survey the river and prepare estimates. It was finished by 22 November 1781 and published.[12] They recommended a horse towpath and some side-cuts, weirs and locks, to take craft of 40–50 tons at a cost of £20,000. A Bill was introduced early in 1782, then withdrawn, probably because supporters thought a cheaper scheme would suffice.

Jessop was now approached to do a new survey, which he carried out during August and September. In his report he refers to 'an Idea, that it was the predominant Wish of Gentlemen ... to avoid the making of Locks and Cuts, if it could be done: I adapted my Inquiries to this Idea ... ' One guesses that the Nottingham gentlemen, like those on other rivers, wanted to save expense and keep tolls down by avoiding expensive permanent works, as well as alterations of river levels that brought problems with riparian landowners.

We may imagine Jessop (and seemingly John Pinkerton) being rowed in a small boat, sounding, delimiting the shoals, studying the banks, going ashore to watch his towpath line, working his way down some 70 miles of river from Cavendish Bridge (Shardlow) to Gainsborough. He reported[13] 67 shoals (including 12 fords) that needed attention down to Torksey, 10 miles above Gainsborough. There were, he said, three ways of dealing with them: contracting the width of the river by weirs of piles and faggots bound and covered with willow; periodical dredging; and deepening a hard bottom. Given his employers' wish to avoid locks, he recommended major cuts past the worst shoals, at Holme, Nottingham Bridge and Wilford.* He also noted the dangerous passage of Trent Bridge itself, where a boat had to travel down a fast-running stream unable to use her rudder, and dependent 'for her safety upon the utmost Degree of Exertion and Dexterity'. His estimates for such modest improvements as a horse towpath, a 30ft channel, and 18in depth in the driest seasons, was £4,321 and £795pa; for a 2ft depth, £7,064 and £1,330pa.

His report accepted, an 18in navigation was chosen. However, a shower of petitions from navigation companies and such concerned cities as Hull, Lincoln, Leicester and Derby, all asking for a 24in navigation, decided the promoters to increase the depth to 27in in the main channel, and 21in over the fords at Sawley, Wilford, Gunthorpe and Holme Pierrepont. Jessop appeared before Lords and Commons committees, and on 24 June 1783 the Act was passed.

At the company's first meeting, William Jessop agreed 'to carry on and see the Business of the said Navigation completed' for £675 in instalments, he to pay normal expenses.[14] On the day following the Royal Assent, the impatient company ordered him to stake out the towpath working down from Wilden Ferry so that land valuers could begin work. He then had to build the path with its gates or drop stiles at land boundaries. He also had to 'improve the worst of the Shoals . . . as soon as possible'[15] to enable tolls to be charged. On 19 December 500 toll-tables calculated by Jessop from his measurements of river distances were ordered to be printed, and on 1 January 1784 the Wilden Ferry-Trent Bridge section was opened, just over six months after the Act's passing. It had been quick work.

Jessop drove on: tolls on the Nottingham-Newark stretch were taken

* Holme is $2\frac{1}{2}$ miles below Nottingham Trent Bridge, Wilford some 2 miles above.

from 12 May, on the Newark-Gainsborough section from 29 September. The job had taken fifteen months and cost £3,100 to date, as Jessop told shareholders on 6 September. What he said gave 'general Satisfaction to the Meeting'.[16]

Severn Navigation

Meanwhile, Jessop's work on the Trent had become known to the Staffordshire & Worcestershire Canal Company, whose line from the Trent & Mersey southwards past a junction with the Birmingham Canal to the Severn at Stourport had opened in 1772. But at Stourport traffic entered the busy but unimproved river. Much moved downstream to Worcester, Gloucester and the Bristol Channel, or upstream to Coalbrookdale, with some beyond to Shrewsbury and above. Yet the Severn, with plenty of winter water from rain on the Welsh hills, often had insufficient during the summer. Above Worcester, shallows of gravel and rock were only passable in low water by small boats, sometimes by none at all. Towing was done by gangs of men, there being no towing path.

In April 1784 the Staffs & Worcs company asked Jessop

... to examine and prove the Shallows in the River Severn and to make an Estimate of the Expence of Removing such Shallows and improving the Navigation of the said River Severn. And also for making a Towing path by the side of the said River for haling Vessels by Horses ...[17]

Jessop was off like a shot. He surveyed in May, and seems to have prepared a report by 17 June. This (it has not been found) probably covered the river from Coalbrookdale to Bewdley, for two others followed, on 10 August[18] dealing with the river below Stourport, and on 30 October[19] with that between Bewdley and Stourport. Taken together, Jessop then had it in mind to build thirteen or fourteen locks between Meadow Lane, Coalbrookdale and Diglis just below Worcester, and a horse towpath. He seems also to have proposed to collect floodwater from the upper river in reservoirs for use in the summer.[20]

A tremendous year-long controversy then broke out, with two main groups of opponents: many of the traders, who much preferred to take their chance of adequate water on a free river to a certain navigation that would charge tolls all the year round, and who thought that a horse towpath would be accompanied by compulsion to use it: and landowners, fearful that their lands would be flooded by the weirs' alteration of river levels.

A year later, Jessop, trying to clear away accumulated misapprehensions ahead of the Staffs & Worcs' proposed Bill, wrote an address 'to the Noblemen and Gentlemen Owners of Land on the Banks of the Severn'[21]

Characteristically, he begins with

> ... as I meet the anonymous Publications of those who may differ or affect to differ in Opinion with me, by giving my Name, and thereby pledging my Reputation to prove what I advance, I trust I shall have credit with candid Men for stating the Truth to the best of my Knowledge and Belief.

The proposed horse towpath has been dropped, he says. What remains is a scheme to improve the navigation from Meadow Wharf, Coalbrookdale, to deep water at Diglis by building locks and weirs to give 4ft of water in the driest seasons.

The final plan was now engraved by George Young of Worcester.[22] It provided for sixteen locks, but dropped the proposal for reservoirs. In this form it came to Parliament, where it met a new opponent in Lord Dudley and the backers of a proposed canal from Stourbridge to Worcester that would parallel part of the river. In spite of a last-minute concession on tolls, it failed in April without having reached the Lords.

And so, except for the later building of towpaths, the Severn remained unimproved until the Severn Commission constructed its first locks in the 1840s. By then industry, hampered by poor transport, had failed to develop along the Severn: Jessop's work had gone for nothing.

Shropshire Canal

Yet not quite. It may have been because he had got to know William and Richard Reynolds the ironmasters while doing his Severn survey that the latter asked Jessop in 1788 to appear as engineering witness before the Lords committee on the Shropshire Canal Bill.

This tub-boat canal, quite different from anything Jessop had so far been concerned with in Britain, must have reminded him of the Tyrone Canal. Intended to run from Snedshill works to Severnside at Coalport, with two inclined planes and a branch to Coalbrookdale, the line was extended in the Commons on the petition of John Wilkinson the ironmaster to Donnington Wood, and a third plane added. Jessop appeared both for the original proposal and the amendment.[23] He played no further part in the canal's building, but the contacts he then made with the Reynoldses probably had something to do with the later iron aqueduct story.

To Leicester and beyond

In May 1785 the proposal to extend the navigation of the Soar upwards to Leicester was revived, with the influential Lord Harborough as its patron. Jessop was in Ireland, but by the middle of August he had returned and done most of the survey. Twelve water-powered mills were one difficulty: the likely opposition of the Leicestershire coalowners in the Coleorton area to the easier carriage of Derbyshire coal from the Erewash Valley to Leicester was another. An editorial in the *Leicester Journal* for 24 September suggested a branch canal to serve them, or else a 'Newcastle Road'.[24] Maybe Jessop provided background for the editorial, and already had a railway in mind for the Forest Line.

On 28 September he attended a Leicester Navigation promoters' meeting, where his report was presented. Then he started to survey for what had now become two projected branches, one to the Coleorton collieries, the other up the Soar's tributary the Wreake to Melton Mowbray. The Melton proposal in turn caused Lord Harborough and others to commission Jessop to survey for an extension by river and canal from Melton to Oakham, Stamford and the Welland.[25] Seemingly, he got Robert Whitworth to do it for him, but the plan was dropped after the Melton Bill had failed.

However, a group headed by Lord Rawdon were also in the field, interested in supplying Leicester and much of the county from collieries round Ashby Woulds, by a canal that would also serve Coleorton, Swannington and Cloudhill. Whitworth and Jessop were commissioned: a fortnight later Lord Rawdon and his supporters declared their opposition to the Leicester Navigation and its Coleorton branch. Neither engineer seems to have been perturbed at employment by two rival groups.

The engineers' reports[26] galvanised the promoters of the Leicester Navigation into action. At a county meeting on 19 January 1786, their new plan was agreed, and Rawdon's alternative defeated. The plan,[27] one takes it Jessop's, shows a canal from Thringstone Bridge, near Coleorton, Swannington and Breedon, level for the first mile, then falling 185ft over $6\frac{5}{8}$ miles on a course north of that later built, to the Loughborough Navigation Cut below Loughborough. Thence it continued level for $3\frac{1}{2}$ miles to the Soar at Barrow, where a cut would bypass Quorndon. Except for that, the $11\frac{1}{8}$ miles from Barrow to Leicester would follow the river other than in short lock cuts.

However, opposition continued. The Bill reached the Commons in March, and Jessop, giving evidence with Whitworth, dealt painstakingly with the opposers' points. Nevertheless, the Bill was lost by 51 to 41 on a division, as was the Melton Navigation Bill also. Neither project was revived until early in 1789.

The year 1785 also saw Jessop proposing reservoirs on the Don to supply Sheffield (see Chapter 12), writing his first drainage report, on Knight's Gool in Norfolk (see Chapter 4), and doing further work on the Trent. As engineer of the Trent Navigation Company, he was asked to comment on a proposed bridge over the river at Gainsborough. A Bill reached Parliament in 1787,[28] upon which he appeared. This three-arched stone toll-bridge had William Weston as engineer-contractor. Weston, almost certainly son of the veteran engineer Samuel Weston, was a young man with Oxford Canal experience. Later, Jessop, having been asked to recommend 'a properly qualified person for investigating and arranging several proposed inland navigations'[29] in the United States, recommended Weston, who later became a well known American canal engineer.

Thames Navigation

With 1786 came other commissions: an appointment as engineer to Rye Harbour at Smeaton's suggestion (see Chapter 12), a major report on the Holderness drainage near Hull (see Chapter 4), and his first work on the Thames. It was also important for his personal life, for it marked the baptism of his fourth son and child, Charles, and in November his election as alderman of Newark Town Council. Aged 41, he was adding public service to his engineering and business activities.

On the Thames downwards from Oxford, there were in 1786 no pound-locks—only flash-locks—until Mapledurham, except for three dating from the seventeenth century at Swift Ditch (Abingdon), Sandford and Iffley. Above, there were no locks and four low and difficult bridges, Folly, Godstow, Radcot and St John's (Lechlade).

The Thames Commissioners, conscious that action was needed to improve the river above Mapledurham for prospective traffic from the

Oxford and Thames & Severn Canals, both nearing completion, called Jessop in to make proposals for a pound-lock at Whitchurch (Pangbourne).[30] In a report of May 1786 he recommended a lock in the central channel, with an approach cut across the curve of land above it just inside the capstan used to winch barges up through the flash-lock in the existing weir (see p 67). He assumes that a timber lock will be built as all but Hurley below, and recommends beech, elm or fir for under water work, and oak 'above water or between wind and water'. This he estimates at £1,054, but he also gives figures for a brick lock with stone quoins and coping (£1,150) and stone backed with brick (£1,700).

He himself recommended a brick lock, which he thinks 'properly constructed, to be in every respect as Good' as a stone one. However, the committee chose timber, and the lock opened in June 1787. Similar locks were built in the same year at Goring and Cleeve.

On 6 March Jessop put in a single-page report on the old flash-lock at Nuneham Courtenay,[31] recommending a pound-lock instead. Eventually, the Commissioners decided in 1793 that a pound-lock was not needed there: a flash-lock survived for some time. On the following day he did another single-page report, this time on Radcot Bridge above Oxford. He proposed to bypass it by straightening, deepening and widening about 220yd of the back cut on the north side of the river, and building a new bridge.[32] The cut and bridge were built the same year. This Radcot note was part of a short report he put in on 9 March 1787 which also included estimates for a lock at Osney.[33]

An Act to authorise improvements to the Thames was passed in 1788, whereupon the committee responsible for getting it recommended that the upper river from the Oxford Canal junction to Inglesham should be improved in consultation with the Thames & Severn Company, and on 24 July 1788 Jessop was again commissioned to make a 'Survey and Level of the River ... between Letchlade and Oxford'. Presumably he was then too busy, for, with a brief now extended downstream to Dorchester, he did the survey in July and early August 1789, dating the Lechlade-Oxford report from Oxford on 4 August, and that from Oxford to Dorchester from London on the 7th.[34]

His purpose being to provide 3ft 6in of water in dry seasons, he begins his first report observing that if there had existed 'An Accurate Plan of the River, describing its various Windings, and the Situation of its Shallows', he would have had an easier task, and suggests that one be made.

Having surveyed the Oxford-Inglesham stretch at a hundred points and listed shallows and obstructions, he doesn't think much of the river:

... in many Parts very crooked and very much obstructed with weeds: but those Circumstances ... I consider as necessary Evils, as by tending to Stagnate the water in Summer, they thereby increase its depth; and if they were to be removed, without substituting Weirs ... the River would be impassable for an empty Boat, in the upper Parts ...

The navigation evils complained of are a want of depth for fully-laden barges, time lost in waiting for flashes, and the lack of a horse towpath. He recommends removing shallows and continuing the flashes, but in aid of these to build six pound-locks whose 'Operation will be beneficial the whole length of the River'. Together with a properly built towpath, as far as possible on the same side of the river, 'a Barge will often make five Voyages, with a full lading, in the time that it now makes one, with half a Burthen'.

Osney Lock should be proceeded with, but 200yd further down than where work had already begun, because

... a tail cut from a Lock on River Navigations should be as short as possible, because after Floods the Eddy that is formed at the Entrance into the River, is generally the Cause of a Bar ... which is most easily to be removed by drawing the Sluices of the Lock ...

and because a long head cut is cheaper than a long and deeper tail cut. His other recommended locks were at Godstow, Pinkhill, Old Nan's Weir (a mile above Rushey), Buscot, and above St John's bridge, Lechlade.

Jessop continues to show his practical approach. He does not think cuts made merely to shorten a river navigation are worth while compared with improving the channel and eliminating waits for flashes: if a great increase in trade should come, cuts can be made then. He suggests ballast lighters should at once dredge a single-width barge channel through the shorter shallows, using some of the recovered gravel to build a 9ft wide towpath raised up to 18in. In this way 'a fifth part of the Expence will remove more than half the Causes of Complaint, and the remaining half may be done more at leisure'.

He now recommends stone locks, the stone to come by the Thames & Severn, as would Aberthaw lime, the best for

Water Works; the Weirs may be made of Oak Timber, and Elm for those Parts which are always under Water.—The Bridges for the

William Jessop: a portrait painted *c*1805 in the possession
of a member of the Jessop family

(*above*) Jessop's house at Newark

(*right*) A portrait by George Dance, 1796

Towing Path may also be made of Oak as they will be very cheap and of sufficient Duration.

His rough estimate is £9,020 for the locks and cuts, 8,300yd of dredging, the towpath (the land for which would be rented), and clearing some obstructions. It was very suited to an impecunious set of commissioners.

He added an interesting passage on building river locks:

The making of Walls at all in the Chamber of a Lock is not absolutely necessary: but without them the Earth would be liable to be washed away, or the Chamber by having too large a Capacity would in Canals waste much water, and where Water is plentiful, will at least waste time in filling and emptying: the only use then of those Walls is to preserve a proper Capacity in the Chamber, and to resist the lateral pressure of the Earth behind them: they are too generally made wide at the Base and narrow at the Top, being lessened by Offsets behind, by which Means, without Earth behind them, they have a tendency to lean forward, and the pressure of the earth increases that tendency; and I have rebuilt many, otherwise substantial Locks, merely because by the overhanging of the Walls Barges have been prevented from passing thro' them for want of the necessary Width.

I would therefore Recommend, that the Walls, should be of equal Thickness, from the Bottom to the Top, even if they should be made so by lessening the Thickness at Bottom: and the Counterforts, which merely are intended as Land-ties, should not be built from the Bottom, but be set on by Steps, on the Slope, of the Lock Pits, so as to lean against the Earth and counteract its lateral pressure; for the wall will never fall backwards: and this construction with much less Materials than are otherwise necessary, will ensure it from leaning forwards.

I have also to remark, that the Sluices for filling and emptying Locks are generally made too small: they should never be less than two feet square, so that a Boat may pass in 5 Minutes.

Jessop's view of the Oxford-Dorchester (Day's lock) section had to be a cursory one, but much needed doing, he thought, especially near Abingdon. His main points were that the weir and lock sill at Dorchester (Day's) should be raised as high as possible to increase the depth of the long reach above; and then that a new flash-weir might possibly be built in this reach as the easiest way to deal with four

35

extensive shallows, two of them hard rock; that Sutton Lock should be left as it was; that a new cut 800 or 900yd long should be made at Abingdon; and a pound-lock at Nuneham. Otherwise there were only shallows to dredge.

On 20 August 1789 the commissioners approved the first report, and referred that part of it which dealt with the Buscot Lock—Thames & Severn Canal junction to a local sub-committee to execute forthwith. On 12 August they agreed to expedite the building of Osney Lock and to remove the shallows between Oxford and Pinkhill Weir as Jessop had recommended, on 3 September to dredge at Lechlade and build pound locks at Lechlade and Buscot. On 29 October the Oxford-Dorchester report was approved, a sub-committee being told 'to carry the same into Execution upwards as far as Cullum Bridge and the remaining part is referred to the next General Meeting'. By the early winter of 1790 the new locks at Osney, Godstow, Rushey, Buscot and Lechlade were open, followed by Pinkhill in 1791. Of the six, only Rushey was differently placed from Jessop's recommendation—a mile from his site at Old Nan's Weir.

Some of Jessop's proposals below Oxford were also carried out. The sill and weir of Day's Lock were not raised, nor a new lock above it built for some years. The enormous private pound-lock, dating from 1638, under part of Sutton Courtenay Mill was left as he suggested, but instead of a new pound-lock at Nuneham and a cut past Abingdon, the Commissioners adopted their engineer, John Treacher's, suggestion of a pound-lock at Abingdon and the recutting of the old channel under Abingdon Bridge.

On 1 April 1791, the first stage of the improvements completed, the Commissioners, clearly pleased with Jessop's earlier work, wanted him to look over what had been done and suggest further improvements. But he was too busy, and Mylne did it instead.

Upper Ouse Navigation

Jessop worked on three other waterways of this earlier period: the Basingstoke Canal (see Chapter 12), the Ipswich & Stowmarket Navigation (see Chapter 12), and the upper Sussex Ouse. His experience with the last-named leads us directly into the canal mania.

Following upon his reports of 1787 upon the lower Ouse below Lewes and on Newhaven Harbour (see Chapter 12), Jessop was asked to survey the Ouse upwards from Lewes, a project in which Lord

Sheffield, the landowner principally concerned, took the lead. He reported[35] on 26 October 1788 from Lewes, with proposals to make the river (in its natural state seldom more than 14ft wide) navigable to Pilstye Bridge just above the Cuckfield-Balcombe (B2036) road, as economically as possible. Apart from locks and weirs, most of the work would be making short cuts to straighten the river, deepening, making a towpath, and altering bridges.

The Act of 28 April 1790 extended the navigation a little beyond Pilstye Bridge, to Hammer Bridge. Jessop did not personally take charge of the work, but was consulted from time to time by Lord Sheffield, and it seems to have been at his suggestion that the Pinkertons undertook the contract, not so much, one may think, because he wanted them to have it, as because he knew of no one else.

On 13 May Jessop sent Lord Sheffield eight drawings of locks and in September he promises sketches for bridges—and sees little point in them having a towpath and so costing more, to save three minutes at each. He encloses

a Sketch of the sort of Boats, that will best suit such a Navigation—they are clinker built of $1\frac{1}{4}$ or $1\frac{1}{2}$ Inch Plank—they are to be as long as the Locks will admit, allowing 4 feet for the Rudder; and 2 Inches less than the width of the Lock:—they are nearly flat bottomed and have not an Inch of Keel—they have generally a covered forecastle, and sometimes a whole Deck—and must have a Mast, that will strike to pass the Bridges—they are worked with a Square or Lug Sail.[36]

Later in the year Lord Sheffield wrote querying items of the Pinkerton estimate, which he now had. On 23 October Jessop patiently replies, then ends:

I should wish your Lordship not to let little matters prevent the progress of the work, for there are at present so many works of this kind in hand, and so many more likely to come forward next season, that workmen will be very scarce especially artificers.[37]

Lord Sheffield must have taken the hint that the canal mania was on its way, for on 17 November a contract was signed with Thomas, James and Francis Pinkerton. They were to build the navigation by 30 May 1792 for what seems to be a seriously under-estimated figure.

Right from the beginning the Pinkertons got behind with their dates, and at the end of 1791 Lord Sheffield complained to Jessop. He in return more than hinted that Lord Sheffield should take a firmer grip on the contractors:

> even under the best management I always find that in the progress of Execution, there are such a variety of unforeseen dissapointments, so many delays arising from the negligence of workmen of all descriptions . . . and so many Knaves among them . . . I can foresee that the impression will wear off when you have put them into a better train of proceeding.[38]

It is a time of boom, labour shortage, and rapidly rising wages and prices. Clearly the Pinkertons had not provided for increasing costs, nor realised the difficulty they would have in keeping their skilled men unless they paid more. The result was to be expected: they ran out of money with much begun, but little finished, and in August 1792 abandoned the contract. On the evidence we have, it seems that the Pinkertons had not done too badly. Much more the trouble was that the Ouse company could not raise the money.

Lord Sheffield then asked Jessop to nominate an agent to take charge of the remaining construction. The engineer replies that 'so numerous are the works now in hand that I know not of one disengaged, that I could by any means recommend . . . if you would give me the Navigation, I could not at present find a man that would suit you'.

Jessop ends with a note of what the canal mania meant to an engineer like himself:

> In two or three works in which I am concerned they are nearly at a stand for want of all descriptions of workmen—and I cannot conceive how the Numerous Schemes now in agitation can be executed in less than double the time that was formerly necessary. For my own part I am harrassed beyond endurance and hate the sight of the Post that brings me Letters.[39]

However, in February the navigation acquired a superintendent in Hodgkinson, and on 2 June Jessop sends in his bill, at well under his normal rates, for four days at Sheffield House viewing the Ouse from 8 to 11 August 1790, and three days from 19 to 21 May 1792, including expenses. He must have felt he had got himself into trouble through trying to help beyond his responsibilities; Lord Sheffield and his committee in turn must have thought they should have had more help, and the Pinkertons reflected, like some successors today, how unwise they had been to undertake fixed price contracts in a time of boom. As for the Ouse, the section to Sheffield Bridge with 9 locks was opened by April 1793, to Freshfield Bridge (11 locks) by 1805, to Lindfield (15 locks) by 1809, and to upper Ryelands Bridge (Balcombe wharf) with 18 locks, by 1812; it never reached Hammer Bridge.

3

THE CANAL MANIA AND THE TRENT

The great outburst of canal investment and speculation that we call the canal mania began in 1789 and ended in 1796. It was most intensely felt in the country in the second half of 1792, and in Parliament in the sessions of 1793 and 1794.

Because he was the premier engineer of the day, most promoting committees tried first to get Jessop to agree their plans and help their Bills through Parliament; only if they failed did they engage others. During those years he appeared before Lords committees on navigation Bills far more often than any other engineer (see p 262) and because he could pick and choose, most of the waterways with which he concerned himself were successful. It is difficult to guess what would have happened to many of the major promotions of the time, and so to the pace of industrial growth, if there had been no Jessop. Indeed, most of his remaining active life in waterway building was spent in finishing what he had begun during the mania. Only one great new work, the Caledonian Canal, postdated it.

We may now divide Jessop's work into three groups: the further improvement of the Trent and the creation of a network of communicating waterways in the East Midlands and East Anglia: the building of five great trunk canals, the Grand of Ireland, the Grand Junction, Rochdale and Ellesmere in England and Wales and the Caledonian in Scotland; and his other work, which took him from Newcastle to Exeter, Lancaster to Doncaster, and London to Gloucester and the Wye. In this chapter we give an account of his Trent area work; in the three that follow of his trunk canals, and finally we say something about the rest.

Cromford Canal

In 1787 a canal had been proposed from the Erewash Canal at Langley Mill to Pinxton, to enable 6 miles of coal-bearing land to be worked. Nothing happened for a year, and then a fresh series of meetings began, which first proposed to make the Derwent navigable upwards to

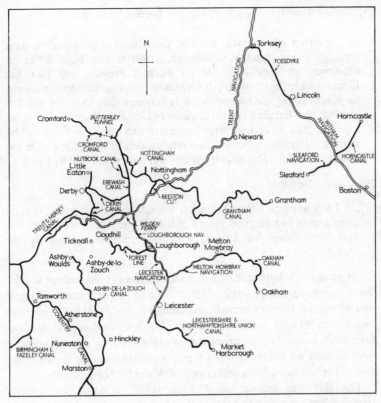

Fig 2 Waterways of the East Midlands and South Lincolnshire

Cromford. However, by 14 August 1788 someone (probably Benjamin Outram) had done a preliminary survey for a canal from Langley Mill to Cromford, with a branch to Pinxton. Arkwright of Cromford then took charge, and at the next meeting on the 30th it was resolved: 'That Messrs Jessop and Fletcher be appointed to make a Survey and Estimate'. The meeting's secretary was Outram.

Jessop did the engineering work, Fletcher the survey. By December Jessop's estimate and businesslike report,[1] free both from nervousness and exaggeration, were ready. They were accepted at a meeting on 18 December that decided to seek an Act. One signatory of the meeting's report was Francis Beresford, solicitor, soon to be a founder of the Butterley Company.

So began Jessop's first major canal, when he had to leave river valleys for hills, and master tunnels and aqueducts, and such problems as carrying a canal along a steep hillside. Indeed, he wrote:

> In a District of Country, such as this Canal is proposed to pass through, rugged and Mountainous, it will at first Sight strike an Observer, as very ineligible for such a Project, and that flat Countries are the most proper for Water Communications; in regard to practicability and Expence, it is obvious that they are so; but putting the Expence of Execution out of the Question, it is as obvious, that its comparative Superiority to Land Carriage will be much greater than in level Countries; especially when the Public are informed that the Distance by Water will not exceed that by Land.

Presciently, he adds:

> ... I know of no better Situation for establishing Iron Works; as there appears to be great plenty of Iron-Stone; which with the Coal and Lime-Stone for fluxing, may be brought together by the Canal ...

He proposes a hybrid: a broad canal of Erewash dimensions to take Trent barges on from Langley Mill to the east end of Butterley Tunnel and along the Pinxton branch, including all the locks, but a narrow-boat tunnel 9ft wide and 1¾ miles long at Butterley leading to Cromford. One other innovation he proposed, to make his long summit level 5ft deep against 4ft below, 'so that it might occasionally be drawn down twelve Inches, and leave a sufficiency of Water for Navigation'.

The Bill was passed on 31 July 1789. Among the original shareholders were Josias Jessop, William's brother, with seven £100 shares, and Francis Beresford with ten; soon afterwards William Handley, Jessop's cotton mill partner, took five.

The first meetings authorised payment of Jessop's preliminary bill for £514 8s 6d (which presumably included Fletcher's), and £257 19s 7d for Outram, and asked Jessop to do further surveying, order bricks and start writing specifications, helped by Outram. On 4 November Jessop was retrospectively appointed principal engineer from 24 August at £300pa plus £50pa expenses, sums calculated on the basis that he would give one-third of his time to the job. He in return stated that 'he considered himself as responsible in point of Honour and Character for the due Execution of the Canal ...'[2] Outram was made full-time superintendent under Jessop at £200pa, and the next day Thomas Sheasby and Thomas Dadford senior were appointed contractors; both were old hands. And so the transport basis was provided for the Butterley Company.

On the Cromford Canal between 1789 and its completion in 1794, Jessop gained more experience than he had bargained for. It must have taught him much.

In January 1791 he was caught out by his contractors leaving the job (they went to Wales to build the Glamorganshire Canal) at a moment when he had overpaid them by £1,332. The money seems not to have been recovered, and he and Outram decided to continue, using direct labour plus some small sub-contracts.

He had a worse failure in January 1792. He was building two major masonry aqueducts—his first of comparable size—one some 200yd long and 50ft high, with three arches over the Amber at Bullbridge near Crich and another over the Derwent near Cromford, also about 200yd long but 30ft high, with a river arch of 80ft span and two smaller ones. In that month part of the Amber aqueduct failed, whereupon Jessop offered to pay £650 from his own pocket to repair it, and to give up his salary retrospectively and until the canal was finished, an offer that was exceptional indeed in the world of canal engineers. The committee took his £650, but not his salary.

Then, after he had become confident enough to hold seven £100 shares, worse happened: in the autumn of 1793 his big Derwent aqueduct developed a crack. Jessop wrote to the committee:

I have been examining the disastrous state of the Derwent Aqueduct ... the failure has happened for want of a sufficient strength in the front walls and I blame no one but myself for the consequence having often seen much profusion of expence by an unnecessary consumption of materials, I have always endeavoured to arrive at the proper medium, in this and a few other instances I have mistaken it. I have reason to believe that the dimentions of the walls would have been sufficient if the materials had been good but from a misapplied oeconomy I suffered it to be built with Crich lime which has not set at all ...

He suggests closing the crack in an arch with tie-bars, then rebuilding the walls to include eight internal counterforts, meanwhile carrying traffic by a railway, and ends:

I think it common Justice that no one ought to suffer for the faults of another ... I shall use every means that I can suggest to have the work effectually reestablished; and no expence attending it shall be charged to the Company ... Painful as it is to me to lose the good

43

opinion of my Friends, I would rather receive their censure for the faults of my head than of my heart.[3]

The Committee agreed, the work was quickly done, and by August 1794 the aqueduct was reported in good condition.

Against his aqueduct troubles must be set his and Outram's success in building Butterley Tunnel with its deep approach cuttings in some four years with no especial difficulty. It was the longest tunnel he was ever to build (2,966yd, longer than Blisworth). When he began it, only two longer had been completed, Norwood by Brindley and Henshall, Sapperton by Whitworth and Clowes. The engineers sank thirty-three shafts to cut it, using a Woodhouse steam engine for pumping that was later sold to the Butterley Co. Most was brick-lined, but in part the rock was left unlined. The section was elliptical, 9ft wide at water surface and 8ft from surface to crown, with a flatter invert. A seam of coal and also iron ore found while building it were later used to supply Butterley Ironworks. Over the tunnel a 50 acre reservoir was made, with a 200yd embankment, 12ft wide at top and 33ft high in the centre of the valley. Two other reservoirs were also built, of 20 and 15 acres.

Again, the upper canal line along steep valley sides, using short tunnels or cuttings to avoid loops round projecting hill spurs, and with several sizeable embankments, was built with no recorded trouble.

Jessop had not done very well on the Cromford, yet his aqueduct failures did his reputation no harm, perhaps because his honesty and his willingness to admit mistakes and to learn from them was so obvious to contemporaries. Out of it all, too, came the Butterley Company and his partnership in it.

The Butterley Company[4]

Shortly after work began on the Cromford Canal, Butterley Hall Estate came on the market. About 200 acres in extent, on the line of the canal near Ripley, and known to possess mineral resources, the estate offered a wonderful opportunity which Outram seized. Francis Beresford of Ashbourne, a lawyer and landowner who had earlier been Outram's mentor in his career as a surveyor, purchased the freehold in June 1790 with Outram as partner; the latter leasing a moiety from Beresford until such time as he could buy his half share.

Small-scale mining began at once; in 1791 and 1792 Beresford purchased land at Crich for a limestone quarry and a wharf with kilns on the canal; a blast furnace was built at Butterley; the quarry opened in December 1792; by mid-1793 2,000 tons of ironstone and about double this amount of coal had been mined; and it was probably at the end of that year, after completion of the canal, that iron production began.

Meanwhile, the partnership had been strengthened by the addition of John Wright, the Nottingham banker, and Jessop. It appears they joined around June 1791, but the deed of partnership, which formally established the firm, is dated 10 December 1792. Until 1806 trading was carried out under the name of Benjamin Outram & Co, though the firm is usually referred to by the later and better known title of the Butterley Company. According to this deed the four men held equal shares. But in fact Outram and Jessop held theirs in the form of a mortgage from Wright, and were to become full partners when they had paid off a capital of £3,000 plus interest at 8 per cent.

From the start until his death in 1805, Outram worked as general manager, engineer and sole active partner. In 1796 his brother Joseph took over much of the paper work, and this no doubt helped Outram to continue his private practice as a canal engineer. By about 1801, however, the firm's activities had grown to such an extent that he devoted himself thenceforth entirely to Butterley affairs, still with Joseph's assistance and with George Goodwin as managing clerk.

Butterley, then, was very much Outram's creation and he saw it become one of the foremost ironworks in Britain; both as regards output and the quality of its products. Yet, despite his prodigious efforts, and partly arising from his personal extravagance (he spent some thousands of pounds improving Butterley Hall, where he lived) he died still owing the partnership a substantial sum.

For Jessop too, Butterley proved to be a heavy investment. More prudent than Outram, and enjoying an immensely successful private practice, he nevertheless did not pay off his partnership mortgage until 1805; and this accounts for the otherwise inexplicable fact that on several occasions, even at the height of his career, he found himself short of capital. It is not possible to say exactly what sums were involved, but in 1806 a quarter share in the company, equal to that owned by Jessop, was sold by Beresford's heir to Wright for £10,000; and a precise valuation in 1813 showed the company's assets to be worth £56,000, a quarter of which is £14,000. Thus, by the end of his life, Jessop possessed a small fortune in the Butterley holding that he bequeathed to his sons. But it was one he never realised, for no dividend had ever been paid to the partners, all profits being ploughed back into the company.

Jessop obviously played no part in day to day affairs at Butterley. But we cannot doubt that the presence among the partners of such an able and highly respected engineer proved of inestimable value. Nor can we doubt that Jessop's close association with the firm added to his knowledge of iron, and it is therefore no surprise to find in him a strong advocate for iron railways or a confident designer of the iron bridges at Bristol. And it was Jessop, in 1804, who produced the designs for the first of the Butterley dredgers, soon to become one of the firm's important engineering products.[5]

Moreover, his son William went as a boy from school into the Butterley works and at the age of 22, in 1805, succeeded Outram in the management of the firm.[6] Here again we sense the value, at this critical stage, of Jessop's experience and advice behind the scenes at Butterley. Indeed, with his family now installed (from the autumn of 1805) at Butterley Hall, for which incidentally the company charged a rent of £52 10s per annum, and with several of Jessop's major works nearing completion, it may well be that he took a more active part in the firm's affairs. Certainly after 1805 the engineering activities expanded considerably: Butterley established almost a monopoly for supplying high quality iron pipes to waterworks, especially in London; they produced the first known I-section iron rails in 1813; William Brunton, appointed as engineer in 1808, developed the Butterley steam engines to a level of excellence rivalled perhaps only by those of Boulton & Watt; dredgers have already been mentioned—they were supplied to the orders of Telford, Chapman and other leading engineers; and in 1814 the company won the biggest iron bridge contract yet awarded in this field, for Vauxhall Bridge over the Thames.

Trent Navigation

Because the Cromford Canal would be likely to bring more traffic from the Erewash junction on to the Trent, Jessop, as the navigation's engineer, was told in July 1789 to view the river near Sawley Ferry and estimate for making a side cut.[7] He proposed a lock at the lower end of the cut, to minimise excavation and allow scouring of the tail cut, with floodgates and banks at the cut's upper end.[8] Sawley Cut and Lock, the Company's first, were made by 1793. Jessop also became involved in the problem of what to do about the dangerous passage of Trent Bridge, and soon decided that a side cut was the answer.[9] In 1791 negotiations for it opened with Nottingham Corporation. But this matter of Trent Bridge led on to a general feeling among the shareholders that ' a further

Improvement to the Navigation ... would be usefull to the Public',[10] and Jessop was asked to survey and report. Proposing a thorough canalisation of the river, it was made in March[11] and considered in September 1791. But other plans were now in the air, and the company decided to take no action.

Other initiatives to avoid the bridge began. One was a large proposal, promoted by the Erewash and Trent & Mersey companies, for a bypass, the Trent Canal, big enough to take keels, from the Erewash in one direction to the Trent & Mersey, in the other to Beeston, Nottingham and the Trent below the bridge. With two other proposals Jessop was himself concerned. One was the promotion of the broad Derby Canal, which would leave the Trent & Mersey at Swarkestone above Derwent Mouth and pass through Derby and across the Derwent to meet the Erewash line at Sandiacre. It would therefore serve the purpose of the western part of the Trent Canal. The other was the Nottingham Canal scheme, for a line from the Erewash at Langley Mill to Nottingham and the Trent below the bridge. This, of which Jessop was also engineer, proposed also to build a cut from its line at Lenton outside Nottingham to the Trent at Beeston, so providing the needed bridge bypass.

Jessop was now engineer to two companies, both of which wanted to build the same cut. However, the Trent committee, having grasped that if they sat tight they would win, commissioned John Smith to survey the river to show the public that it was in good order even in a dry season, and that the Trent Canal was unnecessary. Not surprisingly, he found that Jessop's improvements had made it so.[12]

The Nottingham's Bill reached Parliament first, and only got through at the price of dropping the Beeston Cut at the combined insistence of the Erewash and Trent companies. The river shareholders then decided to oppose the Trent Canal, and 'to employ some able Engineer to survey the River along with Mr. Jessop and to report to them the most effectual means for making ... Improvements ...[13] On the understanding that such a survey should precede any legislation by the river company, the Trent Canal Bill was withdrawn.

Consequently, Jessop and Whitworth reported upon the river from Cavendish Bridge to Gainsborough.[14] They explained that out of 71 miles of navigation, 65 miles had a depth of 3ft or more. In the remaining 6 miles there were about 70 shallows, of which about 42 had 2ft 3in or more of water. Of the other 28, 15 had 2ft or more. The worst was opposite the mouth of the Soar, with 1ft 9in. These shallows, they considered, were caused by soil falling into the river from eroded

47

lengths on curves. The river's average fall was 1ft 3in a mile, but the upper 13 miles had a fall of 2ft 2in a mile, 3ft of which had been absorbed by the new lock at Sawley. They recommended another weir and 5ft lock should be built below Soar Mouth (the later Cranfleet).

They went on to say that 'the passage under Nottingham Bridge is the most troublesome and dangerous Obstacle in the Navigation', and that a cut was necessary. The authorisation of the Nottingham Canal the previous year gave an opportunity to make such a cut from the river at Beeston to this canal at Lenton, which would continue the cut to the Trent again below the bridge. With a weir at Beeston and an entrance lock to the cut (and also a side-cut back to the river below the weir), another 13ft would be taken off the river's fall. Finally, they recommended a cut and lock at Cow Ford (Holme Pierrepont) below Nottingham, more training walls to deepen the channel, and towpath improvements.

Trent boats currently carried 13–40 tons at a draft of 2ft 2in. They now proposed a river depth of 2ft 6in, except at fords. Three of the five would be avoided by their recommendatons, and the other two would now have enough depth.

In August[15] the report and estimate were approved, and a new Act followed in May 1794, both Jessop and Whitworth appearing for it. In June Jessop was told to begin the Beeston locks as soon as convenient. That cut was opened early in 1796, Cranfleet lock and cut in 1797, with its associated river weir that enabled boats to cross on the level between the Loughborough (Soar) Navigation and the Erewash Canal. Holme flood-lock followed in 1800, and on 1 September 1801 Jessop reported to a shareholders' meeting that the works to be done under the 1794 Act were complete.

Fortunately, a note of the days Jessop spent 'In Surveying and directing the Execution of the Works' between 1794 and 1802 exists:[16]

		days
1793–4	Sept–Feb	—
1794	June–Sept	7
1794–5	Sept–Sept	26
1795–6	do	20
1796–7	do	23
1797–8	do	19
1798–9	do	35
1799–1800	do	24
1800–1	do	14
1801–2	do	8
		176

At his new standard fee of 5 guineas a day (expenses were extra, though his were only £34 5s for the whole period) he earned £1,008 5s plus £50 salary for the period September 1793 to February 1794.

An interesting development had meanwhile taken place. At the end of 1796 the Trent Company decided to write to eleven others (colliery proprietors were later brought in) saying that frauds on the tolls were taking place because no proper gauging was being done, and calling a meeting at Nottingham on 28 February 1797. Over the next year the majority decided to set up a common gauging system using standard records of boats, the whole being run by the Trent Company as agent.

The Leicester Navigation

The Leicester Navigation promoters had by now gained the support of Lord Rawdon, their former opponent, and it transformed their prospects. After a meeting on 12 July 1790 that supported a navigation from Loughborough to Leicester, with 'a Cut or Railway' to Coleorton or Swannington,[17] Jessop was sent for by special messenger. He was in Ireland, but by 4 August he had handed in a preliminary report which Rawdon approved. Thereupon Christopher Staveley did the detailed surveys under Jessop's supervision, and a Bill was prepared. Jessop having been examined in both Houses, it passed without opposition in May 1791, and on 5 July Jessop was appointed principal engineer at £350pa including expenses, with Staveley as resident, the same meeting having authorised Jessop's preliminary account for £248 18s.

The Leicester Navigation was in fact two waterways, the River and Forest lines. The first was the Soar made navigable though with extensive cuts, beginning with one $2\frac{1}{2}$ miles long from below the Loughborough Company's basin to the river at Barrow, and soon afterwards another to cut off a loop through Quorndon and be nearer the limeworks. Then, with small straightenings, the line followed the river to Cossington. Between here and Syston the Soar ran near Wanlip and the difficult Sir Charles Hudson, so Jessop took the navigation nearly a mile up the Wreake, straightening as he went, before making the $1\frac{1}{2}$ mile Sutton's Cut back to the Soar at Thurmaston. He again left the river at Belgrave and improved a backwater to Belgrave Gate Basin in Leicester, then went on past North Lock to the river again and a termination at West Bridge. At Barrow he provided a flood-lock (Pilling's) to protect the entrance to the Loughborough Cut, and nine locks elsewhere, nearly all to bypass mills.

The Forest Line, its route changed from 1785, began with a section

49

of horse railway $2\frac{1}{2}$ miles long and rising some 185ft from the Loughborough Navigation's basin at the town to Nanpantan. Thence a $7\frac{3}{4}$ mile canal ran level, though in parts winding, to Thringstone Bridge by the Loughborough-Ashby turnpike road, whence $2\frac{1}{2}$ miles more of railways ran to Thringstone, Swannington and Coleorton Common. A mile-long canal branch from near Thringstone Bridge to Osgathrope was to have had short connecting railways to the Barrow Hill and Cloudhill limestone quarries, but these were not built. A reservoir on the Blackbrook would supply the canal level. The railways were single-track, with passing places every 400yd.

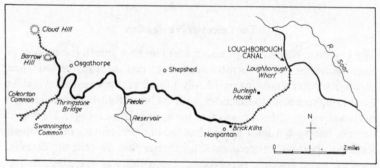

Fig 3   The Forest Line of the Leicester Navigation

We have seen that in 1785 the Forest Line had been thought of as all-canal, and that in July 1790 'a Cut or Railway' had been an open question. Though the plan showing the mixed canal-railway route, surveyed by Staveley and signed by Jessop, had been made and dated in 1790,[18] it was not until after the Act's passing, on 1 July 1791, that the company finally decided that because water supplies were insufficient for lockage, the canal section should be built level, and railways do the rest.

Jessop seems to have envisaged barges carrying rail waggons;[19] rather over a year later, he was to propose a similar plan for the Derby Canal's Little Eaton branch (see p 54). Some waggon-carrying boats seem indeed to have been used.

In September 1791 the Leicester Company signed up with James, George and Francis Pinkerton to build the River Line, and in February 1792 the Forest Line also. However, the Pinkertons seem not to have had the working capital or the skilled manpower to stand the pace and quality of work the company—and Jessop—required, for on 29 August he reported that the 'Contractors do not execute the works on the Navigation to his satisfaction'.[20] They were taken off, and direct labour substituted, with Staveley in charge. Both lines were formally opened on 24 October 1794, though the Forest Line was far from finished. A discussion of the type of rail used will be found in Chapter 8.

By early 1795 work on the Forest Line was nearly done, though some leakage was showing, for which Jessop recommended puddling. It was time to build the Blackbrook reservoir: Jessop recommended this on 4 June, and with this minute book entry his work for the navigation ended, Staveley being in charge thereafter. It was the latter who built the ill-fated Blackbrook reservoir by direct labour. Not completed till mid-1797,[21] it burst after a rapid thaw in February 1799, doing much damage to houses, property and the canal. Jessop, called back to report, said the disaster had been due to insufficient capacity in the discharging head, and recommended enlarging it. This was agreed, and rebuilding began. But the canal never reopened: within a few years the reservoir had been drained, while the unrepaired canal and railways sank into disuetude.

The River Line had been a success from the beginning, the Forest Line not. Its canal-rail admixture was probably not the main reason for its lack of use—that lay elsewhere in colliery politics—for some canal-rail lines elsewhere worked reasonably well: for a time on the Grand Junction, for longer on the Derby and the Lancaster Canals.

The Melton Mowbray Navigation and Oakham Canal

We saw in Chapter 2 that Jessop had surveyed the Wreake to Melton Mowbray in 1785. His bill unpaid in May 1788, he took proceedings, whereupon a special meeting of subscribers was held which probably raised the money. Revived early in 1789, it was authorised in 1791 soon after the Leicester Navigation, Jessop appearing for it in Parliament along with Christopher Staveley junior, who then built it to Jessop's plan,[22] with twelve broad locks. The line began in the Wreake where the Leicester Navigation swung away into Sutton's Cut, and followed the river all the way.

The idea of a canal from Melton to Oakham was revived in 1792. Jessop did a report. A newspaper account of a meeting on 5 September 1792 says that after it had been received, Christopher Staveley junior was told to prepare a plan and estimate, and 'that Mr. Jessop examine and verify the same'.[23] Both Jessop and Staveley appeared before the Lords committee on 29 April 1793; the Act was passed soon afterwards, following which Jessop drafted a sheet of useful hints for Staveley.[24] William Dunn replaced Staveley in 1798, and the canal opened in 1802.

Nottingham Canal

The Cromford Canal Act of 1789 meant that coal from its line would supplement that mined along the Erewash, to reach Nottingham by way of Trent. Thus, collieries nearer Nottingham, dependent on road transport, would decline. Why not therefore build a canal from the bottom end of the Cromford directly past the city to the Trent below Nottingham Bridge? It would serve the intervening collieries, and profit also from Cromford traffic. So, at a meeting on 26 October 1790, the Nottingham Canal was launched. A few days later Jessop was invited to become engineer: he accepted, and on 19 November was asked to survey the proposed line, and also 'a collateral Cut from the Trent through Beeston Meadows to unite with the proposed Canal at or near Lenton'.[25] Jessop, busy and also for a time ill with an abcess in his cheek, could not do the survey, and recommended James Green of Wollaton, who worked for Lord Middleton, a land and coal owner prominent among the promoters (and also Jessop's landlord at Newark). He made his recommendations in September 1791, and the Act was passed in May 1792, Jessop supporting it in the Lords. Then appointed engineer, he had Green as resident.

The canal's line left the Trent by a lock just below Trent Bridge and passed through Nottingham, rising by three locks to Lenton, junction for the Beeston Cut. Thence it swung to the north and climbed by sixteen more broad locks in under 3 miles to the summit at Wollaton. From there, rather like the upper Cromford Canal, it ran level along the east side of the Erewash Valley, winding in and out of side valleys, to its junction with the Cromford at Langley Mill, on its way tapping collieries at Bilborough, Eastwood, Awsworth, Wollaton and elsewhere.

There were no tunnels or important aqueducts, but one reservoir near Awsworth. By an agreement reached with the Erewash Company and the millers on the Erewash river, this had a self-regulating sluice that released regular supplies to the mills and the Erewash Canal.[26] Another reservoir was built at the expense of the Nottingham Canal at Butterley to compensate the Cromford Company for their water loss.

Short of time to give proper supervision to his resident, and perhaps finding his connection with the Trent Company a little embarrassing, given the arguments that went on between the two concerns, Jessop seems to have given little time to the canal, leaving Green to get on with construction. It opened on 26 April 1796, and within five years was carrying over 100,000 tons of coal a year.

Nutbrook Canal

Jessop was also asked to help with another colliery line, the Nutbrook, built as a branch from the Erewash Canal.[27] With a local man, John Nuttall, he surveyed it in 1791, did an estimate on economy lines, and supported the scheme in Parliament. It failed there on the proposed company structure, whereupon Jessop again went over the line for a new survey by Nuttall, after which a second Bill in 1793 succeeded. It provided for a broad canal, not now economy sized, rising through thirteen locks to Shipley. The account[28] he sent in is interesting as showing us first that an eminent engineer wrote out his own account, and second, how much of his time was spent in parliamentary work. In 1793 he attended in London on the Nutbrook Bill for eighteen days in March, April and May. His charge was then 3 guineas a day, plus $\frac{1}{2}$ guinea a day expenses in London and two guineas travelling expenses; surely modest figures, even though on some of the days covered he was probably engaged also on the Nottingham Canal and Sleaford Navigation Bills, which were then going through.

Jessop was not concerned with construction, this job being done by Benjamin Outram, who finished it in 1796. The canal was a straightforward one with no special engineering features.

Derby Canal

Another canal north of the Trent was promoted in 1792, the Derby. The original plan had been drawn up by Outram, for a line from the Trent to the Trent & Mersey Canal at Swarkestone, thence to Derby and on to collieries round Denby, with a branch to cross the Derwent and join the Erewash Canal at Sandiacre. Outram's first proposals seem to have been thought too expensive, whereupon he suggested changes. The promoting committee then engaged Jessop to survey and report, which he did on 3 November 1792.[29] Unfortunately, while we have Jessop's report, no copy of Outram's original scheme, or note of the alterations he proposed, seems to have survived.

Jessop approves Outram's line from Sandiacre to Derby, but suggests improvements which were adopted in that from Derby to the Trent & Mersey and on to the Trent. Interestingly, Outram seems to have proposed canal lines right through to the collieries round Denby; certainly the Druty-Lowe papers[30] make it reasonably clear that he was thinking of a canal up the valley at any rate until 22 October 1792.

Jessop confirmed that canals would be practicable and could be supplied with water. However, he proposed instead a canal from Derby as far as Little Eaton, and then railways for the steeper ascent:

> If those Railways, which should be of Cast Iron, are substantially laid upon Stone Foundations, and ascend on a regular Acclivity from Eaton to the Collieries, one Horse will easily draw down two Waggons with two Tons on each; and empty, they will as easily be drawn up again, as I understand the Ascent is only one-sixth of an Inch in a Yard in length: those Waggons may be drawn on to Boats and conveyed to Derby, and may be so constructed as to be carried into the Town without unloading.—Putting Tonnage out of the Question, they cannot be carried so cheap by a Canal the whole Length as by the proposed Railways.

This paragraph raises points of much interest. At the time it was written, the mixed canal and railway Forest Line of the Leicester Navigation was being built. Taking the two together, it seems clear that Jessop considered that in reasonably level country (the Little Eaton branch had four locks in $3\frac{1}{8}$ miles) the big barges of broad canals, carrying some 60 tons, offered economies of horse and man power that more than offset their higher construction cost, whereas on hilly and relatively short lines the advantage lay with railways.

His proposals for transferring railway waggons to boats and then on to road carts is an early one for what amounts to a container. Box containers had been used earlier by the Duke of Bridgewater on his coal boats to Manchester; these were loaded in the mine on to the boats, but at Manchester probably hoisted only to be unloaded.[31] Earlier still, Kemmett on the Stroudwater Navigation had used containers to tranship goods from one boat to another over intervening mill weirs.[32] The previous year, Jessop had envisaged waggon-carrying boats on the Leicester's Forest Line, and later such boats were also used on the Don and the Forth & Clyde Canal.

In fact, while Jessop's proposal to end the canal at Little Eaton and continue by railway was agreed and carried out by Outram, transferable waggons were not used, but boxes each holding rather less than 2 tons. Such demountable bodies for railway/canal/road transfer were used about 1788 on Joseph Butler's Ankerbold & Lings railway.[33] Outram probably therefore followed Butler's practice.

Ashby-de-la-Zouch Canal

Jessop also worked on three other East Midlands canals, the Ashby,

Leicestershire & Northamptonshire Union, and Grantham, of which the third has special importance.

In 1794 the Ashby Canal was authorised as a broad waterway, to leave the Coventry Canal at Marston. Canal branches were intended to Breedon and other limeworks, though in fact they achieved canal-linked railways.

The canal's originating idea went back to 1781, Robert Whitworth having done the early plans. By 1792 the promoters were seeking a Bill against considerable opposition, and called in Jessop to support Whitworth in Parliament.[34] He was there in mid-December. By early 1793 the company had run into further trouble with the Hon Penn Assheton Curzon of Gopsall House, who feared that the spring that supplied his estate with water would be affected by the canal, which anyway he did not support. In March, both Jessop and Whitworth averred that nothing would happen to Curzon's spring, whereupon the company pledged their whole capital upon its intact survival, an astonishing mark of confidence in their engineers. Nevertheless, their 1793 Bill was lost, seemingly with Curzon's help.

Thereupon Jessop was asked[35] to resurvey the line before a further application to Parliament. He must have written two or three reports, but we have only one, of 14 June 1793.[36] In it he approves Whitworth's lines, but suggests certain changes, one of which was to make Marston Bridge the point of junction with the Coventry Canal, as was later done. In November Whitworth and he signed the survey by John Smith that was the basis of the new deposited plan.[37] This time, in May 1794, Jessop having appeared in the Commons and Lords, the company got its Act. Whitworth, jointly with his son Robert, was appointed engineer and Jessop stepped out, having done his part, though later Outram was to build the company's railways with iron from Butterley.

Leicestershire & Northamptonshire Union Canal

Once Jessop had begun to make the Soar navigable to Leicester, extensions were thought of. What began in 1792 as a proposed canal onwards to Market Harborough soon became the broad Leics & Northants Union, for which he was too busy to do more than appear before the Commons and Lords committees on the Bill in early 1793,[38] John Varley having done the survey. It was passed, and authorised a canal from Leicester to join the navigable Nene at Northampton, and also a broad canal branch from the Grand Junction, through which there would be access to London. It was no fault of his that the company ran out of money in 1797, and ended their line at Gumley Debdale. It was extended to Market Harborough in 1809, and linked with the Grand Junction by the narrow-locked Grand Union in 1814, the year of Jessop's death.

Grantham Canal

The Grantham Canal was promoted and thought of as a corollary of Jessop's Nottingham Canal. As first planned, it was to run from Radcliffe-on-Trent below Nottingham for some 30 miles through the Vale of Belvoir to Grantham, and provide a market along its line for coal brought down the Nottingham. It was surveyed and laid out by Jessop, who supported it in Parliament in 1792. There the Bill had to be withdrawn before its second reading on the opposition of bodies interested in the waters of the Devon and Witham.

Thereupon Jessop began again: he moved the Trent entrance of the canal to Nottingham almost opposite the Nottingham Canal, and redesigned the 33 mile line to get virtually all its water from flood reservoirs at Knipton (60 acres) and Denton (20 acres), a new concept in British canal building. Seemingly, only a few days after the loss of the Bill, he wrote *Observations on the Use of Reservoirs for Flood Waters*[39] which he then used to convince the promoters, and afterwards circulate to members of Parliament[40] before a new Bill in 1793. This public relations exercise, helped by his parliamentary reappearance in April 1793, succeeded, for the Act was passed. Jessop's success here in convincing opponents that flood-water reservoirs could do the job, must have helped him to do the same to the recalcitrant mill-owners of the Rochdale Canal's line (see Chapter 6).

William Hodgkinson and James Green marked out the line, Green and William King built it, but Jessop kept a general eye upon it, during construction and after completion in 1797.

Witham Navigation

Finally, on the tributary Trent water line that ran from Torksey by Lincoln to Boston on the Wash, one that lay not far from his home at Newark, Jessop did three interrelated jobs, on the Witham, the Sleaford and the Horncastle Navigations. Each has something of interest for us.

By 1791, when Jessop was called in, both the Fossdyke from Torksey on the Trent to Brayford Pool in Lincoln, and the Witham thence to the Wash, were being improved: the first by its lessee, Richard

Ellison, the second by its Navigation and Drainage Commissioners. Two navigable branches from the Witham were also being talked of, to Horncastle and Sleaford, and these helped the feeling which Ellison encouraged, that markets for corn outwards from the Witham and coal back existed to the north in Yorkshire, along the Don and the Aire & Calder.

Yet in the centre of the water line stood the medieval Lincoln High Bridge with its single arch:

> The width of the passage is about 20 feet, confined between walls for a considerable length. The High-bridge is built upon a Wooden floor, which is about 18 Inches under the surface of the water at its lowest state.[41]

Only small boats drawing about a foot could pass. What to do? And how to do it without increasing flooding danger to lands around? And so Jessop was called in, and made his first report:

> It would be very practicable to take up this floor without any danger to the Bridge, to deepen the Channel all the way through, and underpin the Walls that confine it, so that it might admit Vessels of the largest size to pass through it; for the Arch of this Bridge is sufficiently high . . .

though, he says, there is no towpath, and in wet weather floodwater coming from Brayford Pool causes a strong current. This factor, together with an impression he had got that the Common Council would object to any tampering with the bridge, caused him to propose a bypass instead, using 800yd of the Sincel Dyke and 400yd of new cut, with a lock at its upper end to control the water flow.

However, after a favourable public meeting on 17 November, Lincoln Common Council agreed to the High Bridge route. Jessop thereupon wrote a second report,[42] recommending *inter alia* that the levels of Brayford Pool and the bridge floor should be lowered, and Stamp End Weir (on the bridge's Boston side) raised to give 3ft 6in depth above the bridge's newly lowered floor.

The Witham Drainage Commissioners then agreed to proceed at the joint expense of the Witham, Horncastle and Sleaford concerns, the work being authorised for the sake of convenience in the forthcoming Horncastle Act. By 1797 the improvement, giving a maximum navigable width of 15ft 6in, had been completed. This width, normal for a keel, was thereupon used for the new Horncastle and Sleaford navigations—the Yorkshire trade was to become a reality.

The Fossdyke and Witham about to be linked efficiently, Jessop in September 1792 surveyed the latter's whole length, reporting in June 1793.[43] He put in a cheap and practical report, but, presumably because they were so hard up, the commissioners took no action. Eventually, after the High Bridge improvement had many times increased their takings, Rennie, who had previously surveyed the river in 1803, proposed a more radical and expensive scheme which formed the basis of an 1808 Act. This authorised a new lock, to be built at Bardney, and the removal of three others. Two were indeed removed and the new one built, but Stamp End remained.

Early in 1808 Jessop was asked by Lincoln Corporation to comment on its proposals. In his report[44] he is conscious of the deficiencies both of the section between Stamp End Lock and the High Bridge to serve as a commercial port for the increased traffic expected up the Witham, and of the Grand Sluice at Boston. He proposed a bypass to the first that would also be an extended basin, and supported Rennie's suggestion for another round the Grand Sluice that would also give Boston a floating harbour. The suggestions were, however, too expansive and expensive for the time: Lincoln did not get its commercial cut, nor Boston its floating harbour and alternative to the obstructive Grand Sluice. When, later, an enclosed dock was built there, it was made north of the Witham and not to the south, as Rennie and Jessop had proposed.

Sleaford Navigation

In 1773–4 and 1782–4 there had been proposals for a navigation from Sleaford to the Witham by way of the River Slea and the Kyme Eau, Jessop having worked with James Creassy on the first.[45] These lapsed until Jessop and John Hudson were commissioned in 1791.[46] Their report and estimate were published on 25 November. The line they proposed was partly along a deepened existing drain, the Kyme Eau, partly along a widened mill-stream, and partly by the River Slea, with 7 locks 60ft x 15ft to overcome a fall of 41ft 6in in some 13 miles, the two lowest to have flood staunches. It was a straightforward job, except in one respect. From Flax Dyke (just below the confluence of the mill-stream and the old river) down to the Witham, there were 'several Tunnels laid through the Banks for watering Cattle in dry Seasons'. Some, Jessop and Hudson said, would not need altering. Others must be raised and their width regulated, as locks raised the water levels, so 'as to give them such capacity for discharging Water, as they are now by Law entitled to', or they would drain the navigation. This applied especially to the biggest, Holland Tunnel through the south bank of the Kyme Eau, 38in high and 22in wide. Landowners' concern lest Holland Tunnel should be deprived of some of its water had been the cause of the earlier Bill's failure.

The report's proposals were agreed. When the Bill came to the Lords committee, Jessop appeared for the company and against James Creassy for the objectors, first on the provisions for the dimensions and safety of the banks protecting Holland Fen from the Kyme Eau, then on ensuring that the rebuilt Holland Tunnel would not be deprived of water. An Act followed on 11 June 1792. Part-river and part-cut, $12\frac{1}{4}$ miles long, the Sleaford Navigation's contractors were William Bonner for the digging and John Dyson, an old associate of the Pinkertons, for lock construction. It was opened in May 1794. Jessop had probably found Dyson to do the job.

Horncastle Canal

Not far away, a short private line, Gibson's Canal, with one lock, ran from the Witham to Tattershall. In 1791 Jessop was asked to recommend a link between the Witham and Horncastle. He proposed two alternatives in his report of 30 June 1791,[47] either to canalise the River Bain upwards from Dogdyke to Horncastle; or, basing himself on a previous survey by Bullivant, to cut a new canal from the Witham at Kirkstead to the town. Both would have twelve locks and both would cost much the same. The promoters chose the river line, after which a further survey made by Robert Stickney and Samuel Dickinson suggested only minor changes. Jessop had not mentioned Gibson's Canal in his report, but the survey showed a proposed link with it at Tattershall that was later made. An Act followed on the same day as for the Sleaford, Jessop having given evidence to the Lords committee.

Naturally enough, Jessop was then asked to find an engineer to build it. With difficulty he produced William Cawley, who had worked on the Chester Canal in the 1770s. He came at £300pa, but proved unsatisfactory. After complaints of his work, in some of which he had deviated from Jessop's plans, he left late in 1793. Jessop then revisited the works. He found the second lock being built wrongly, 'and I thought it very necessary to tell the workmen so on the spot, that they might as far as they were able correct it, but take better care in the third lock.'[48] In 1794 he was appointed arbitrator between the company and local contractors, after part of a lock had collapsed and a bridge had had to be taken down. On 3 May he found against the contractors.[49] John Dyson, who had with John Gibson made the original Gibson's Canal, then took on the job. Like many others of the mania period, the company got into financial difficulties and the 11 mile long canal was not opened until 1802.

Jessop created the navigable Trent. He also played a vital part in originating every navigable tributary between Derwent Mouth and Torksey except the Erewash Canal, as also in developing the Witham water line. The total was $316\frac{1}{2}$ miles and 165 locks, all of it broad waterway except for the $10\frac{1}{8}$ miles of the upper Cromford. Thus was brought into being the transport base upon which for decades flourished local collieries, quarries, factories and agriculture. Details are set out in Table I. Of all the projects he handled, only the Leics & Northants Union and a part of the Horncastle were unfinished ten years after the authorising Act; most were completed much more quickly.

His work was far more than local, for it looked to the development of great through transport routes. By making the Trent fully navigable he brought to fruition what Brindley and Henshall had done in building the Trent & Mersey Canal, which otherwise might have remained as frustrated as was the Staffs & Worcs by the state of the Severn. And by creating a through keel passage at Lincoln, he enabled the growth of a great corn/coal exchange with Yorkshire that endured until cheap American corn imports began.

Lastly, the Leics & Northants Canal that he helped through Parliament was intended to run to Northampton to link there with a broad canal branch of the Grand Junction, itself broad and Jessop-engineered. If this line had been completed—and it was no fault of Jessop's that it was not—he would have created that barge canal line from the Trent to the Thames that was to be an object with canal companies up to the time when Foxton inclined plane was built as a last effort to make it a reality.

Table I

Name	Length (miles)	No. of locks	Authorising Act	Completed
Cromford Canal	$16\frac{7}{8}$	14	1789	1793
Trent Navigation	$69\frac{5}{8}$ (a)	3 and 2 flood-locks	1783 1794	1787 1801
Leicester Nav.	$15\frac{3}{4}$ (river) $8\frac{3}{4}$ (canal/rail)	9 and 1 flood-lock	1791	1794
Melton Mowbray Nav.	$14\frac{3}{4}$	12	1791	c1797
Oakham Canal	$15\frac{1}{4}$	19	1793	c1803
Nottingham Canal	$14\frac{3}{4}$ exc branches	19 and 1 stop-lock	1792	1796
Nutbrook Canal	$4\frac{1}{2}$	13	1793	1796
Derby Canal	$14\frac{1}{2}$ plus railways	8 and 1 flood-lock	1793	1796
Ashby-de-la-Zouch Canal	30 plus railways (b)	1 stop-lock	1794	1804
Leics & Northants Union Canal	$23\frac{3}{4}$ (c)	25	1793	1797 Gumley 1809 Market Harboro'
Grantham Canal	33	18	1793	1797
Witham Navigation	$31\frac{5}{8}$	(3) (d)	1792 (d)	1797 (d)
Sleaford Navigation	$12\frac{1}{4}$	7	1792	1794
Horncastle Canal	11	12	1792	1802

(a) The length includes $2\frac{1}{2}$ miles of canal in the Beeston Cut, with 2 locks, 1 a side-lock. Jessop also built a towpath throughout.
(b) Length as built. Railways were substituted for canal branches.
(c) Length as built. Intended to be $47\frac{1}{2}$ miles.
(d) The dates are those of the High Bridge works. Jessop did not build the locks.

4
DRAINING THE LOW GROUNDS AND CARRS

As part of the general agricultural improvement and expansion throughout Britain in the period from about 1760 to 1830 many thousands of acres of fen and low ground were drained and reclaimed. Like most leading civil engineers of that time Jessop was frequently consulted on such works. Six schemes with which he was involved are described in this chapter; five others are mentioned in Chapter 12.

Norfolk Marshland

In the late eighteenth century the main drain of the country of Marshland, in Norfolk, ran roughly north-east for a distance of 8 miles from point A in Fig 4 to an outfall in the old course of the River Ouse at point B, known as Knights Gool.[1] Several branch drains radiated from the main drain into relatively high land to the north. This area had long been settled, and defended from the sea by embankments bordering the salt marshes from Wisbech to King's Lynn. In the fenland to the south, Magdalen Fen had its own system of drains and banks; Marshland Smeeth and the low grounds north of Magdalen Fen were drained in part by the so-called New Drain, running parallel to the main drain for much of its length and discharging at Knights Upper Gool; but Marshland Fen lay almost permanently under water.

The administration of Marshland drainage, excepting Magdalen Fen, came under the Norfolk Commissioners of Sewers; funds for maintenance and occasional new works being raised by rates levied on the parishes in proportion to the area and value of the land drained.

In October 1784 the Commissioners resolved to improve Knights Gool by building a new sluice, with pointing doors, nearer to the river and a little to the north of the old outfall, and approached Smeaton. He recommended Jessop, who attended a meeting at Lynn on 5 January 1785

and laid before the Commissioners ... a Plan, Section and front View of a Sluice proper to be erected near Knights Gool, an Estimate

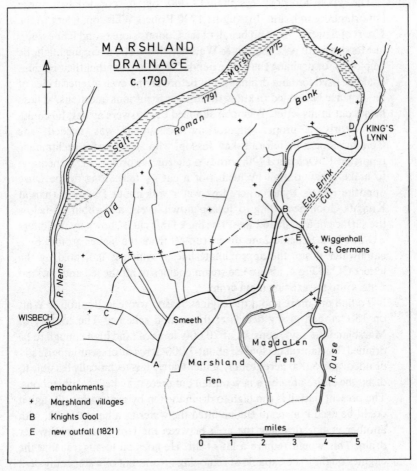

Fig 4

of the Expence of erecting such a Sluice and doing the other necessary Work ... and his Report as an Engineer on the Situation of the Outfall and on the means of improving the same from a Survey thereof taken by him in December last.[2]

All this was approved; construction started soon afterwards with John Pinkerton as contractor and by November 1785 Jessop was able to certify that the work had been completed satisfactorily.[3] The sluice had an opening about 15ft wide and its floor was 5ft below low-water level in the river.

The whole job cost less than £1,000, but it soon led to a more important commission. In August 1790 Robert Whincop, Clerk to the Court of Sewers, wrote on behalf of the Commissioners and landowners in Marshland to ask Boulton & Watt whether a steam engine might be employed for draining the low grounds.[4] Watt replied that their engines could be used for land drainage, but before giving even a general idea of the expense he needed to know the answer to various questions.[5] These he set out in his letter. Whincop supplied the answers as best he could, but clearly a proper engineering assessment was needed; the Commissioners therefore asked Jessop, who submitted a preliminary report on 12 October 1790, with two alternative proposals.[6] Scheme 1: to make a new outfall by means of a cut $4\frac{1}{2}$ miles long to the Ouse opposite King's Lynn, where low water was about 5ft lower than at Knights Gool, according to Jessop's own levels, and about 3ft below the surface of Marshland Fen. The line of this cut is shown by the letters BD in Fig 4. Scheme 2: to divert run-off from the higher ground by a catchwater drain, the approximate line of which is indicated by the letters CC in Fig 4, and to use steam engines to lift the fen and lowland waters into the existing main drain.

To find out more about the engines Jessop wrote to Boulton & Watt on 15 October, giving details of the second scheme.[7] The country of Marshland, he says, consists of 20,000 acres of land high enough to be drained 'by natural declivity'; about 7,000 acres at present imperfectly drained, and 5,000 acres totally under water. It is technically feasible to drain the entire area by a new outfall but there may be local objections. The present outfall is too high to drain the fen by gravitation, though it could be used if a steam engine lifted the water to a height of 6ft, with another engine draining the area between the fens and a catchwater drain. This would require a lift of 3ft. He goes on to suggest that the engines ought to be capable of removing an amount of water equivalent to 2in net rainfall in a week, although the drains will act in some degree as reservoirs to smooth out the peak flows. Jessop concludes his letter with the following remarks:

There are many of the gentry, advocates of Wind Engines. I have told them that the uncertainty of them is a great objection. I think if Steam Engines are once introduced into the Fens, they will increase and multiply; and even where Wind Engines are already established, it will answer well to have steam Engines in aid, for Calm weather, or very wet Seasons.

Watt was keenly interested in the possibilities of draining land by steam power. In 1788–9 he had been involved in some disappointingly vague proposals for draining Middle Fen near Ely,[8] and the Marshland scheme showed signs of going the same way. But now he had a sensible, quantitative set of engineering proposals to consider. Several sheets of his calculations have survived, tucked into and written on the back of Jessop's letter. The results he communicated to Jessop on 3 November.[5] A total of 84hp would be required, allowing about 80 per cent hydraulic efficiency in the pumps or scoopwheels, with fuel costs of £700pa based on twelve weeks' operation in the year and the engines working 20 hours a day. But he remarks that in view of the 'reservoir effect' it might be sufficient to reckon on an effective rainfall of 1in a week.

On 6 December Jessop replied that he accepts this modification, as engines designed accordingly

> will be large enough to erect in the first instance; and if it should be found necessary afterwards to erect another it would be more eligible to work two small Engines on an emergency than to work one large Engine when there is but little for it to do.

He also says, however, that he now finds the engine for the 5,000 acres of drowned fen should be designed for a lift of 8ft, and that more accurate surveys[9] have shown the intermediate area bounded by the catchwater drain amounts to 12,000 acres.[7]

Watt could now complete the calculations, which he sent to Jessop on 21 December.[5] These showed that 40hp would be required for draining the 5,000 acres with an 8ft lift, and proportionally for the larger area with a smaller lift. The engine for the fen would have a 45in diameter cylinder and 8ft stroke: dimensions not in any way exceptional.

Jessop presented his second report on 27 December 1790, with estimates, in which we have the first carefully considered and realistic proposals for the drainage of land by steam power.[6] Suggestions for draining fens by steam engines had been made before, and were to be made several times during the next two decades; but the proposals were not worked to their logical engineering conclusion.

This is the point of critical importance in the Marshland scheme of 1790; Jessop and Watt had produced practical recommendations which can be expressed thus: provide 8hp for every thousand acres to be drained requiring a maximum lift of 8ft, and add to this only if experience shows the necessity for doing so. When, around 1820, steam engines began to be used in the Fens they were distinctly under-powered: typically around 4–5hp per 1,000 acres. Later in the 1820s the figure rose to 6 or 7hp and in the period after 1830 when Joseph Glynn, chief engineer of the Butterley Company, had become the recognised authority on this subject he usually allowed 10hp per 1,000 acres.[10] It will therefore be seen that the pioneer calculations by Watt and Jessop in 1790 were well founded. Indeed, the modern practice in designing land drainage pumping stations is to provide a capacity equivalent to about $1\frac{1}{2}$–$2\frac{1}{2}$in of rainfall per week[11]—figures which bracket Jessop's original assumption.

Nothing directly came of the 1790 proposals for Marshland. In 1791 investigations were carried out by James Golborne, John Watté and Robert Mylne on the feasibility and expense of making what was to become the Eau Brink Cut (see Fig 4), which would short-circuit a long bend in the Ouse and cause an appreciable lowering of low-water level at the upper end of the cut where a new outfall for Marshland drainage could be made. This, of course, was only one reason for making a new channel; it would also benefit very large areas of fen further inland. However, the advantages to Marshland were thought to be so considerable that the Commissioners of Sewers in April 1792 advised support for the Eau Brink Bill. Meanwhile, the proprietors had employed John Watté to make more detailed surveys of the catchwater drain. They now sought Rennie's opinion; in January 1793 he reported in favour of the cut, whilst pointing out that the catchwater drain would be most beneficial and that in any case a steam engine would still be required to drain the lowest parts of Marshland Fen.[12]

During the progress of the Eau Brink Bill, which extended over three sessions from 1793–5, Jessop gave evidence on behalf of the Marshland proprietors. He concluded that the proposed cut and new outfall for Marshland would be very effective except for the deepest part of the fen, where the assistance of mills or engines might be required.[13]

Though the Act dates from 1795, the works were not carried out until 1818–21, at great expense, and even so the cut had to be enlarged before its full effect could be felt. The results then exceeded expectation, with a lowering of low-water level near the new (1821) Marshland outfall sluice of rather more than 6ft.[14] Nevertheless, had steam engines been installed in the 1790s their cost, after thirty years, would have been more than repaid.

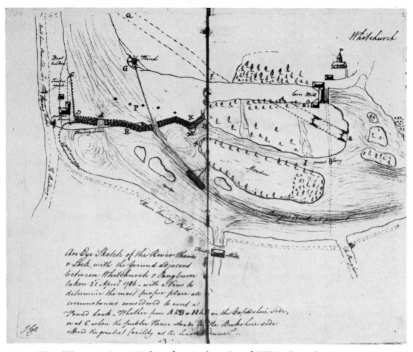

An Eye Sketch of the River Thames
& Lock, with the Ground adjacent
between Whitchurch & Pangburn
taken 21 April 1786 - with a View to
determine the most proper place all
circumstances considered to erect a
Pound Lock - Whether from A & B & H &c on the Oxfordshire side,
or at C where the public House stands on the Berkshire side
afford the greatest facility at the least Expense. -

The Thames in 1786: (*above*) sketch of Whitchurch
flash-lock at Pangbourne; (*below*) and that for the site of
Jessop's proposed new pound-lock

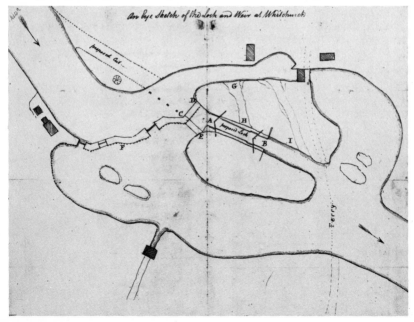

An Eye Sketch of the Lock and Weir at Whitchurch

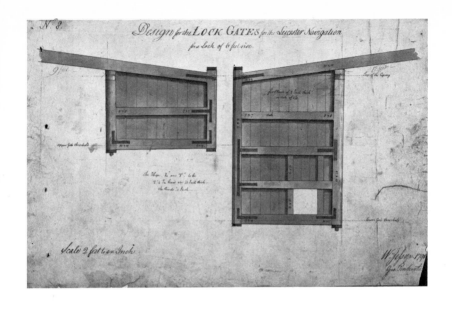

Leicester Navigation: (*above*) Jessop's drawing for lock gates, 1791; (*below*) iron anchor for lock gate heel post. Both are countersigned by George Pinkerton on behalf of the contractors

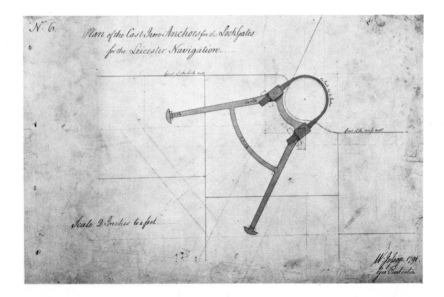

The first important improvements in draining 11,200 acres of low grounds and carrs in Holderness had been accomplished by Trustees appointed under an Act of 1764, with John Grundy as engineer and Smeaton as consultant. The southern and middle parts of this area are shown by hatching in Fig 5. The essential features may be described as follows.[15] Embankments along the east side of the river Hull provided defence against flooding; the main drain from the northern carrs and the drain from Sutton joined in Fore Dike (F), whence a 4 mile outfall channel led to Holderness Sluice, just upstream of Hull North Bridge. The sluice had two openings each 10ft wide with pointing doors, and draw doors on the land side for penning water in the summer. The sills were 1ft below normal low water in the river, the surface of the carrs ranging from 6ft (in the south) to 9ft (in the north) above this level.[16] The drain from Swine and Ganstead carrs fell into Ganstead Stream, which led through a new eastern cut into the main outfall channel about a mile above the sluice. Lambwath Stream, with a a large catchment in higher land to the east, and also Kelwell Water (K), and two streams further north, all flowed into the main drains.

Holderness Sluice, the outfall channel and the new cut from Ganstead Stream were completed by 1767, but deepening of the drains and raising the river banks continued until 1775. The Commissioners then issued their Award,[17] from which we learn that much of the drained land had an annual value of 5s per acre and some over 10s per acre.

Nevertheless, the drainage still left much to be desired. Areas near Leven in the north and in the neighbourhood of Weel remained under water and widespread winter floods were frequent, chiefly because the drains had to cope with rain falling in the carrs while they were overburdened with water brought down from the uplands by Lambwath and other streams. Moreover, the Trustees, through a misguided zeal for economy, had insisted on smaller dimensions for the outfall drain than those recommended by Smeaton and Grundy, and the River Hull itself had been allowed to deteriorate by the dumping of stones and other rubbish.

The landowner's discontent was expressed in a strongly worded pamphlet written by 'A Friend of the Undertaking' and submitted to the Trustees in May 1786.[18] This ended by recommending

the Trustees to ask Mr Smeaton, Mr Jessop, or some other experienced engineer, his opinion of the undertaking in its present state, and agree implicitly to abide by his determination.

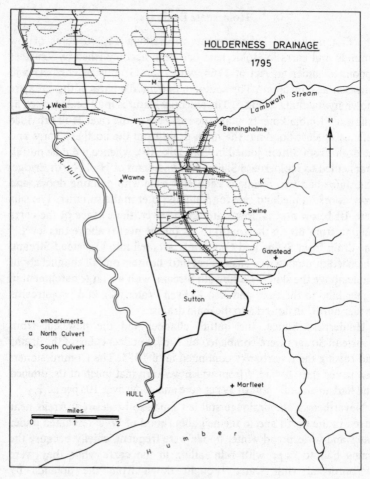

Fig 5

Grundy, it may be noted, had died in 1783.

The Trustees, to their credit, immediately ordered the pamphlet to be printed and circulated. They also decided that

> a copy be sent to Mr Jessop, and that he be desired to take a View of the Works of the Drainage, and of the River Hull, and to report what Measures in his Opinion ought to be pursued to give the best Effect to the Undertaking; what will be the probable Expence of these Measures, and whether a Navigation be Compatible with the Drainage.[19]

70

REPORT

OF

WILLIAM JESSOP, Engineer,

ON THE

STATE of the DRAINAGE,

OF THE

Low Grounds and Carrs lying in the Parishes, Townships, Hamlets, Lordships, Precincts and Territories of Sutton, Ganstead, Swine, Benningholme, Benningholme-Grange and Fareholme, North-Skirlaugh, Rowton, Arnold, Long-Riston, Leven, Heigh-holme and Haily-tree Holme, Brandes-Burton and Bursall, Eske, Tickton, Weel, Routh, Meaux, and Waghen otherwise Wawn, in Holderness, in the East-Riding of the County of York; and on the means of compleating the same; and on the present state of the River Hull;

AND ALSO

On a Proposition for making Navigable the Drain from Hull to Monk Bridge:

From a Survey taken in the Month of June, 1786.

─────────────────

HULL: Printed by J. FERRABY, in the *Butchery*.

Fig 6   Title-page of Jessop's report on the Holderness Drainage

Jessop visited the site in June and submitted his report on 17 July 1786.[20] Ten days later the Trustees ordered it to be printed and asked Jessop to attend a meeting in September. Following various discussions, a plan of action was agreed in June 1787; Jessop paid another visit in July and work began soon afterwards.

The guiding principle of Jessop's scheme was expressed in his report as follows:

71

The Low Lands within the Drainage, are not only subject to the downfall Waters that immediately belong to them, but also the drainage of upwards of Ten thousand Acres of higher Country to the Eastward; the greater part of which is brought down by the Lambwath Stream. It is obvious upon the slightest consideration, that the intercepting of this water, and discharging it . . . as near the outfall as may be, will afford great relief to the present Drains; and there hardly remains a doubt with me that, if this is done, the present Drains properly regulated, as I shall presently describe, and the River Bank made secure, the greatest part of the Carrs may become fit for the Plough, and even Weel Deeps and the lowest Lands in Leven, will be in much better state of drainage than the general Surface of the Carrs is at present.

The new drain for Lambwath Stream and the stream itself would be embanked across low ground and led into the eastern outfall; and the waters from Swine and Ganstead low grounds would be passed

under the new Drain by a Fox[21] or Culvert, and led by Foredike; where they will find a compleat outfall, when that Drain is deepened, and unencumbered by upland water.

Jessop then goes on to specify the dimensions for the drains, with sections and profiles and detailed plans which could be seen on application to George Plummer, surveyor of the works. Briefly, the drains were to be graded to a slope of 6in per mile with widths proportional to the drainage, and the drain from the sluice to the junction of the two outfall drains was to have an average depth of 10ft with a bottom width of 20ft and sides sloping to $1\frac{1}{2}$:1. Jessop also surveyed the lower reaches of the river, and emphasised the need for improvements there.

Between the submission of his report and the start of work some modifications were made in the line of Lambwath drain.[22] As completed in 1792 that part of the scheme involving the separation of Lambwath and Ganstead streams from the internal drainage is shown in Fig. 5. The main features may be summarised as follows:

1 Head Dike (H) was embanked and extended $1\frac{1}{2}$ miles south-east to join Ganstead Stream and the eastern outfall, and the embankments were continued where necessary along Lambwath Stream to the edge of the low ground at Benningholme.
2 The water from Swine and Ganstead was taken in a new drain

72

through the South Culvert to join Sutton Drain and thence to Fore Dike.

3 Water from Benningholme pastures passed under Lambwath Drain in the North Culvert.

4 A dam was placed across the drain which had previously discharged into the north end of Head Dike and a new cut joined this drain (which was regraded to reverse the direction of flow) to the south end of Monk Dike (M).

5 In Fig 5 Kelwell Water is shown embanked and diverted into Head Dike, with a tunnel beneath it for Benningholme Drain. This part of the scheme was proposed and agreed in 1791[23] but not executed until the 1830s.

The principle of separating upland waters from internal drains is of outstanding importance. It was partially adopted by Sir Cornelius Vermuyden in his drainage of Hatfield Chase, but seems not to have been widely acknowledged, even in theory, until the period around 1770,[24] and the first applications in practice may well have been Samuel Foster's remodelling of the Hatfield Drainage (see p 77) and the slightly earlier work by Jessop at Holderness. In any case the subtle means by which the principle was realised there, by modifications to an existing drainage, are surely to be admired.

Within a year of the submission of his Holderness Drainage Report, Jessop received a request from the East Riding Commissioners of Sewers to survey the River Hull, in order to provide a factual basis for action to improve the river outfall. The request came in May 1787.[25] He carried out detailed surveys in October 1787 and June 1788. In addition, he viewed the river and the adjacent low grounds in February 1788 during flood conditions.[26]

As a result the Commissioners ordered their surveyor, the same Mr Plummer who was acting as resident engineer on the drainage works, to make arrangements for the river to be widened wherever necessary to a minimum width of 45ft at low-water mark and for all stones and obstructions to be removed by dredging.[27]

By 1792, then, the main objectives in the remodelling of Holderness Drainage and improving the river outfall had been accomplished. Jessop's attendance was no longer required; he had visited the area seven times, and charged £246 for his fees and expenses.

However, much still remained to be done in widening, deepening and regrading the drains to Jessop's sections, which appear to have been meticulously followed. This programme was carried out during the years 1793–5 under the direction of Anthony Bower, who took over the duties of surveyor from George Plummer in December 1792.[28]

Strickland gives the expenditure on Holderness Drainage from 1764 to 1808 as £54,000 and says that the drainage, though still imperfect, has greatly improved the land, much of which, from having been of little or no value (before 1764), is now let from 15s to 30s per acre.[29] This figure can be broken down approximately as follows:

1764–75	£24,000	Grundy's scheme
1775–87	£4,000	minimal maintenance
1787–95	£16,000	Jessop's scheme
1795–1808	£10,000	good maintenance

After 1795 there is litte to note for many years. In 1797 Jessop advised the Trustees, and also the Driffield Navigation Commissioners, on protective clauses to be inserted in the Act for Beverley & Barmston Drainage,[30] and he was the engineer who piloted the Bill for this drainage scheme, located on the west side of the River Hull, through Parliament.[31] Later, in 1804, he and Rennie reported jointly with Chapman on the need for raising the Holderness barrier banks by an extra foot and on the consequential works necessary to be done on the banks then under construction on the opposite side of the river for the Beverley & Barmston Drainage,[32] and finally, in December 1805, he reported on proposals which had been put forward by John Dalton for leading Lambwath Stream to a new outfall at Marfleet.[33]

In his report Jessop says that the discharge of Lambwath water into the Humber at Marfleet had often been suggested. He personally felt some reservations about the advisability of the project but did not doubt that it could be achieved if the outfall drain had larger dimensions than those suggested by Dalton and if the aqueduct over Fore Dike were to be laid at a lower level, to improve the fall. The aqueduct could with advantage be made in the form of a cast iron trough, he said.

On the basis of this mildly favourable report, the Trustees asked Dalton to take accurate levels and prepare estimates. But, except for removing the central pier of Holderness Sluice in 1808 to increase the clear waterway to 26ft, nothing happened until 1832–7; and then the Marfleet outfall was constructed as part of a thorough remodelling of the entire drainage scheme, designed by Edward Page.[34] Lambwath Stream and all the other upland waters were taken along Fore Dike to Holderness Sluice, and the lowland waters were led under Fore Dike to a new outfall, at a lower level, at Marfleet.

Isle of Axholme Drainage

In February 1795 a petition was submitted to Parliament for the inclosure and drainage of 'several large tracts of common or waste ground, known by the name of the Isle Commons, . . . within the several parishes of Epworth, Haxey, Belton and Owston in the Isle of Axholme, Lincolnshire'. John Dyson gave evidence, and the Act was obtained in June. Nine General Commissioners were named in the Act; Joseph Young and Jonathan Teale were nominated as surveyors; William Jessop and Joseph Hodskinson as the appointed engineers. Hodskinson, an eminent land surveyor with a small additional practice in civil engineering, had been consulted in 1793 by the Participants (ie the proprietors) of the Level of Hatfield Chase on problems arising from the construction of the Stainforth & Keadby Canal.

Jessop and Hodskinson presented detailed plans in a report written at Epworth in October 1795.[35] Referring to the map in Fig 7 their recommendations were:

1 To transfer that portion of the Participants' Idle South Drain marked by the letters CDE to a new cut from C to E.
2 To construct the main 'Isle Drain' from Idle Stop, passing under Snow Sewer at H, running in the re-excavated course of the abandoned north branch of the River Idle to point A, then a new cut to join the existing drain CDE, and finally in another length of new cut from E to an outfall sluice at Derrythorpe.
3 To drain the carrs south of Haxey by cutting 'Ferry Drain' parallel to Snow Sewer with a new sluice at Owston Ferry.
4 To make a branch drain leading from the carrs north of Misterton Soss and passing under Snow Sewer in a tunnel to join Ferry Drain at point J; the tunnel to have two apertures each 5ft wide and 4ft high.
5 To drain the low grounds east of Epworth to a sluice at Butterwick.
6 To protect this area from upland floods by a catchwater drain.

The bottom widths and the depths of the drains, the widths and heights of the sluices, and the levels of their sills, are all carefully specified in the report. Derrythorpe Sluice, for example, to have two openings each 8ft wide and 10ft high with the sills laid 2ft below low water in the Trent; the drain leading to the sluice to have a bottom width of 18ft with side slopes of 1:1 or flatter if required by the nature of the soil; the dimensions to decrease progressively towards the extremity of the drain, where there would be a 10ft bottom width and a minimum depth

75

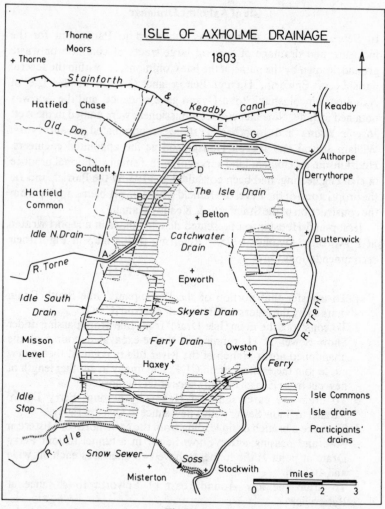

Fig 7

of 3ft. In the length of this drain, about 13 miles, there was a fall of 6ft from the lowest carrs south of Snow Sewer to low-water level in the Trent. In additon to the main drains, numerous secondary drains were to be constructed by Special Commissioners for each parish.

It is clear that Jessop and Hodskinson produced their plan in close collaboration with Samuel Foster, engineer of Hatfield Chase, as agreement with the Participants would be required for the alterations to Idle South Drain and for tunnelling under Snow Sewer.

Initial efforts to drain the Chase and adjacent lands were due to Vermuyden in the early seventeenth century. A feature of his plans had been the removal of upland water, by diverting the rivers Don and Idle; in the latter case by building a dam, at the aptly named Idle Stop, to direct the flow of this river along its eastern branch to Stockwith, and a barrier bank to protect the southern parts of the Isle drained by Snow Sewer (Fig 7). But he had not dealt at all successfully with the River Torne. The first basic suggestions for improvements here seem to have been those of Smeaton in a report of 1776. They were incorporated in an Act of 1787 under the authority of which Samuel Foster, adding some important modifications of his own, achieved a logical scheme with the Torne, embanked where necessary, running to its own outfall at Althorpe and the Idle North Drain flowing to a new sluice at Keadby.[36] Foster's work had been completed by 1789 and it was this system of drainage that Jessop and Hodskinson modified still further to accommodate the Isle Drain.

Unfortunately, the Isle Commissioners' Minutes are lost, though we have those of Haxey. From these we learn that excavation of the Isle Drain and Ferry Drain was well under way by the summer of 1797, while references to John Dyson show he held the position of resident engineer for the Isle works. A map of Hatfield Chase dated 1801, which shows the Isle Drain, proves that this was by then completed.[37] The Commissioners' Award can be dated at August 1803; it lists the area of drained land as 12,600 acres, distributed almost equally between the four parishes. The main or 'public' drains are described and evidently have been set out as recommended by Jessop and Hodskinson, though in some cases the 1803 widths are slightly larger.[38] A map accompanying the Award shows the drainage areas illustrated in Fig 7;[39] and Thomas Stone, the principal Commissioner, is quoted as stating that the works cost about £20,000.[40]

Without the Minute Book we cannot say when Jessop came to the site, but probably he did so on most if not all the six occasions between 1796 and 1801 that he visited the neighbouring Everton, Gringley and Misterton drainage scheme.

Everton, Gringley and Misterton Drainage

The first works for draining the carrs south of the River Idle, located principally in the parishes of Everton, Gringley and Misterton, in Nottinghamshire, were carried out around 1630 by building a sluice across the river with embankments from the sluice to join the Trent bank at Stockwith, and by cutting several drains across the carrs into the river.[41] The sluice, known as Misterton Soss, kept Trent water out of the carrs but they were inundated whenever the Idle rose in flood. The drains certainly accelerated the run-off of flood water and subsequent drying out of the land, but as the entire flow of the Idle now came down the eastern branch (often referred to by its old name, Bycarsdike), following the diversion at Idle Stop, winter floods were frequent and extensive. Nevertheless, some 4,000 acres were by these means converted to 'summer grounds'.

In the 1670s Misterton Soss was rebuilt as a lock for boats navigating the Idle to and from Bawtry; mitre gates, pointing to the Trent, still preserved its function as a drainage sluice. After an exceptional flood during the winter of 1763–4, which damaged Bycarsdike bank near Isle Stop, the Participants called on Smeaton for advice on improvements to the river and also to Snow Sewer. Smeaton reported in September 1764 and incidentally mentions some levels taken by 'my clerk': that is by Jessop—his first visit to the area.[42]

Smeaton notes that the Soss had a height of 16ft above the sills and a waterway of 17ft 8in. As this was far less than the width of the river, he recommended the construction of an additional sluice beside the lock, thus reducing the height to which floodwater could rise and increasing the rate of run-off from the carrs. He also suggested modifications to Snow Sewer and its outfall sluice. The latter works were in due course carried out, but the Participants, having relinquished many years ago all interest in the carrs south of the river, merely raised and strengthened their embankment.

The idea of building an additional sluice at Misterton Soss was not forgotten, however, and we find it incorporated in a scheme put forward by George Kelk in 1773 for the comprehensive drainage of Everton, Gringley and Misterton carrs.[43] As well as the river sluice, he proposed to cut a main or 'mother' drain running parallel to the river and separated from it by a barrier bank; the drain to extend from an outfall sluice just below Misterton Soss up to the parish of Scaftworth (Fig 8), and the carr drains to be led into the main drain.

The advantage of this plan can readily be seen. The river, given an adequate waterway at the Soss, would be contained within the embankments leaving the drains to deal with rainfall and the few small streams coming in from the high land to the south around Gringley and Everton.

A partial move towards Kelk's scheme came in the late 1780s when the Commissioners for Misterton Inclosures built an 8ft sluice in the

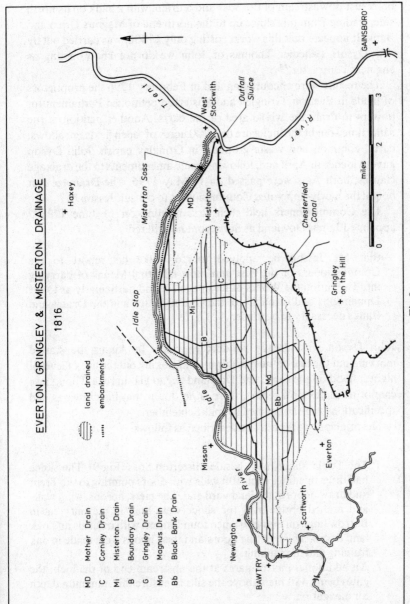

EVERTON, GRINGLEY & MISTERTON DRAINAGE

1816

MD Mother Drain
C   Cornley Drain
Mi Misterton Drain
B   Boundary Drain
G   Gringley Drain
Ma Magnus Drain
Bb Black Bank Drain

land drained
embankments

miles

0   1   2   3

Fig 8

bank just downstream of the Soss and a drain, with a bank on its north side, leading from this sluice up to the north end of Magnus Drain and Bank. It appears that this work, costing only £1400, was carried out by 'Mr Dyson' (whether Thomas or John we do not know) acting as engineer-contractor.[44]

The results were encouraging and in February 1796 the proprietors of lands in Everton, Gringley and Misterton petitioned Parliament for powers to drain the whole area of the carrs. Another petition at the same time sought the inclosure of 3,200 acres of 'open fields, meadows, carrs, common and waste grounds' in Gringley parish. John Dyson gave evidence in April and, following some amendments to the drainage clauses, both Acts were passed on 14 May 1796. The Drainage Act bound the newly-appointed Commissioners to consult Jessop.[45]

The Commissioners held their first meeting on 11 June 1796,[46] appointed James Dowland as Surveyor and ordered

that Mr Jessop be applyed to, to make his report to the Commissioners of the best and most effectual Means of carrying into Execution the Works of Drainage . . . and particularly as to the Dimensions and Capacity of the Outfall Sluice and the Drains and Banks necessary to be made.

John Dyson was already resident engineer. In August he started marking out the line of the main drain and staking out the line of level of highest flood on the carrs, and Dowland began his surveys. Though we cannot trace Jessop's report, there is no doubt that his drawings and specifications were completed by mid-September.

The principal works may be described as follows:

1 The Triple Sluice, built beside Misterton Soss (Fig 9). The sluice had three openings each 10ft wide with doors pointing to the Trent and draw doors at the landward end. The piers, aprons, wing walls and arched bridge over the sluice were built in masonry set in Barrow lime, on timber framed foundations, with oak sills and oak land doors. The pointing doors and their hoods were made in oak framing and fir planking.

2 An additional pair of gates at the upstream end of the lock; the gates being $4\frac{1}{2}$ft high above the sills to ensure this minimum depth for navigation.

3 The Mother Drain, $8\frac{1}{2}$ miles in length, extending from the Soss up to a point 1 mile north of Scaftworth. As originally made, the drain near the Soss had a bottom width of 14ft and a depth of 10ft.

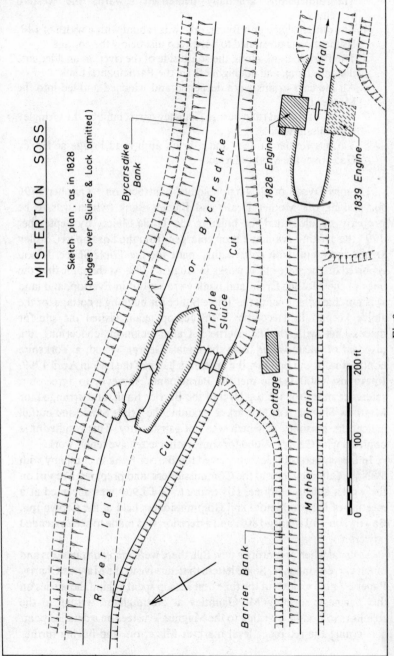

MISTERTON SOSS

Sketch plan, as in 1828
(bridges over Sluice & Lock omitted)

Bycarsdike Bank

Triple Sluice or Bycarsdike Cut

1828 Engine

Outfall

1839 Engine

River Idle Cut

Cottage

Mother Drain

Barrier Bank

0   100   200 ft

Fig 9

The dimensions gradually decreased towards the western extremity.

4 The outfall sluice into Bycarsdike was rebuilt with a width of 14ft. Its location is presumed to have been just below the cottage.

5 The Barrier Bank along the south side of the river, at an adequate distance from, and not higher than, the Participants' bank.

6 All the carr drains were deepened and widened and led into the Mother Drain.

7 A new drain and road across Gringley carrs, built by the Gringley Commissioners.

8 Various timber bridges and a brick arch road bridge at Haxey Gate, over the Mother Drain.

Thomas Dyson of Newington signed contracts on 1 October 1796 for making the Mother Drain and Barrier Bank (which was to be properly puddled) and for building the Triple Sluice. By September 1797 the existing drain had been enlarged from the Soss up to Cornley Drain and a cut, with cofferdams, made for the Triple Sluice. Jessop reported on the state of the works in August 1798. At the same time the lines of the Mother Drain and bank were set out in Everton, and land was purchased adjoining the Triple Sluice for building a cottage for the sluice keeper. In December 1798 Jessop again visited the site for discussions with the Chesterfield Canal engineer concerning the disposal of waste water from the canal. George Wood, a Yorkshire contractor, began building the upstream gates of the lock in April 1799. In August 1800 Jessop met the Participants' surveyor to agree on a reference mark for the top level of the Barrier Bank, and arranged for Matthew Sheppard of Newark to examine the Triple Sluice and outfall sluice, the masonry of which was not satisfactory. This resulted in a contract with George Wood for some rather extensive repair work.

In December 1800 Jessop viewed the Barrier Bank in company with William Gauntley, one of the Commissioners, and prepared a report on the works still to be done. His estimate of £3,900 was accepted at a meeting of the proprietors and Commissioners held at the Crown Inn, Bawtry, on 16 January 1801, and a decision was made to seek extended powers.

As usual when preparing a new Bill, there were many discussions and much correspondence. Some letters that survive in the Magnus Charity Papers,[47] give an idea of the time that Jessop spent behind the scenes on this business: meeting Mr Gauntley at Nottingham, writing to the solicitors in London, writing to the Magnus Trustees on a detailed point concerning the reference level mark at Misterton, and having further discussions with the canal people as well as Chapman, who had been brought in to help. Finally, in June, Jessop gave evidence to the Lords, and the new Act was obtained on 2 July 1801 apparently to the satisfaction of all parties.

William Gauntley the younger, nephew of the Commissioner, was appointed Surveyor of the Works in December 1801 in place of John Dyson. By May 1803 the Commissioners were able to report that the works had been completed, and on 29 September 1803 they presented their Award, recording the acreage of each proprietor to be assessed for drainage rates. The total area of drained land amounted to 5,700 acres.[48]

This marked the formal conclusion of the undertaking. But for several years the bank had to be raised occasionally to compensate for settlements, and constant maintenance was required to keep the drains scoured to their proper depths. Jessop visited the site again in January 1804 regarding further troubles with the Chesterfield Canal and, later that year, Rennie was called in for another independent opinion. He considered that the Mother Drain should have been extended to the Trent, thereby gaining an additional fall of 4ft or thereabouts in an extra distance of only $\frac{3}{4}$ mile, and commented that 'Mr Jessop is much to blame here'.[49]

Jessop is bound to have considered this point and obviously decided, with the limited funds available, to avoid the cost of an outfall at Stockwith. Indeed, it is clear that he had every hope of the less ambitious scheme proving satisfactory.[50] However, as events were to prove, he had been too optimistic. Following a particularly bad flood in December 1810, during which the drains were quite unable to cope, the Commissioners met, with Jessop attending, to discuss extending the main drain to the Trent. Later, in June 1812

The Commissioners with Mr Jessop viewed the intended line for making a new Cut and erecting a Sluice near Stockwith Bridge for bettering the Outfall, and Mr Jessop delivered in his Report thereof with an Estimate of the Expence attending the same, he being of the opinion that the proposed works ought to be carried into effect.

Moreover, at a meeting of the Commissioners held in Chesterfield in November 1812, Jessop, as his last contribution, recommended the use of a steam engine. This could lift the water into the drain by several feet, over a temporary weir, and so keep the outfall sluice doors open even with the Trent in flood.

By 1813 Jessop was ill and Joseph Thackray of Gainsborough became consulting engineer to the Commissioners in July. In 1814 his plans for the Stockwith outfall were approved and the work reached completion in 1816. Then in 1828 a 40hp steam engine was installed by Joseph Glynn,[51] the first to be built for land drainage outside the Fens. With the addition of another engine in 1839, and only minor subsequent improvements, the drainage continued to give total protection to this valuable agricultural land until so recently as 1941, when the scheme was remodelled and a new diesel pumping station erected on Gringley Carr.

Axe and Brue Drainages

The Axe and Brue run in a westerly direction across the Somerset Levels to the sea between Bridgwater and Weston-super-Mare. In doing so they flow for several miles through low grounds, chiefly peat moors, and then through a broad coastal clay belt standing at a slightly higher elevation. Most of the peat land was reclaimed in the second half of the eighteenth century, but little had been done to improve the rivers themselves. As a consequence, severe winter flooding occurred quite often; the low grounds were entirely flooded in 1794 and again in 1799, when the Axe Valley remained under water for five months.[52]

The means of remedying this state of affairs were clear, in general terms, to leading agriculturists such as John Billingsley,[53] and it proved easy to obtain acts in 1801 and 1802 (for the Brue and the Axe respectively) setting up commissions with powers to build outfall sluices, to make new cuts on the rivers, to deepen the main drains in some places and to cut new ones elsewhere. Unlike the schemes described earlier in this chapter, it was not necessary in the Levels to do much embanking of the rivers, given a good outfall sluice and adequate sea banks, nor to go very far in separating the drains from upland waters.[54] Two reasons for these differences were: (1) a lower low-tide level at the outfalls, owing to the exceptionally large tidal range on the Somerset coast, and (2) a higher ground water table, and even a small amount of winter flooding, could be accepted as the land was used for pasture, not arable farming.

Though administered separately, the Brue and Axe works had the same technical staff. Jessop designed the sluices, cuts and bridges; William White made the engineering and land surveys, and Robert Anstice was resident engineer. The principal contractors were James Parry for the structures and William Tyley for excavations. The areas of land affected by these improvements amounted to about 27,000 acres in the Brue Valley and 16,000 acres in the Axe.[55]

Jessop and White gave evidence on the Brue Drainage Bill; in August 1801 they marked out the new cut and outfall sluice at Highbridge; Jessop produced plans and specifications in October; Anstice took up his appointment that month, at a salary of £218pa, and work began.[56] In December 1802 James Mills, perhaps as Jessop's assistant, examined the sluice works and in February 1803 Jessop marked out more river cuts further upstream, wrote specifications for the sluice doors and also examined plans for the Axe. After another site visit to the Brue in October, work started in August 1804 on a new main drain (the South Drain) 6 miles in length[57] and major improvements were made in the North Drain. In July 1805 excavation began on a cut across Little Moor, seemingly to White's plans, and by September 1806 Anstice was able to report completion of all works. A few days later, the Commissioners signed the Award[58] and, when the accounts were settled in February 1807, the cost amounted to £53,000.[59] Jessop's fees came to £276.

During the passage of the Bill for Axe Drainage, White gave evidence in April and May 1802. After the Act had been obtained the rest of the year was devoted to land surveying.[60] Jessop inspected plans and viewed the site in February 1803, and decided where the outfall sluice should be built.[61] But much discussion ensued, including a meeting between Jessop and White in London, on the need for a navigation lock at the sluice. Meanwhile, excavations began in July 1803 on a deep cut 1 mile in length at Loxton and, later, on a cut near Rackley. A decision having been made against a lock, Jessop sent his drawings for the sluice in January 1804; it was to be at the west end of a new cut at Bleadon. He and White checked tenders while on a joint visit to their Bristol job, and the contract was let in May. Construction took longer than expected, owing to difficult foundation conditions. In a report written in May 1805 Anstice mentions boring to a depth of 40ft at the sluice and contemplates the possibility of 'laying a temporary weight to consolidate the substrata' before building the structure.[62] In the event, he used piled foundations and planking, but his reference to preloading anticipates the use of this technique by Jessop and Telford at the Clachnaharry Lock on the Caledonian Canal (Chapter 7).

All works on the Axe scheme were completed by 1810, at a total cost of £41,000.[63] Jessop's fees, amounting to £126, were settled in June 1805. Afterwards, Anstice carried on alone except for a single consultation with William Bennet in 1808.

5
JESSOP IN IRELAND

When Smeaton and Jessop visited Ireland in 1773 (see p 16), the Grand Canal Company[1] had only been in existence a year, during which time, with John Trail as chief engineer, they had tried to give the enterprise a new start after Thomas Omer's over-ambitious beginning. Smeaton's recommendations[2] had included a reduction in lock dimensions to 60ft × 14ft (with 4ft 1in on the sills) against Trail's 80ft × 16ft, itself a great reduction on Omer's 137ft × 20ft.

Trail had contracted himself to the company, but early in 1777 he resigned; Captain Tarrant took over, and in 1779 opened the canal as far as Sallins, some 20 miles from Dublin. Soon afterwards Richard Evans took charge, Tarrant thereafter acting as consultant. Robertstown, 7 miles beyond Sallins, was reached in 1784, by which date the directors had decided that before going further towards the Shannon they would link the part of their canal completed to Lowtown, a little beyond Robertstown, by a branch to the River Barrow, then being made navigable,[3] at Monasterevan, as Smeaton had in 1773 recommended. They began on this in 1783, and early in 1785 the link was made. However, navigation difficulties between Monasterevan and Athy lower down the Barrow must have persuaded the company to extend their lateral canal, for this was being built in mid-1789. Evans, who was taking on other jobs as well, was now told that he must give all his time to the Grand Canal: he refused, and was dismissed in December 1789. Soon afterwards Archibald Millar, promoted from overseer, took charge of construction with William Rhodes and James Oates as assistants.

The Grand Canal records are missing between August 1785 and August 1789. We know that Jessop visited Ireland in the summer of 1785[4] and again later, because a reference exists to a report of his of 1789, and because in 1790 he told the company that he would spend two or three months in Ireland 'as formerly'. Henceforward until 1802 we can regard Jessop as being consulting engineer to the Grand Canal Company: as Ruth Delany says in *The Grand Canal of Ireland*, his reports clearly carried great weight with the directors, and were entered in full in their minutes.

86

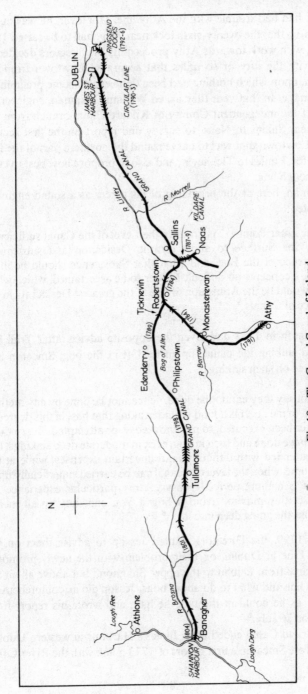

Fig 10   The Grand Canal of Ireland

Millar had had trouble with the Athy line. Moreover, he was out in his levels, so that the twenty-sixth lock near Athy had to be raised 18in. In 1789, with work towards Athy proceeding, the directors decided to get on with the fifty or so miles that separated Lowtown from the Shannon, upon which nothing had been done except some preliminary bog drainage. In that year they asked William Chapman, engineer-in-charge of the independent County of Kildare Canal branch from the Grand near Sallins to Naas, to survey and report on the first section beyond Lowtown that was to curve round the northern part of the Bog of Allen for 7 miles to Ticknevin, and also to propose how best to cut a canal through bog.

Chapman, here at the beginning of his career as a sound engineer, commented:

> ... the great Point ... is, to have the Level of the Canal sufficiently below the Surface to allow for the Desication and subsequent subsidence of the Bog, and what that Subsidence should be in all Cases, I conceive no difficult Matter to be ascertained, which when done would be the Aquisition of one of the greatest Desiderata in the Science of Canals.[5]

But Smeaton in 1773 had given the opposite advice, after Trail had suggested sinking the canal for up to 33ft in the bog. Smeaton had commented on such sinkings:

> I do not say they cannot be done, yet cannot be done by any method known to me ... It is a kind of undertaking that has, in this degree of it, never been executed, to my knowledge, or attempted. Every thing that I have done and seen in bog, even in moderate deep sinkings, has been attended with difficulty, and uncertain expenses, while at the same time, when the level of a canal can be carried superficially upon bog, it is a thing perfectly easy ... my particular experience ... suggests this maxim, avoid a bog if you can, but by all means possible, the going deep into it ...[6]

Now, in 1790, the Directors wanted Jessop to advise them on the Circular Line at Dublin, on their problem with the newly-promoted Royal Canal from Dublin to the upper Shannon,[7] but above all on the Shannon line and what to do about bogs. Jessop did as comprehensive a survey as he could in the time he had, and wrote his report from Newark on 26 July.[8]

The Grand Canal ended at St James's Harbour in western Dublin. From before Smeaton's first report of 1773 a link with the River Liffey at Ringsend below Dublin had been talked of, and in 1785 Chapman proposed and later surveyed a circular line round the city with seven locks. The idea fell in with the Directors' own for wet-docks at Ringsend, and Jessop was asked to comment on Chapman's survey. He says that he had told them in person his opinion on the works of the Circular Line, had 'left with you plans for the Locks & Bridges & of which you have been pleas'd to approve', and had marked out lock sites and proposed deviations from Chapman's line. Jessop also suggested a basin beside the Liffey and the River Dodder (which enters at this point), 'whence boats may occasionally discharge over the wall into sea-vessels lying on the outside of it'. He goes on:

When I formerly view'd the ground for the termination of the Canal & presum'd to look forward to a time when a suitable accommodation wou'd be made to the encreasing trade of Dublin I flatter'd myself that before now the Gentlemen of Ireland who have power to promote her prosperity wou'd have effectually adopted some sound plan similar to what I took the liberty of suggesting for keeping Ships constantly afloat. ... I consider the little accommodation at the Dodder but as a temporary expedient, but when the great object may be hereafter decided, it will afford the means of convenient entrance from the Liffey.

For which reason also he wants the last part of the canal through 'the low grounds' to be at least 100ft wide.

The Royal Canal had been proposed to run from Dublin for 90 miles past Mullingar to the upper Shannon at Cloondara above Lough Ree. Given the closeness of the Royal's proposed line out of Dublin to that of the Grand, the latter's Directors tried hard to head it off by suggesting that to avoid duplication, they themselves should make a branch from their canal at Lowtown northwards to Kinnegad, and that the Royal should start there and continue to Cloondara. Jessop surveyed this branch, following Chapman, but making some changes in his line. He thought the idea beneficial to the 'adventurers of the Royal Canal'; but the adventurers disagreed, and Jessop's labour was wasted. Given their subsequent financial history, they might have done well to compromise.

Jessop also remarked in his report that whereas the early Grand Canal locks had been made too big, some later ones were too small: he asked for standardisation at 69ft length. This was done, locks thereafter taking craft 63ft 6in × 14ft, and having 5ft 6in on the sills. But had Jessop forgotten that it had been Smeaton who had proposed locks of 60ft in 1773?

Finally, he made proposals for constructing the canal through bog. He had, of course, already had experience of drainage works, though nothing on the scale of the Bog of Allen, where many miles of canal had to be taken across undrained peat.

His problem was to drain the water away from a strip of land wider than the canal, upon which sides and banks could be built able to take the weight of clay puddle. His solution was developed as he gained experience—its gaining can be followed in successive reports. Whether to begin with he really agreed with Smeaton we cannot tell. His old master was then alive, and it would have been difficult for Jessop publicly to disagree with recommendations that had been so forcibly expressed in 1773 to the directors of the same company for whom he himself was working. But if he did, he soon moved towards Chapman's view, with which he may indeed have agreed from the beginning.

In its final form his method is well described by the Mullins'. Bernard Mullins when young had been an overseer on the worst stretch of bog construction, that at Edenderry to which we shall return. Later he became a partner in the great Irish canal, railway and road contracting firm of Henry, Mullins & McMahon:

> Parallel drains, at ten perches* from the centre line on either side, were made, and at two perches distant from these, and from each other, a series of parallel drains to the extent of 34 perches from the centre line on either side, were then made, embracing a breadth of 68 perches; these were crossed at right angles, at two perches distant from each other, so that the area of the bog, from the 10-perch drain to the 34-perch drain, on each side of the embankment, was divided into squares or ramparts of four perches area each. The drains of those squares were continually widened and sunk, and the spoil thrown on the ramparts. When the spoil became dry it was wheeled, together with an 18-inch lift of the ramparts, into the embankment in which the material was firmly trampled and chopped, and while all the dry ramparts were so disposed of a new set were being similarly prepared by sinking the drains. The formation of the canal thus proceeded until the navigation was opened.[9]

It must be added to this account that only after the water had by this method been drained away from the centre to the outermost parallel drains, and after the building up of the embankments, was the canal itself excavated by having the central core removed. Finally,

* A perch is 5½yd.

Great quantities of clay were then boated for the lining of the bottom and sides, soling the trackways,* and covering the whole surface of the banks . . . the banks were . . . perfectly retentive.

Jessop sought to obtain a stable canal lining without necessarily having to cut down to the bottom of the bog. His system required great care and diligence from the contractors, for it depended entirely upon deepening the outermost drains over and over again, a little more each time, one step ahead of the same thing being done on the inner drains, until the centre had dried and sufficient firm material to build the banks had been obtained.

It must have been wet, cold work, and tempting to scamp, for it often was scamped. Jessop was to write in 1801: 'The Directors will recollect that . . . much money (has) been thrown away for want of system in the cutting thro' Bogs', [10] and in 1802 Richard Griffith (father of Sir Richard Griffith, the well-known engineer) was to say of contractors' failure endlessly to recut and deepen the back drains as the inner parallel drains were also deepened: 'the want of these precautions has frequently irritated Mr. Jessop, who is not easily moved to anger, and it has cost us much time and many thousands of pounds to remedy'.[11]

When Jessop first began to extend the canal from Lowtown across the bog, canal construction seems to have followed too quickly after the preliminary draining to allow fully for probable subsidence. Therefore he found himself carrying his canal upon unnecessarily high embankments. But certainly by 1794 he was agreeing with Chapman that the extent of subsidence should be allowed for when deciding the canal level, for he wrote in one of his reports of 19 September:

Whatever line may be adopted I hope it will be remembered, that no time should be suffered to elapse without beginning on the Drainage of the Bogs, after the purchases are effected . . .

In the draining of the Bogs, where they are deep and wet are found to settle to one half of their original Section; they have hitherto been set to Contractors at the measure of their original Section . . . it has been found difficult to restrain them from working improperly and taking out the Core prematurely.

It will be advisable in future cases not to Contract for the Core at all until the side drains are cut down to the Bottom . . .[12]

On the stretches beyond Tullamore built after 1801, the time gap

---

* The Irish term for towpaths.

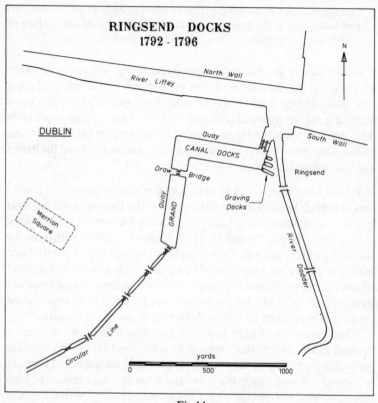

Fig 11

between drainage and construction was widened, so reducing embankment height.

In 1791 Jessop was back in Ireland to plan the extensive docks that the Directors of the Grand Canal had decided to build at Ringsend and for which an Act had been obtained in May (Fig 11). His report cannot be traced, but from several letters written to Boulton & Watt, ordering two steam engines for draining the excavations, we know he was in Dublin for at least three weeks during July and August.[13] A sketch of somewhat later date (Fig 12) is almost certainly copied from Jessop's design, made on this visit, for the massive structure of the triple entrance locks.[14] On returning to England, he left Chapman to deal with further correspondence about the engines and pumps, and other preliminary matters to do with the docks, and at about this time Millar, having completed the canal to Athy, became resident engineer on the Circular Line. James Oates continued on the Shannon Line.

92

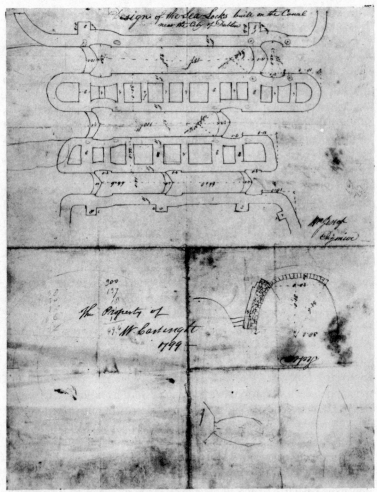

Fig 12 Sketch of Jessop's design for the triple entrance locks to
Ringsend Docks, Dublin

On Jessop's next visit, in the summer of 1792, he looked first at the
Circular Line and in a report dated 25 June wrote detailed comments on
it, lock by lock and bridge by bridge.[15] He also gave instructions for
building the dock wall foundations. Draft contracts had by now been
prepared for his approval and on 14 July, before leaving Dublin, he
produced a dozen drawings including plans and sections of the graving
docks and designs for the gates of the ship lock.[16]
Construction work at Ringsend started soon afterwards, probably

with Millar in charge, and the first steam engine was in operation by September.[17] This 3hp sun and planet engine, with a 10½in diameter cylinder and a 3ft stroke, is one of the earliest ever used for pumping in foundation works.

During the same visit, Jessop considered the route to be taken towards the Shannon. The first proposal had been to meet the river at Banagher. Chapman had now surveyed this, and Jessop liked it, as offering the prospect of building a branch from the main line short of it to the Shannon higher up: to Athlone at the south end of Lough Ree would be too expensive, but Shannonbridge might be possible. However, Jessop asks that Chapman should do further surveys that should 'trace the Levels of all the passes that may invite attention between Ballycoven Castle and Belmount Bridge on the Brusna' and thinks it possible that the canal might run north of the river Brosna to the Shannon, so shortening a northern branch.[18]

On the Athy line, completed in 1791, he looks at the need for an aqueduct at Monasterevan where the canal crossed the Barrow by locking down into the river and up again. Chapman had suggested this, and Oates had done plans and estimates. Jessop, however, thinks it would not be worth the expense unless in connection with a talked-of branch towards Mountmellick.[19] He approves Oates' proposal for the point at Athy where canal should meet river.

1793 saw the seven locks and 3¾ miles of the Circular Line completed, followed by Millar's departure to the Lancaster Canal and the appointment of Chapman's brother Edward as resident engineer at Ringsend, with a salary of 300 guineas.[20] Jessop on his visit to Ireland in 1793 was cheifly concerned with the Royal Canal. A committee of the Irish House of Commons was set up to investigate what had happened to £7,000 granted the company in 1792 to make docks, but which they had instead spent on canal construction. Much disputation followed, Richard Evans the engineer being attacked by Brownrigg, who seems to have hoped to get the job himself, with Thomas Hyde Page for his consultant. The Directors called Jessop in on four points:[21] whether between Blanchardstown and the ninth lock, to raise embankments 9ft or to cut that much deeper through rock; whether the single-arched Rye aqueduct was being properly built; what the effect of constructing a three-rise staircase near Dublin would be; and, lastly, to check levels throughout to decide between Evans and Brownrigg. This last Jessop declined to do for lack of time.

On the first point he recommended cutting as cheaper than embanking. As for the second, the Rye aqueduct was really a large culvert in a long, high embankment, the works of which had been begun in 1791, but damaged by floods in 1792. They were not to be finished till 1796. He said of it that it 'appears to be well executed, and the Walls are very substantial, much more so than I should think necessary; and I did not see any Point that in my Opinion wanted strength'.

As regards the proposed three-rise set of locks, he said:

> Where the Saving of Water is a very material Consideration single Locks are most adviseable where there is no Passage-boat Trade to require a Lock-keeper at each Lock; but where a Lock-keeper is necessary at every Lock this will more than counterbalance the Expence of obtaining Water, and in this Case double Locks are better; a treble Lock will consume more Water than a double one where the total Rise of each is the same.

Thomas Hyde Page strongly attacked Jessop's report, but in the event Evans survived and Page's relationship with the company did not.

These visits to Ireland caused a pile-up in Jessop's other work. He writes to Mr Taylor at Bridlington on 1 September 1793: 'I am just returned from Ireland, and find your letter among a multitude of others which call me to various concerns, which I am obliged to attend to. . . .'[22]

Back in Ireland in the summer of 1794 he wrote three reports, all dated on 19 September from Dublin.[23] One discussed the pros and cons of a northerly and a southerly line from Tullamore to the Shannon. Jessop is now inclined to prefer a higher level line from Tullamore that Chapman has found. He fairly points out, however, that the older northern line would be both cheaper and slightly shorter, and leaves the choice open to the Directors.

In his second report of September 1794 Jessop is pleased with the progress at Ringsend and makes some helpful suggestions regarding execution of the works. At the same time he sends in the remainder of the design drawings required. A second, larger steam engine, purchased locally, is now installed[24] for the entrance lock foundations.

He also deals with problems presented by the worst bog section on the whole canal, the half mile or so across the deep and intractable Edenderry bog beyond Ticknevin and short of Philipstown (Daingean). The bog here was too deep to drain properly, and Jessop had to face draining it 'as far as is necessary to carry a floating Embankment over it'. He asked therefore for construction to stop while repetitive drain cutting lowered the water level as far as possible.

95

Looking beyond this difficulty to the canal's eventual completion to the middle Shannon, the question of what trade might be expected to pass into and out of the river began to loom. Northwards of the likely junction near Banagher lay Athlone and Lough Ree; to the south, Portumna and Lough Derg. Some work to improve navigation had been done from 1755 onwards on this stretch of the river, but when William Chapman surveyed it for the Limerick Navigation Company in 1791, he pointed out how much was wrong with it.

This naturally worried the Grand Canal Board, for their prosperity would depend upon easy navigation of the middle Shannon.[25] They therefore began negotiations with the government for financial help in exchange for themselves improving the central river. A committee of the Irish House of Commons reported favourably in 1794, and Jessop was then asked to survey the whole river. His third report was the result.

He covers the Shannon from Lough Allen in the north to Lough Derg, having used reports and plans made by John Brownrigg and Chapman when they were working for the Grand Canal Company, and having examined the river himself. The result is a proposal for comprehensive development.

The two great Objects that call for an Opening of this Navigation are, the Collieries in the Vicinity of Lough Allen and the Cultivation of an extensive Country in ten Counties bordering on or near to the Banks of the Shannon.

As Coal is found on both Sides of Lough Allen, and at Points widely extended from each other, the Strata inclining with a gentle Dip, it is reasonably presumed that there are many thousand Acres; it is good and easy to be worked, and as much of it can be drained without Steam Engines, it may be got at an easy Expense; it is found excellent for smelting Iron Stone, of which there are immense Quantities of the best Quality.*

For want of Markets for Barley and Wheat, the Agriculture of the Country is limited generally to the Growth of Potatoes and Oats; this Fact, independent of other Arguments, speaks too forcibly to need other Proof of the very great national and local Benefit that will be derived from the Opening of this River with its Branches to the Sea, and to the Inland Communications which are approaching it . . .

* The centre for coal mining was, and is, Arigna. But though coal has been mined in the area from Jessop's to our own day, the seams were not rich enough to justify Jessop's hopes of substantial traffic, and output has always been low and barely economic. There were also ironstone deposits, there being ironworks at Arigna from 1788 onwards, which operated intermittently till 1838. The iron content of the ironstone was, however, low. Whoever gave Jessop his information was, we fear, being wildly optimistic.[26]

The Shannon, he explains, is wide and slow, with low banks over which water floods easily, and much obstructed by eel weirs. If is to be efficient, it must have a trackway, to be built usually on the western shore so that craft may be sheltered from the wind, 2ft above flood and 5ft above land level. This, however, will require that where the characteristic bankside reed beds are wide, a navigation channel should be cut through them beside the trackway. For the rest, improved navigation required a series of short and longer bypass and linking cuts at critical sections, together with lock rebuilding to modern standards.

The great lake of Lough Ree could not, however, be given a trackway and navigation channel:

> Boats must . . . trust to their Sails; the Rocks and Shallows must be marked by Buoys or Beacons; if the Islands were planted it would much improve the Navigation by affording Shelter for Vessels which might moor to the Leeward of them; so provided, decked Vessels that will pass on the Canals may navigate with Safety on the Lake by the Assistance of Lee-boards to be used occasionally; it will be only in stormy Weather that they will be liable to Detention, or when the Wind is directly against them.

He did, however, suggest that 'a Branch from the Grand Canal to join the River above this Lake' might be considered. He concludes:

> The Estimate annexed will shew that the Expence of completing the Navigation of the Shannon bears little Proportion to the Benefits which will result from it.

It was for £72,819 from Lough Allen to Lough Derg.

The Grand Canal board, having ordered all three reports and estimates to be entered in their minutes, added:

> Resolved Unanimously that the thanks of the Directors be given to Mr. Jessop for his eminent services to the Company, and that he be particularly requested to give to the Company as much of his time as he can possibly afford. The Directors feeling that the Services of Mr. Jessop are of the utmost Value to the Company upon all occasions.[27]

The formal opening of Ringsend Docks took place on 23 April 1796 (p 102). With a total area of 25 acres this was the biggest single wet dock so far built, though soon to be surpassed by Jessop's West India Docks (Chapter 10). There were three graving docks and three entrance locks: one for barges and two for ships, the larger of which had a clear width of 28ft, a length of 149ft between gates and a depth of 18ft on the sills at high-water spring tides. The locks were built with inverted arch foundations, and the dock walls had a curved vertical profile. The north wall moved forward a little during construction and in a letter of 16 January Jessop sketches his idea for the remedial measures. consisting of buttresses and additional piling at the toe.[28] Apart from this there seem to have been no serious mishaps; the Directors expressed their complete satisfaction with Edward Chapman's conduct of the job[29] and in a report of 16 September 1796, written during his visit to Ireland that year, Jessop's only criticism is that he himself would have made the long graving dock slightly wider.[30]

In the same report he has much to say on the Shannon line, where the Edenderry embankment was still a major anxiety. Of the latter Captain Evans had reported:

> The Edenderry Bog has again got into a bad state since the rain, and that what we have done latterly has been of little use, as the Bog has sunk, cracked and given way as formerly, so much that I conceive it lost labour to persevere in wheeling Bog Stuff on the bad parts as when the Top weight is added, the bottom stuff gives way.[31]

Though Jessop hoped this embankment was

> in a fair way to completion, I cannot divest myself of anxiety on that subject, since the last failure of an attempt to open it; it is proceeding in the best way that can be devised, but the time & expense is yet uncertain.

And so he suggested a procedure that was to cause much controversy.

> ... when about 3 feet of water can be let into it, it is proposed to give it every possible security by sinking a Rib of Clay on each side of the most precarious part of it, this rib shou'd be begun about 3 yards in thickness, and as it gradually sinks shou'd be gradually reduced, so that when the Clay may be sunk, if it will sink to the bottom of the Bog, it may be left 2 yards in thickness at the Top, the trench for it shou'd be cut progressively in short lengths, not exceeding 3 or 4 yds at once, it may be about 2 yards in depth of more, if it can conveniently be done; the distance of the trench from the verge of the

Canal, may be about 55 feet, and the rib of Clay shou'd be made to lean gradually towards the Canal, so that it may be ultimately at the distance of 50 feet, in order that it may counteract the tendency of the Bog to press outward, its section, when compleated, will represent, and have the effect of a battering wall, I expect that each rib may cost about £5 a running perch, and it may possibly require about 50 perches in length on each side; its progress in sinking must be ascertained from time to time by boring rods, in order that its gradual diminution of thickness may be properly preserved.

In other words, these walls were intended to sink down to the gravel and clay beneath the bog, and so stand firm to hold the loose light stuff of the embankment, itself floating on the bog, from slipping sideways.

Near Tullamore, beyond the bog, Jessop gives instructions for building the line in such a way that earth and stone should quickly be made available for embankments and walling, and some parts made navigable so that they could be used for building the rest.

His report, accompanied by main estimates for the Tullamore-Shannon line and several subsidiary estimates, was so well received that 50 guineas were added to his bill 'as a small testimonial of the continuance of our esteem for him', making the payment £346 18s 9d in all. And here we must make an obvious point: what Jessop wrote formally, we have; but what he said, we do not know. But he must have talked to, encouraged, explained to, enlightened, men from directors to junior engineers and navvies, and from one end of the canal to the other.

In November, back at Newark, Jessop received a letter from the Board. There had been disagreement upon the Edenderry embankment, and therefore he was sent a situation report, and asked to say what should be done. He replied:

.... under all the circumstances of the case, I do not feel much apprehension of danger in taking in 3 feet of water. In the progress of strengthening & finishing the embankment, the Bog stuff to be laid on the tail or foot of the Slopes cannot be too heavy, & it may be got as heretofore from behind;—the black Bog will be best;—but on the top of the embankment, the stuff cannot be too light, and Bog earth as nearly dry as may be so as to be capable of being trod solid, will be best got by boating; before Clay is laid on, there should be laid on the Banks a Stratum of the Sods of heath, to prevent the Clay from sinking . . . . .[32]

Jessop had not meant to return to Ireland in 1797, the year in which the canal was opened to Philipstown (Daingean), some 50 miles from

Dublin and 40 from the Shannon. But in August the canal breached at the point near Edenderry where the clay walls were being built. One of the canal's Directors, Richard Griffith, whom we can describe as a gentleman engineer, wrote to him in November, before he arrived[33]

> Tho I entertain as high an opinion as any man can, both of your knowledge and good sense', yet 'I was convinced at the time and am now still more by the event, that you were entirely wrong on that occasion, and I am persuaded that if you had seen the state of the Bog you would not have decided as you did.

Griffith thought there had been four causes of the breach: insufficient lining to the canal, unstable banks, lack of attention to the back drains and, above all, damage to the canal's precarious foundation from the clay wall on the south side. He thought that this last,

> having no other foundation than that on which the whole of this part of the Canal is erected, namely water . . . . sunk down from its own weight, and in sinking displaced part of the base on which the Canal was erected, made cracks and fissures in the Banks, into which the water of the Canal rushed and carried away the whole body.

Griffith admitted that had the clay walls been built before the canal itself, 'it would have been the safest Mode of proceeding', but as it was, he recommended 'a small body of clay at the bottom of the Canal which is already done and a mixture of clay and Bog stuff on the Banks upon a very broad Base with one general and equal pressure . . . upon the principle of the Broad Snow Shoe'.
He ends:

> You deservedly stand too high in the public esteem to be afraid to confess an error when you are convinced of it . . . I sincerely hope I have converted you—the very existence of the Canal now depends on your determination . . .

Jessop replied from Newark on 30 November in a long and technical letter which, however, ended: 'Whatever may have been the immediate cause of the Breach I cannot impute it to the clay wall . . . '[34] He then crossed to Ireland, and was there for much of December and part of January. His report of 27 December dealt only with Edenderry:[35]

> I have again examined the state of the Embankment on the Bog near

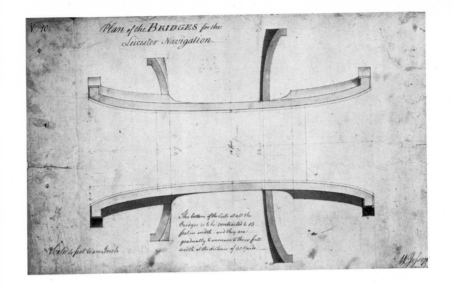

Leicester Navigation: (*above*) Jessop's drawing for a standard
design of bridge and (*below*) for flood sluices

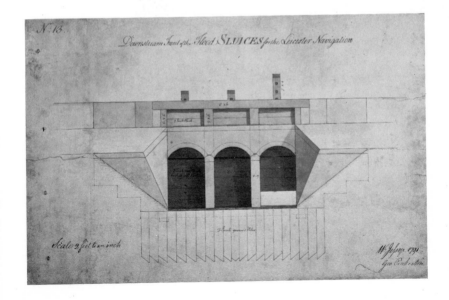

(above) Dublin: the opening of the docks at Ringsend, 23 April 1796

(below) One of Jessop's drawings of 1794 for the Ellesmere Canal

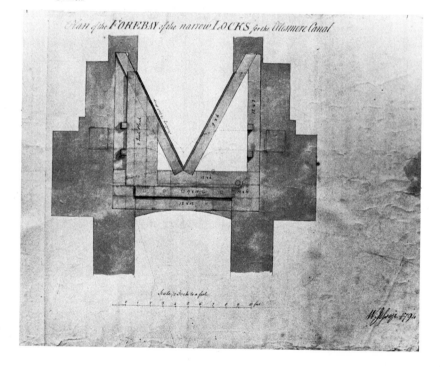

Edenderry, and from the appearance, and the consideration of its having had so many Months of tryal in a very wet season I am almost inclined to think it safe: but as the existance of the Canal to the Shannon depends entirely upon the security of this Embankment, I must still recommend the addition of a wall or abutment of Clay or Gravel: I am perfectly satisfied that no injury can arise from it: and in the way that I have now to propose it may be carried on in a Mode that will give gradual security.

He now suggests building the walls 75ft instead of 55ft 'from the verge of the Canal', and

instead of carrying it on progressively, I would recommend that it should be done in detached pieces of about 9 feet square at the Base and at the distance of about 5 Perches from each other, those to be carried on until they have sunk to a foundation and are finished; they will immediately give a degree of support to the Bank; the intervals may then be subdivided by an equal number of similar pieces or abutments, which will reduce the interval to 2 Perches: those may again be subdivided until the whole is united, or until experience may produce a feeling of Security, which may dictate the propriety of stopping the proceeding.

His reasons follow, and then he gives the addition of more clay to the bottom and sides, together with keeping the back drains open, as the best other means of keeping the canal watertight,

for though it can never be drained below a certain Depth, and the Canal and Banks must ever float, like a huge Vessel upon an imperfect fluid below it, it is material that this Vessel should have the thickest possible bottom to it, and every inch that the Drains can be lowered will add an inch to its thickness . . .

He ends:

I hope and trust that the combined effect of those several operations will give permanent stability to a work to which in all probability there is nothing similar in the world.

And so, in 1798, the canal was opened past the bog to Tullamore some 20 miles from the Shannon. But in January 1800 it once again breached at the same place near Edenderry. John Killaly, in immediate charge, first 'wheeled dried bog material into the breach, firmly ramming it into its place, and incorporating it thoroughly with the broken sides'.[36] He then lessened the water depth, which he thought too great, and afterwards puddled the bottom. Finally, he suggested that the clay walls should be moved still further back.

Jessop came over to Ireland in April 'at the pressing desire of Sir John Macartney and Mr. Griffith on a business of very great importance', to survey the proposed ship canal from Ringsend Docks to Kingstown (Dunleary, Dun Laoghaire).[37] He had not the time to visit Edenderry. However, he concluded that the clay walls had not reached firm ground, as he had intended they should, and recommended holes to be cut between them to help new walls to sink right down to firm gravel. Griffith disagreed again, considering the embankment was being carried on a bog crust firm enough to bear it, and that the walls would puncture and weaken this.

Killaly had recommended putting more clay into the canal bottom to reduce the depth from the 10ft it had reached. He then cut it down to 6ft, and also widened the canal's inner slopes. These measures seem to have remedied the trouble: indeed, we may guess that the main cause of the breach may well have been, not Jessop's walls, but allowing an excessive depth and so weight and pressure of water. No further clay walls were, however, built, Jessop writing:

> . . . tho' I feel the strongest impression that a wall of Clay executed according to the true intention of it would be the most probable means of obtaining security, I feel myself no longer inclined to advise it until any further symptoms may make its security, in its present state, doubtfull.[38]

This letter from Jessop, incidentally, reveals an odd fact about such an eminent man: that although he was writing from his home at Newark, he had there no file of his earlier reports on the canal, but was relying on his memory for what he had said some years before.

With the advantage of hindsight, the Mullins' were later to criticise the way the bog had been crossed at Edenderry. The canal there, they said,

> furnishes a two-fold instance of the difficulty of making a canal through bog, where the level of the substratum is below that of the adjacent river, and of the ill-effects of not going deeply into the bog. It was supposed that the level chosen, which afforded from 6ft to 9ft of cutting, was such as would enable the undertaking to be completed at least possible expense . . The excavations and drainage

were carried on concurrently, and that which was expected to be an unusually cheap reach of canal in shallow cutting, ended, after several years of unremitting labour and enormous expense, in the formation of a bank on either side, 45ft high for a distance of 80 perches, so that the canal with the carrying up of its sides and bottom to the required level, containing six feet of water, was in the centre of a high artificial embankment, having a base of fully 400ft.[39]

We in Britain are familiar with this result, both in the Fens where the rivers have risen higher and higher above the countryside, and where coal and salt subsidence have caused canals to finish on high embankments.

The breach having been repaired, the line from Robertstown to Tullamore gave no further troubles of any great consequence for many years. 32 miles long with eight locks and crossing the most extensive peat bog ever traversed by a canal, the line had been under construction since 1789 with Jessop as chief consulting engineer throughout. The costs of this and of the two other works carried out entirely under his direction are summarised in Table 2.

Table 2

Works carried out under Jessop's direction

	Construction period	Cost £	Resident engineers
Line from Robertstown to Tullamore	1789–1800	174,000	James Oates and John Killaly
Circular Line	1790–1793	52,000	Archibald Millar
Ringsend Docks	1792–1796	113,000	Edward Chapman

Surveys had been made by Chapman, Killaly and Oates for the canal's line beyond Tullamore to the Shannon, but no decisions taken, when Jessop did his own survey and set out his findings in his report from Dublin of 26 December 1797. Chapman had proposed a southern route through Birr to Banagher, Killaly and Oates a northerly one nearly to Athlone. Jessop made two proposals for a more central line: either to continue from Tullamore on the same level through Frankford (with possible branches to Birr and Roscrea), and then fall through a flight of locks to the Shannon at Banagher, or to keep further north and drop down the valley of the Brosna to join the Shannon north of

Banagher. Of these, he preferred the Brosna route. Because of floods at the time of his survey, however, he could not decide whether the river itself could be used, though he thought it probably could from Ferbane downwards.[40]

In June 1801 the company chose the Brosna Valley line. Killaly thought it impracticable to use the river, and proposed a route he had surveyed with 22 miles of canal, 8 of them through bog. Jessop, asked to look over Killaly's line, confirmed that the 6 miles he had had time to see on a fine day were 'very judiciously laid out'.[41] In a postscript written two days later, after seeing the remainder of the line, Jessop authorises a very rare—for him—staircase pair of locks: 'I see no objection to the double Lock* as I believe there will be plenty of Water'.

Richard Griffith was asked to take charge part-time of construction. Again, the bog lengths proved the worst problem. Griffith wrote early in 1802 that 'there is no serious difficulty to encounter in this line, but the Bogs, and they are tremendous'. And within this problem was that of making the contractors endlessly recut and deepen the back drains as the inner canal boundary drains were also deepened.

Jessop did not revisit the canal again, and Killaly had to struggle with more leakage troubles on the section through Glyn and Belmont before the canal was permanently opened towards the end of 1805. At the Shannon junction a basin was built—Shannon Harbour—reached from the river by two river-sized locks 80ft × 16ft × 6ft. The Grand Canal was finished.

As a result of Jessop's 1794 report on the Shannon, the canal company had offered to take responsibility for the navigation of the river for the whole distance between Lanesborough (at the head of Lough Ree) and Killaloe (at the foot of Lough Derg) and work it with low tolls, if the government would provide the capital sums Jessop had estimated to be needed. Nothing had happened, but as the canal had neared Shannon Harbour and action became urgent, they began negotiations with the newly-appointed Directors of Inland Navigation, using Jessop's report and figures as a basis.

The Directors agreed to the company's suggestion that they should immediately 'lay out a few hundred pounds on some of the locks'. The Grand's committee then asked Jessop to accompany Killaly on a survey of the Shannon in 1801, being anxious to establish the current state of the navigation because of the negotiations to take it over.

They must have given him an optimistic brief, for he wrote in his report dated 1 December 1801 from Dublin:[42]

* No 33, at Belmont

I have been instructed to consider this work as a great National concern unfettered by local considerations or parsimonious frugality, and that it was to be fitted to embrace and accommodate all Collateral Canals which may hereafter communicate with it, and be adapted to the largest size of Vessels which can Navigate on any such Canal, now made or making.

I therefore must look on the River Shannon as the great Artery of Ireland, destined by future Ramifications to circulate its commerce and give animation to the Country.

Therefore, instead of taking the Shannon's older cuts as settling the dimensions for new ones, Jessop estimates them to be 6ft deep instead of the Grand Canal's 5ft, 'to accommodate vessels which may use other Canals', and therefore 26ft wide at bottom against 24ft, craft to be able to pass anywhere, with bank slopes 18in to the foot instead of 15in 'to provide for the wash', and with benched trackways in cuttings instead of the path running along the top. Other improvements included a better trackway embankment with timber bridges every half mile to allow flood meadows to continue and to pass side streams, and also over the river itself when the trackway changed, whereas previously he had provided for ferries.

These improvements, coupled with an increase in wages 'in the proportion of 9 pence to a shilling' compared with his former estimate, nearly doubled the figures. His total was now £175,275, of which £119,454 was for the Lough Allen to Lough Ree stretch, and £55,821 from the south end of Lough Ree to Lough Derg. However, he said, as if hinting that all this was too good to be true, if it proved necessary to do the work 'with that rigid economy which might be an object to a private Company who might naturally look for Emolument as Adventurers', then 'large sums might be saved', and the total reduced to £131,000 without lessening lock, bridge or channel dimensions. The level of wages, he thought, was unlikely to fall to produce further savings and, 'considering the condition of the laboring Inhabitants of Ireland it is perhaps not to be wished or desired that it should'.

He gave 29 days to this Irish visit—from 8 November to 6 December—charging 145 guineas and 35 guineas for expenses going and returning.

Israel Rhodes followed with a detailed middle Shannon survey[43] in 1802. In some respects he differed from Jessop. He thought the sills of all the locks were too high, and wanted parallel canals cut 'in the Meadows' instead of using the natural stream, because the river

107

navigation would be tedious and difficult for nine months out of the twelve, and because the trackways might be damaged by surge. Jessop did not agree to either proposition, of the first saying it 'may possibly in some cases be advisable', but 'it cannot be done generally', in the second case instancing 'Banks similarly constructed exposed to the lash of the German Ocean without materially suffering'.[44]

The canal to Shannon Harbour being almost finished, a decision was urgent, so the canal company went ahead to rebuild the middle Shannon locks without the sanction of the Directors General. With prices and wages still rising, the canal company asked them for two thirds of the cost, against a limitation of tolls to 1d a ton-mile. It was not, however, until March 1806 that agreement was reached, the Directors General granting £54,634 towards the middle Shannon works between the north end of Lough Derg and Athlone.

These were completed in 1810, and remained in use till the major reconstructions of the 1840s. No trackways were, however, built, boats having to be part-sailed, part-shafted until the beginnings of steam navigation. On the upper Shannon, little was done for many years except to build the Lough Allen canal in the 1820s. Therefore little traffic developed: in 1830 only 14,368 tons on the middle Shannon, in 1835 9,770 tons on the upper.

Jessop's last visit to Ireland, in January 1806, was concerned with the Barrow. This river navigation from the Grand Canal's branch to Athy down past Carlow to its tidal lock at St Mullins, led to the south coast and also to the navigations of the Nore and the Suir, the latter navigable past Waterford to Carrick-on-Suir. Work on making the river navigable had started in 1751, but only a small part had been finished by 1790 when the Barrow Navigation Company was authorised to take over the work from the Board of Inland Navigation. They started to follow a report of William Chapman's of 1789, which proposed raising the size of boats using the river from 20–40 tons as it then was to 80 tons, by building new locks and rebuilding old ones to a standard 80ft × 16ft.

It seems that in 1801, when General Tarrant surveyed the Barrow, Jessop had accompanied him, for the Grand Canal minutes of 4 October 1805 refer to a letter from the Barrow Company asking to see Killaly's adverse report on the Barrow, which was influencing the Grand Canal in planning to build a canal from the collieries to Athy to avoid the river, and say that Killaly's report differs greatly from that of 'Jessop and General Tarrant'.

In his report[45] of 4 February 1806 from Dublin, the 61 year old

Jessop said that he had surveyed the river from Athy to the tideway and was clear

> that the River Barrow may be made navigable with a five feet depth of water in every part of it in the dryest seasons not only without injury to private property but with a considerable benefit to all the existing Mills on the River and to the lands on the borders of it.

That this depth had nowhere yet been reached had been due to the policy of gradual improvement along the whole navigation that the Barrow's engineer, Humphrey Mitchell, had been following, and which Jessop thought sensible, 'considering it unnecessary to raise the Weirs and Trackways to their full height while any obstruction in other parts may call for more immediate attention'.

But to dispel 'the too prevailing doubts of the public which have probably generated from an apparently slow progress of the works without the true causes of it having been known', he suggests that as a public relations move the top stretch from Athy to Carlow should be finished that year at a cost not exceeding £1,500, so that it might 'induce many to be prepared to take advantage of the full completion who might not otherwise begin to prepare until they should see the whole completed'.

And so, in that same year, William Colvill, a flour merchant of Dublin and chairman of the Barrow Company at the time, presented Jessop with an Irish silver snuff box as a 'token of the high sense he entertains of his matchless abilities as an engineer and of the application of these to the improvement of the navigation of the river Barrow'.[46]

But the work was never fully done, nor the depth obtained throughout, and the Barrow remained a good deal less perfect than Jessop had hoped.

At the last moment before Jessop left Ireland, the Grand Canal Company wrote to him at Dublin, this time as a railway engineer, to ask him to estimate for a railway from the coalfields of Doonane near Castlecomer to the Cardington, or long level, of the Barrow line above Athy. But 'the wind is fair for me', and so he excused himself. His Irish experience had extended over more than thirty years, and taken in four of the country's principal navigations: his reports make clear how much he had enjoyed it, the bogs notwithstanding.

6
THREE GREAT CANALS:
THE GRAND JUNCTION, ROCHDALE AND BARNSLEY

Jessop engineered three great canals over almost the same span of years: one the main heavy traffic line joining the industrial North and Midlands to London; one the first canal to link Lancashire and Yorkshire over the Pennines; one a major coal carrier and part of the Aire & Calder—Don waterway link. All three were instant and continuing commercial successes.

Grand Junction Canal

From the end of 1791 ideas of bypassing the lower Oxford Canal and the Thames to London had been publicly discussed,[1] and in early 1792 a group, led by the Marquess of Buckingham, commissioned James Barnes, then rising 52 and five years Jessop's senior, to do a preliminary survey. Barnes had worked for the Oxford company between 1786 and end-1791. By then his ability was bringing him so many outside commissions that they gave him notice, so enabling him to move straight into the arms of their rival.

Barnes' line ran from the Oxford Canal at Braunston by way of Blisworth, Fenny Stratford,* Tring, Hemel Hempstead, Watford, Ruislip, Southall and Hanwell to the Thames at Brentford, with an alternative line from near Hemel Hempstead via Rickmansworth, Denham and Uxbridge to Southall. Branches were proposed to Daventry, Stony Stratford, Northampton and (for the first line) Uxbridge. A crowded meeting at Stony Stratford approved Barnes' survey, decided to seek an Act, and appointed a committee whose chairman was the very able banker William Praed. This decided to invite Jessop to report on Barnes' line.

As planned, the canal rose 35ft 6in from the Oxford Canal at Braunston to its first summit that took it through Braunston Tunnel

* Bletchley, now part of Milton Keynes.

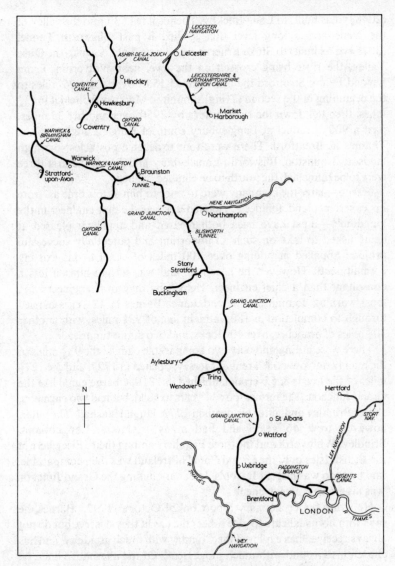

Fig 13   The Grand Junction Canal

$(2048\frac{1}{4}\text{yd}$ as built) to Long Buckby. Thence it fell 63ft into the valley of the Nene and a long level that carried it past Blisworth Tunnel $(3075\frac{2}{3}\text{yd}$ as built) to Stoke Bruerne and a long flight down to the Ouse Valley, the river being crossed on the level near Wolverton. From beyond Fenny Stratford the line climbed 155ft over some 25 miles to the beginning of the second (Tring) summit at Marsworth, held it for $3\frac{3}{4}$ miles, then fell down the river valleys by 295ft over another 35 miles, past a 900yd tunnel at Langleybury south of King's Langley, to the Thames at Brentford. There were four expensive obstacles: the high lands at Braunston, Blisworth, Langleybury and Tring: the first three were to be tunnelled, the fourth to be climbed by locks.

Jessop—later the company were to refer to him at this time as 'from his experience and abilities . . . looked upon as the first engineer in the kingdom'[2]—must have been both pleased and appalled: pleased at being asked to take on such an important and potentially successful project; appalled at adding over 100 miles of canal to his existing commitments. However, he accepted, and was to find himself less a consultant than a chief engineer. Helped by divisional engineers and local working committees, he and James Barnes in 12 years carried through to completion in 1805 a main line of $93\frac{1}{2}$ miles, with another $30\frac{3}{4}$ miles of branches, over 100 locks, and two major tunnels.

There were in England only two comparable canals: the $93\frac{3}{8}$ miles of the mainly narrow-boat Trent & Mersey, opened in 1777, and the $127\frac{1}{4}$ miles of the Leeds & Liverpool, finished in 1816, a barge canal like the Grand Junction. The former took 11 years to build, but had two engineers, James Brindley and, after his death in 1772, Hugh Henshall. The latter, however, took 46 years and had many engineers, Longbothom, Brindley, Whitworth and the three Fletchers among them. Elsewhere in the British Isles only the Grand Canal of Ireland was then comparable, and that too was largely Jessop's. In canal-building the Grand Junction was his greatest achievement.

He wrote his preliminary report on 24 October 1792.[3] Barnes, he says with his usual care to give others the credit they deserve but do not always receive, 'has explored the Country with much assiduity, and has chosen his Ground with much judgement'. Of the alternative lines, he prefers that by Uxbridge; on the proposed branches, he says of that to Northampton that 'the proposed communication with Leicestershire will probably bring a very considerable trade through it'. This last remark refers to the proposed Leicestershire & Northamptonshire Union Canal (see Chapter 3), the appointment as engineer of which Jessop had refused two months before.

112

He assumes that the Grand Junction will be a barge canal, and proposes locks to take 50–70 ton craft as will navigate 'with safety on the Thames, on the Trent if communication should take place with the Navigation to Leicester, and on the Mersey if the present Canals should hereafter be widened, which is not improbable'. Such locks would take two narrow boats, 'and those Boats may pass each other in the Tunnels'. Exclusive of branches, his estimate was £372,175.

As always, Jessop gave special attention to water supply, in this case to the two summits at Tring and between Blisworth and Braunston. On the latter, Barnes had found streams to supply thirty locks a day and more could easily be got by a reservoir to hold floodwater off the clay soil. Tring, however, with its chalky, gravelly soil, would be more difficult. However, Barnes had found thirty locksful a day from streams; if more were needed, 'any quantity may be got from Streams at a lower Level by means of a Steam Engine'. It was to tap these streams, three of them, that Barnes was to plan the Wendover feeder.

The Grand Junction's Act was passed on 30 April 1793, for its main line and branches to Daventry, Northampton, Old Stratford and Watford; the authorised capital was £600,000. Jessop, who had appeared before the Lords committee, became a foundation shareholder, with ten £100 shares (later he took twenty half-shares also), which meant that he could—and did—attend shareholders' meetings which, being held in London in June, could often be fitted in with parliamentary business.

At the first committee meeting, on 3 June 1793, James Barnes was appointed full-time engineer, 'to consider himself as responsible for the Works and people employed', and told to start setting out the line. Jessop was named 'Chief Engineer to this Company'. Not present, he was to be written to 'for Plans and Sections of Locks, Bridges and Tunnells', and desired to apply to 'Mr Wodehouse and Mr Bolton[4] for a Plan of their respective Fire Engines, and for an Estimate of the Expence that will attend the same'.[5]

In May 1793 work began at both ends, as also at Blisworth Tunnel and Tring cutting, until by December, when the committee asked Jessop to survey all works, 3,000 men were employed. In that month the committee noted that a contract had been made 'for executing the several Tunnells between Charles Jones, and John Biggs on their parts, and Mr Barnes on the part of the Company prepared under the direction of Mr Jessop'.[6] It provided for Langleybury to be finished by 1 June 1796, Braunston by 1 January 1797, and Blisworth by 1 June 1797.[7]

Dunstable and St Albans branches were soon withdrawn, but Bills went forward for Buckingham (a continuation of the authorised Old Stratford arm), Aylesbury (its building to be postponed till after Jessop's time), and Wendover, now to be a navigable branch as well as a feeder. These three were authorised in March 1794, and were followed in 1795 by the important Paddington branch and the reinstated St Albans line that was never built. Jessop appeared in Parliament on them all.

Surveys apart, he was quickly involved in all the problems inseparable from building a large canal. By May 1794, for instance, he had found a 68 acre reservoir site at Aldenham to compensate the Colne millers for loss of water, and also a Thameside home for the company's depot at Whitefrairs (upstream of Blackfriars Bridge on the north bank), where he later helped to buy and lay out a three-storeyed building and covered wet-dock.

In the same month, work stopped on preparations for Langleybury Tunnel, with 200,000 bricks made. It had been planned to avoid opposition from the owners of Grove and Cassiobury Parks. However, after Jessop had estimated what the company would save by avoiding the tunnel, a financial settlement was reached with the landowners, which also provided that the canal through their parks should be built to be pleasing to the eye. It still is.

On 3 November 1794 the first section of canal at the southern end opened, from Brentford to Uxbridge. The cut reached Hemel Hempstead in 1797, Tring in 1799 (when the Wendover branch[8] was also finished), Fenny Stratford in May 1800, the Old Stratford branch and to the bottom of Stoke Bruerne Locks in September.

At the other end, Braunston Tunnel had been begun in 1793. In May 1794 Jessop let fly in his report:[9]

> In the Tunnell, they have begun the Walls and Arches in two places, I wish I could say they were proceeding with vigour; they are tolerably busy in the Brick Yards ... I found it necessary to condemn what they have made as deficient both in size and quality ...

Work had also been going on upon the considerable cuttings and embankments between Braunston and Blisworth Tunnels. Apart from the deep cuttings of the tunnel approaches, there was a 36ft high embankment at Weedon, one of 20ft at Heyford and of 40ft at

Bugbrooke, and the crossing of rough country between Gayton and Blisworth. Jessop wrote of this stretch:

> Those works of cutting and Embankment ... tho' little in point of length, have necessarily cost more than all the cutting will cost between Blisworth Tunnel and Marsworth.*[10]

Both Biggs and Jones were working on Blisworth Tunnel. Of Biggs, Jessop said that he had been making good bricks and cutting stone, but had not begun tunnelling. 'Upon the whole', he thought, 'there is an appearance of his conducting it with method and energy'. However, by September Biggs had said that he could not complete his contract on the agreed terms, and thereafter was directly employed under Barnes. Of Jones, Jessop had no opinion at all:

> ... he has done in three places about 24 Yards of Arching in the Tunnell, but part of it must some time or other be taken down again; his Brick Yards are much behind hand, he has no Gins prepared for drawing soil out of the Pits, and he is much wanting in management and economy: I wish he may not be found to be incorrigible.[11]

Jones then voluntarily gave up the contract, Barnes taking over.

By mid-1795 the committee began to realise that money was no longer as easy to come by as it had been in 1793. On 5 May Jessop was asked to estimate the remaining cost of completing the main line and Wendover branch. He did so, and with Barnes added a recommendation to begin cutting the Paddington branch, for which in June he and Barnes were asked separately for proposals for starting work. In August, too, the two engineers, 'thinking it necessary that a reservoir or reservoirs should be provided for furnishing the Braunston summit with an additional supply of water and having discovered near to the same two places which they adjudge to be proper situations ...'.[12] land purchases were agreed. These became Braunston (5 acres) and Drayton (27 acres), to which in 1804 the 100 acre Daventry Reservoir was added.

In May 1795 Biggs and his family were dismissed; in the same month Jessop gave a report on the tunnels and the whole line. The committee heard it on 1 June, and after taking

into consideration the Works at the Tunnells ... Ordered That Mr

---

* At the beginning of the Tring summit.

Barnes do devote as much of his time as he possibly can to the same, and that he do allow nothing but the most pressing circumstances to call him away.[13]

Soon afterwards, on 16 June, Jessop amplified what he had said about Braunston by writing to the company's chairman, William Praed, about Biggs's work there:

I had observed in the month of February last that in one or two of the pits which were nearly open to each other* that his lines were wrong and I particularly charged Mr Hollingsworth to see that they were immediately corrected and to examine the lines in all the other pits ... which he promised me he would do, but he neglected his promise...[14]

However, Jessop went on to say that except in this one instance he had found Hollingsworth 'a valuable servant to the Company', and asked the committee to 'endeavour to forget what is past'. The committee did so, by reprimanding instead of dismissing him. After trouble with a stretch of quicksand 320yd long that preliminary borings had missed, and which cost £4,800 to deal with, Braunston Tunnel was finished in June 1796. Today it still has a small S-bend in it as a souvenir of Hollingsworth's lapse.

Then, four months after Barnes had taken direct charge of Blisworth, on 30 October 1795, '20 yards of that capital Brick-work (for so it was to all outward appearances) fell in altogether without giving the least notice ...'[15] More followed, and work had to stop. The Blisworth story is odd and unclear. Seemingly, the original line of the tunnel as surveyed by Barnes, approved by Jessop, and laid down in the agreed plan and profiles was that of the present tunnel.[16] Then the company's agents and contractors, so Barnes said, agreed to vary the line, seemingly without Barnes' (still less Jessop's) active agreement, began to cut it on a different and longer course, and reported favourably on their progress. Then drainage tunnels driven from the Stoke Bruerne end hit rock, while at the Blisworth end successive falls of arched brickwork occurred.[17]

Jessop, after inspection and consideration, wrote to Praed on 24 November 1795, saying

that the Rock at the Stoke end of the Tunnel dips in such a manner

---

* He means that the tunnels driven outwards from the bottom of neighbouring pits towards each other had nearly met.

into the line of it, as to make it more than probable that the execution of it will be attended with much more difficulty and danger than there was heretofore any reason to apprehend.

Therefore,

to save Expence, to save time, to prosecute the execution of the Canal with comparative ease and absolute certainty, instead of contending with difficulties and very considerable hazard, it will be adviseable to desert the Tunnel entirely and pass by Locks over the Hill[18]

with a 30ft summit cutting, a steam engine to pump up water, and a small reserve reservoir. Such a solution, he said, would be a little cheaper than a new tunnel and, more important, would get the canal open sooner.

Jessop's point of view is clear. He disliked the uncertainty and delay then inherent in tunnelling. In 1794 he had added locks in order to eliminate the 3,000yd summit tunnel Rennie had proposed for the Rochdale Canal, and cut down the same engineer's proposed 4,312yd bore on the Kennet & Avon to 500yd by raising the summit and providing for steam pumping (see Chapter 12). Again, what he was proposing at Blisworth had, on a larger scale, been done at Tring: no tunnel, but a summit cutting reached by lock flights, soon to be provided with reservoirs and steam engines. Finally, he had a keen economic sense. He wanted the canal open, and knew well the extra cost of delay when so much trade was waiting. One cannot help feeling, however, that he should have been less precipitate, letting the situation clarify itself and making sure that he could carry Barnes and the principal committee men with him. He would not then have suffered a serious—though temporary—reverse.

The committee met on 21 January 1796 with Jessop present. They asked him and Barnes to report on the causes of the tunnel failure, and Jessop also to put in writing his reasons for preferring lockage.

On the 26th, Jessop wrote to Boulton & Watt, telling them that he proposed lockage and steam pumping:

... by so doing I have raised a Nest of Hornets about me ... In vain have I urged that there is no uncertainty in a supply by Steam Engines ... I shall have much difficulty in combating their Prejudices.

And so he asks for a brief:

> I know I can maintain my ground on every other Position, and have
> little doubt, that you will enable me to convince them, that a supply
> by Steam Engines is neither impracticable nor uncertain—be the
> future increase of trade what it may . . .[19]

The firm replied that they could supply an engine able to pump 44 locks
of water per day of 12 hours.

Jessop's and Barnes' report[20] was a careful one. It amounted to a sad
confession of insufficient supervision:

> . . .probably much has been amiss from the want of that vigilant
> attention which has latterly been bestowed on the Tunnel at
> Braunston . . .

More particularly, they were

> most inclined to impute the failure generally to the want of the
> necessary hardness in the bricks and mortar.

For the rest,

> To attempt to state precisely the cause or the continued causes of
> this failure would be in vain. If we could compel confession from the
> Many who were employed in the execution much light might be
> thrown on the subject, but their secrets are buried in the ruins.

As the tunnel was being built under Barnes' direct supervision, it must
have been a more than ordinarily awkward report to write, and not
much less so for Jessop, who had probably over-estimated his
reliability.

Barnes then put his own views on what should be done.[21] He said
that he had begun with a predilection for building locks, but had come
to prefer a tunnel as less wasteful of water and expensive in time,
especially as narrow boats would be able to pass in it. He agreed that
Jessop's solution was perfectly practicable, would carry the likely trade
and complete the canal earlier, and

> to the Engineers must be much more agreeable, for though danger
> and difficulties are constant attendants on Tunnelling, Credit and
> satisfaction are always Strangers.

Nevertheless, he recommended tunnelling on the original shorter line, using existing headings, and making better bricks using mills to grind the clay, as had been done at Braunston.

One remark he added was perhaps unwise: 'Tunnels when completed require little Expence to keep them in repair', a forecast hardly borne out by the history of Blisworth itself, let alone such as Harecastle, Norwood or Butterley. Jessop also wrote a separate report[22] in which he summarised what he proposed: 29 locks, a 30ft summit cutting, a small reservoir and a steam engine. They would handle 20 boats a day, and at an average 25 tons a boat for 300 days a year at 1d per ton-mile, would yield the company £77,400pa in net revenue. If traffic grew beyond that, a second engine could be put in. The capital cost would be slightly less than a tunnel, the completion time two years against three or four, and the supervision problem would be removed.

The committee met on 9 February 1796, considered both reports, and decided to ask the opinion of Robert Whitworth and John Rennie. Whitworth Jessop would have regarded as a respected engineer of an older school, but he must have found Rennie's appointment hard to bear: a man sixteen years younger, whose plans he himself had been accustomed to revise. However, at the same meeting, perhaps as a gesture of confidence in the company, Jessop subscribed for five half-shares.

They reported on 7 May 1796,[23] saying that 'a Line over the Summit by Locks and a Steam Engine is perfectly easy of execution', though they thought the cost would be higher than Jessop's estimate, both for construction and pumping. Given this, the extra maintenance of locks, cost of lockkeepers and expenditure of water, 'the balance we apprehend will in the end be in favor of the Tunnel'.

And thus, at the committee meeting held at Blisworth on 17 May 1796, and after inspecting the old and new tunnel lines 'with particular attention', it was unanimously agreed to cut a new tunnel, Barnes himself contracting to complete it in three years for £48,000, the subsequent shareholders' meeting of 7 June ordering 'that Mr Barnes have the entire direction of it'. They were also firm 'that the Tunnel ... be executed in the line originally proposed by Mr Barnes, approved by Mr Jessop, sanctioned by Parliament and directed to be adopted by the resolutions of the Company'.

Jessop's proposals had been rejected. In retrospect, what are we to say? He had economics on his side. If the locks had been built as and when he proposed, the canal would have opened in or before 1800 instead of in 1805. The company would have saved the cost of building first a road and then a tramroad over the hill (perhaps some £12,000), and gained five years of higher takings, which we may estimate at £260,000.* One may guess that if the shareholders had known the immediate future, they would have backed Jessop to a man.

On the other hand, the additional 29 locks were much more than Jessop had needed to eliminate the summit tunnels on the Rochdale (14 locks) and the Kennet & Avon (9 locks). They would certainly have taken longer to pass, even in legging days: as for maintenance, who can estimate the costs of keeping the tunnel in repair against that of the locks? We who now take pleasure cruisers through Blisworth Tunnel may, however, be thankful that we have not to work those 29 extra locks.

For the moment Barnes was in full control, being once referred to as 'chief engineer',[24] and began to set out the Paddington line. At the new Blisworth Tunnel he continued to drive drainage headings from either end, and was soon to begin building a $3\frac{1}{2}$ mile toll road from Blisworth Wharf over the top of the tunnel line to join the Northampton-Old Stratford Turnpike (A508) to give a southern outlet for goods brought by canal to Blisworth. We still have most of it.

Jessop must have smiled a trifle wryly when in mid-November Barnes was told to keep expenditure down on the tunnel and approach cuttings,[25] and then, on 15 March 1797, 'to discontinue all the Works at Blisworth except such as he may judge necessary for the Preservation of those already executed . . . in order that the greater Exertion may be made in prosecuting the Works towards Fenny Stratford and to form a Junction with that part of the Canal which is already completed . . .'[26] The drainage headings were continued: those apart, work was not to restart for six years.

For a year Jessop, his standing with the company impaired, was only asked to clear up outstanding matters, until in September 1797 the committee, involved in economy cuts, minuted that they had taken

> into consideration the charges incurred by Mr Jessop's survey of the works on the Canal, and conceiving Mr Barnes to be in full possession of his sentiments respecting the works now under execution, and that the same do not require his services so frequently as they have hitherto been wanted . . .

Praed was asked to tell Jessop, and to add that he would be told when

---

* The 1806 figure of takings, the first year after the tunnel was open, was £87,392. If we take this sum back five years and subtract from the total the actual takings for those years, the difference is £259,974.

'any occasion shall appear to them to call for his advice and assistance'.[27]

We cannot be sure how much Jessop had earned for his early work on the Grand Junction, but traceable payments for fees and expenses between December 1793 and early 1798, when his balance was settled, total £2,291 14s 5d. Reckoning his fee at 5 guineas a day and expenses at £1 15s a day, this gives some 327 days of work in some 6 years.

In January 1798 Joseph Wilkes took a hand. Wilkes, a colliery owner and businessman from Derbyshire, a committee-man of the Grand Junction and of the Trent Navigation, knowledgeable about railroads as well as waterways, knew Jessop and Outram well. We may indeed guess that Jessop had talked to him about Grand Junction affairs and perhaps warned against over-estimating Barnes' ability. Wilkes began[28] by sending in an estimate by Outram for a railroad from Blisworth to Northampton, but the committee postponed considering it. In September [29] he moved that Outram should accompany Barnes in viewing the canal works and then report. This was negatived, and Barnes alone reported to the November shareholders' meeting.

Thereupon Wilkes wrote to the committee,[30] Barnes replied, and Wilkes then asked for a special meeting. It was held on 22 February 1799 and minuted:

The Committee having discussed and considered the several Matters continued in Mr Wilkes's remarks and Mr Barnes's reply, Resolved That a General Survey on the whole line of the Canal be made by the Committee as soon as the Season will permit ... and that an Engineer be called in to attend them. Resolved that Mr Jessop be desired to attend the Committee upon such Survey, with Mr Barnes.[31]

Jessop was back. Writing in March,[32] even before the survey had taken place, he recommended joining the two ends of canal by 'a temporary Cast Iron Railway from Blisworth to Cosgrove'.*

After visits to other railways had been made and experiments carried out, a committee meeting in August 1799 asked Jessop how long the tunnel would take to build: he replied commonsensically that it would take between two and three years. Barnes said twelve months from the time the canal was finished, but upon being asked whether he would take a contract to complete it in that time, 'he declined entering into an

---

* 10 miles away, the point of junction of the main line with the Old Stratford and Buckingham branch.

121

Engagement for that Purpose, but only gave it as an Opinion that the same was practicable'. Whereupon the committee unanimously decided to build a railway, to be finished by the time the canal approaching from Tring should have reached it. Jessop's and Barnes' report, plan and section were to be sent to Outram (Jessop's partner, of course, at Butterley) who should be asked his terms for building it and then maintaining it for four years. It was to be a double-track plateway laid on stone blocks, each waggon to carry up to 2 tons. The Duke of Grafton as landowner then making difficulties, the proposed track was realigned to keep to the parliamentary line.

In December, Barnes put in a report suggesting that instead of the planned level crossing of the Ouse near Wolverton, with its four falling and four rising locks, an aqueduct and embankment should be built, advantages being freedom from Ouse Valley floods and economy in water consumption. It was the first mention of what was to prove a very troublesome work. He was told to prepare a plan of the necessary embankment, to consult 'Mr Harrison and the several Proprietors of Land that will be affected by it', and to report back.

In February 1800, Jessop was asked to view the whole line with Barnes; he reported in April [33] that Barnes' proposed embankment to avoid eight Ouse locks 'will be a valuable inprovement', but as it would take two years to build, he proposed a level crossing on its upper side using temporary locks, the gates and much other material from which could later be used on the Stoke Bruerne flight. Elsewhere he reports good progress, and finishes by suggesting changes in the proposed layout of wharves at Paddington on the almost completed branch. The company had been thinking of how best to implement the powers given them to supply water in that neighbourhood, for Jessop suggests running waste water into a reservoir, a point picked up in July when the committee agreed to negotiate for land for such reservoirs. [34]

At the end of September 1800, the canal coming north from Fenny Stratford past the temporary Ouse level crossing reached the bottom of the future Stoke Locks, to meet the southern end of Outram's plateway, which he reported finished in October. The Grand Junction's line from Braunston to London was open without the tunnel, as Jessop had so much wanted in 1796, but using rails as a temporary solution.

In October Jessop was asked to survey the completed railway, in November to buy some ice boats, in February 1801 to say whether it would be practicable to run 'Passage and other Boats of small size' on the canal by enabling them to 'pass the Locks by means of a Railway', in July to collaborate with Rennie in making suggestions upon supplying the Paddington area with water, and in September, again with Rennie, to survey the whole canal and especially to advise on water supplies to the summit levels and to mills that might be affected. It was a varied programme for a busy engineer.

And then, on 3 November 1801, the committee decided to seek tenders for Blisworth Tunnel to be built by contract.[35] Three weeks later[36] the committee asked for a section and specification: Jessop provided them on 1 May.[37]

Here is Jessop at the height of his powers. There is now no diffidence about tunnelling. The specification is terse, precise and confident. Internal width is to be 16ft 6in, with an invert 7ft below water level and a crown 11ft above it, the internal radii of the side walls being 20ft, of the arch 8ft, and of the invert 15ft. The side walls and arch are to be two bricks (17in) thick, the invert $1\frac{1}{2}$ bricks (13in).

His covering letter to Praed said:

I have designed the height of it one Foot less than that of Braunston on the faith of its being carried into execution under the particular inspection of Mr. Barnes. I should have otherwise thought it adviseable as I did in that of Braunston to have made the allowance of a Foot for the inaccuracy of Workmanship, and for a degree of Settlement, which will not take place if executed in the manner now specified.

And so he gave Barnes both responsibility and warning.

Barnes having explained that 6 tunnel pits had already been sunk for a total of 102yd, with 2,218yd of drainage heading parallel to the tunnel, and 404yd of cross-headings,

And such Specification and Explanation being very satisfactory to the Committee It is Resolved and Ordered that a Tunnel at Blisworth Hill agreeable to Mr Jessop's Section and Specification be set about without delay . . .

To be on the safe side they proposed to allow contractors $2\frac{1}{2}$ years to finish.

At that time Jessop proposed to build a 100yd tunnel at the Blisworth end, then a short curved cutting, and then the 2,900yd main tunnel, the short tunnel being planned to avoid having to cut deep through ground that held springs likely to cause slips, and which was thought dangerous. However, a heading was able to drain the springs, and more experience discovered that the soil was workable. Barnes therefore proposed a change of plan, which Jessop recommended in December 1802.[38] This was to extend the main tunnel slightly at the Blisworth end, and have the rest in cutting. And so it was, the tunnel, cut from nineteen vertical shafts, being opened on 25 March 1805. As far as we know, Blisworth was the first canal tunnel in Britain to be built using pre-cut drainage headings.

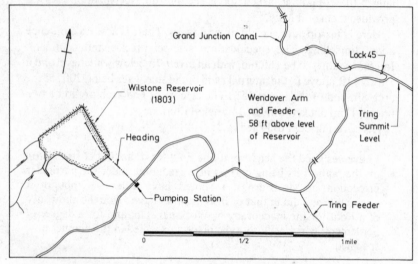

Fig 14   Jessop provides Tring summit with water

The canal had opened throughout late in 1800, whereupon traffic had leaped up. When Jessop and Rennie reported in October 1801, they stressed the urgent need for more water, especially to supply the temporary Ouse crossing. Therefore on 31 October[39] Jessop was asked to seek sources of supply. He must quickly have decided that the Wendover branch was no longer adequate to supply the Tring summit, for on 2 November he and Barnes were told to prepare plans for a reservoir there. He did so, and in February 1802[40] it was given the go-ahead. This was the original (smaller) Wilstone Reservoir of some 40 acres, fed by streams, the beginning of the great reservoir complex of today. Wilstone was below summit level, so a tunnel was run from it to a well at Whitehouses by the Wendover branch, where a steam pumping engine supplied by Jonathan Woodhouse was installed, able to put thirty lockfuls a day into the branch, and so the summit. The tunnel proved difficult to drive because of the water that was encountered, but by June 1803 Wilstone was done.

Given Jessop's concern with Tring summit supplies at this time, the trouble he was having with millers on the Gade, and his known awareness of earlier Continental proposals to use side-ponds, it was probably on his initiative that Benjamin Bevan put in what are thought to be England's first such ponds at Berkhamsted in December 1803. They saved almost half the water used in lockage for a delay of $3\frac{1}{2}$ minutes a lock.[41]

Jessop did another general report in 2 June 1802.[42] One point in it still interests us. He considers that the Fenny Stratford-Wolverton section had been built over-hurriedly to get the canal open. Therefore, through intervening rocky ground, the canal had had to be filled first, and then puddled by boating clay to it. The work was still going on, though nearly finished, and meant that there was shallow water for 2 miles. 'There are now to remedy this two temporary Gates putting down, to pen twelve Inches of Water in this part till the Banks below are gradually raised and made Water tight'. Here we have the origin of the famous shallow lock at Fenny Stratford, with its $10\frac{1}{2}$in fall, for it never was removed, and stands today to puzzle the boater.

Towards the report's end he finds himself writing:

> With the Collateral Branch to Buckingham and that to Wendover there is now open 124 Miles of Canal, connecting the Metropolis with most of the Northern Canals, the great Manufactories attached to them, and with the Ports of Liverpool, Bristol and Hull.

a statement that was as near as Jessop ever got to self-congratulation.

Jessop's connection with the Grand Junction was one of some vicissitudes and great successes. Trouble at Blisworth had to be set against the building and successful opening in only $7\frac{1}{2}$ years (using the railway) or 12 years fully of a canal which, still much as Jessop left it, carried commercial traffic for over 150 years, and has now begun a new and busy life as a pleasure waterway. In 1815, 10 years after full opening, the Grand Junction's takings were £147,857 and dividend 8 per cent. It can justly be described, in Samuel Hughes' words, 'as one of Mr Jessop's principal works'.

The Rochdale Canal

For almost the same spread of years Jessop was also concerned with the construction of another great trunk waterway, the Rochdale, to link the Bridgewater Canal at Manchester with Smeaton's Calder & Hebble at Sowerby Bridge by a broad canal over the Pennines. Not comparable in length—it was 33 miles long—it was indeed comparable to the Grand Junction in the number and dimensions of its locks: it had 92, to take barges 74ft × 14ft 2in. Comparable in importance also, for, first to be finished of the three trans-Pennine canals, it flourished exceedingly.

The Rochdale, the building of which turned out to be almost a pattern-card of trouble-free engineering, is Jessop's unknown achievement. Samuel Hughes does not mention it among Jessop's works, while Samuel Smiles attributes it to Rennie:

> No more formidable difficulties, indeed, were encountered by George Stephenson, in constructing the railway passing by tunnel under the same range of hills, than were overcome by Mr Rennie in carrying out the works of this great canal undertaking. The skill and judgment with which he planned them reflected the greatest credit on their designer: and whoever examines the works at this day—even after all that has been accomplished in canal and railway engineering—will admit that the mark of a master's hand is unmistakably stamped upon them.[43]

The tribute is just, but it is to Jessop and the resident engineers that it should be addressed. This misapprehension has been carried forward to contemporary writers, and has even led the canal company itself to erect a Manchester lockside plaque in Rennie's honour.

The truth is that Rennie was much concerned with the canal promoters' two unsuccessful Bills of 1792 and 1793, less with the Act of 1794, not at all with construction. It was Jessop who wrote the crucial report that changed opinion, and he that piloted the 1794 Act through Parliament. He then laid out the line (which of course owed much to Rennie's previous surveys), designed the structures, and from time to time inspected it while it was building.

At the second meeting of the Rochdale's promoters in April 1791, William Jessop was the man they wanted for their surveyor.[44] He demurred, so that a later meeting in May sent two committee members and William Crosley (later to be Jessop's resident engineer) to try to persuade him. They failed, and 'John Rennie of London, Surveyor and Engineer' was appointed instead.

The vicissitudes of the promoters that led to the failure of the first two Bills are described elsewhere. Both foundered mainly on the opposition of the industrial mill-owners of the Pennine valleys, who depended upon the water of the hill streams for power to drive their machinery. They were not going to jeopardise the water supplies upon which their businesses depended, and tough opponents they proved.

After the second Bill had failed in 1793, the anxious promoters pressed Jessop to persuade the mill-owners.[45] This time he wrote back that though 'much engaged', he would try to come.[46] And so he did, his report of 10 February 1794 being printed in full in the *Manchester Mercury* in the interests of wide publicity.

This report was decisive. It said firmly that, the soil being suitable, the canal could be supplied from reservoirs alone 'without taking any water from the mills which could be useful to them'.

If, therefore, the Act were to provide that all principal feeders to the mills should pass under the canal, only surplus water being taken into the reservoirs, and if a compensation reservoir were to be built in exchange for any small streams cut while the canal was being built, the mill-owners would be amply protected. He identified the sites of two such reservoirs, that became Hollingsworth and Blackstonedge.

Rennie seems to have had little to do with the third Bill, though the deposited plan was surveyed by Crosley under his direction. Jessop appeared in Parliament on it, a shower of petitions supported it, and on 4 April 1794 it was passed.

Before the parliamentary committee, Jessop was asked how much of the proposed line he had himself seen. He replied:

> I viewed the Line by walking over part of it, riding over other parts of it and seeing other parts as I travelled along the Road where there were to me no objects of particular Inquiry. The Information I received was by using my Eyes, making such Inquiry as I thought necessary on the spot and by Evidence before this Committee . . . . .*

He admits that he knows of no canal with so great a rise and fall as the Rochdale, or of so great a length, that is supplied from reservoirs, but sees no danger from water washing against reservoir dams:

> I have seen Banks made secure exposed to the wind and Sea on the German Ocean. I think it very easy to make those secure where the waters that they are to resist amount only to a few acres.[47]

His evidence must have been greatly helped by his willingness to agree to protection clauses for the mill-owners, given his conviction that reservoirs of ample capacity could be built.

Jessop now went over the line that Crosley had staked out, and wrote a long report on 17 June from Rochdale.[48] This is of great interest, partly as being the only English one we have of his that goes over the whole line of a new canal and proposes how it should be built, but also because of engineering ideas it embodies.

* He means on previous Bills.

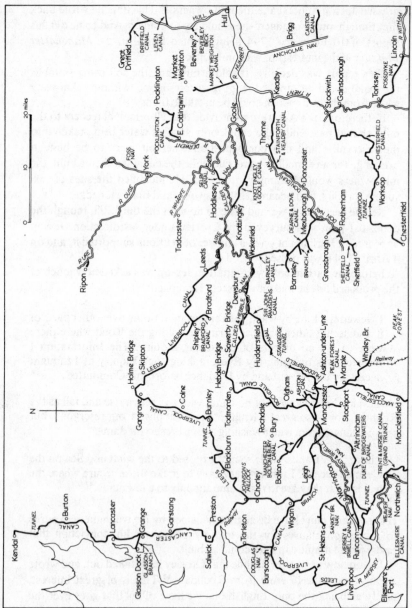

Fig 15   The Rochdale, Barnsley and other waterways of the North

He begins with an idea that he was also working out on the Barnsley Canal:

> Circumstanced as this canal will be respecting its supplies of water, by receiving it, at or near its summit, I have thought it adviseable to make the Locks equal in their rise and fall, with one Exception, and have found that they may be made so without any material inconvenience. Being so made, the Water which serves one, will serve the Rest without Waste, where the Ponds between them can be made capacious enough, to retain it. And it will hereafter be found no small convenience that two sets of spare Gates, kept in readiness would fit any lock when by accident the original one may be damaged.
>
> I have also thought it adviseable that the rise of each Lock should be Ten Feet (Except in Manchester).

This proposal was in fact carried out very exactly. We cannot be sure that measurements taken a century later correspond with the originals, given rebuilding and earth movements meantime. However, figures of 1905[49] show that on the Sowerby Bridge to summit stretch, omitting Mayroyd Mill and Blackpit Locks, 7ft 10in and 8ft 4½in respectively, the rise of the 34 remaining locks is 333ft 5½in, almost exactly 10ft. From the summit to Manchester Piccadilly Basins, the combined fall of the 45 locks is 435ft 6½in. No lock on the canal between these points is under 7ft 10in or over 10ft 9in. The lock flights especially are close to Jessop's figure: eg Sowerby Bridge 4 at 38ft 11½in, Gauxholme 5 at 49ft 10in, Walsden 6 at 60ft and Ten Acres 7 at 71ft 0½in. Many lock gates must indeed have been interchangeable, and canal working unusually economical in water.

Jessop then starts at the Sowerby Bridge end of the line, notes difficulties, and suggests deviations. We can only look at one or two of his points.

At the summit Rennie had proposed a tunnel about 3,000yd long, which Jessop estimated at about £45,000. At this time Jessop was beginning to feel hints of troubles to come at Braunston and Blisworth Tunnels and had no mind for more:

> This Tunnell may be avoided by seven additional locks up and seven down, and about 30 feet[50] of deep cutting, on the summit.
>
> These locks, with the Bridges, the deep Cutting, the Purchase of Land, and the Reservoirs to supply the Summit, will cost less by £20,000 than the Tunnell, and if the supply by the Reservoir shod prove deficient, this deficiency may be made good by a small Steam

Engine which, with the Annual Expence attending it, would not be more than Equal to the sinking of £6000.

At the canal's other end, between the proposed basins at Piccadilly and Castlefield, he recommended 7ft or 8ft falls for the locks because of the likely great local trade. In fact, the 11 built had a total fall of 79ft 2½in, or just over 7ft each.

In an addendum to his report, Jessop recommended which works should be started immediately, and again gives us interesting technical information. First, the reservoir dams:

Those of the Healees (Hollingsworth) reservoir should be made 10 foot wide at the Top, to admit of Roads over them. The Slopes on each side should be two foot horizontal to one perpendicular from which by a Level, the breadth at the Base will be found.

Thro' the middle of the Bank should be a puddle, nine foot in Thickness, and the trench for the Base of the Puddle sho^d be cut into the ground down to the Clay, or other firm soil. Towards the top, where it may be cut into the Rock, the Fissures of the Rock should be choaked with sand (if it can be procured), worked in with water, until it turns water'.

The Bank of the Blackstonedge Reservoir should not be less than 12 foot wide at the Top, with Slopes and puddle as before mentioned and if the principal part of its substance should be peat Earth, it had better be 18 feet at the top. The Peat should be laid, as much of it as may be, in the Base, and the top should be heavier matter, such as sand, stone or earth . . . .

The great embankment at Slack's Valley,[51] 54ft wide at the top, including side banks of 10ft each, should also be made early to allow it time to consolidate. Then,

The deep cutting at Dean head[52] may be begun at each end, if only a few men work they will most easily keep themselves clear of water . . . . the Ground will probably be inclined to slip by the pressure of water from springs on the side of the Hills, for when a crack takes place if that water should not be more than a Hogshead, it may press with a force of 10,000 Tons. To provide as much as possible against this, where it may be likely to happen, it will be prudent to sink drains at the distance of 40 or 50 yards from the Canal . . . . down to some stratum that is impervious to Water, below the Springs, and at the Bottom to lay a sough of a foot square, covering the sough up to the surface of the Ground with Rubble Stone or Faggotts. This will not only intercept the Springs but also the surface water in Showers, and by insulating the Banks of the Canal will keep them dry. Those soughs should have some declivity and proper Vents for discharging the Water.

Finally, he gave instructions for the building of locks, bridges and culverts.

William Crosley had been engaged as resident engineer before Jessop's report, which was clearly intended for his guidance in laying out and building the canal. Equally clearly, the company wanted Jessop to be available for advice, for on 16 July the committee minuted:

> That Mr Jessop be written to for his opinion respecting the propriety of preparing the masons-work for Locks, etc.

The only surviving Rochdale Canal working sketch, of a bridge, is signed by Jessop, and we must assume that he provided Crosley with his working drawings. Therefore we must assume also that the two skew bridges called Gorrell's and March Barn, on the main line between the Rochdale and Heywood branches, are his. L T C Rolt says:

> Both are skew bridges, crossing the waterway at an angle of 60 degrees. Gorrell's bridge solves the structural problem created by the oblique crossing by the use in the face of the arch of very large stones, some 6 ft long, laid in courses parallel with the abutments. Its neighbour, March Barn Bridge, on the other hand, is an example of true skew arch construction using winding courses.[53]

William Chapman, asked by the Directors to maintain the line of roads crossing the canal, had built a skew bridge[54] in 1787 on the County of Kildare Canal, an independent branch of the Grand Canal. Given Jessop's association with the latter, it is likely that he had seen it, and used the idea on the Rochdale. The attribution of the Rochdale Canal to Rennie has led to his being credited also with these bridges, but this is of course not so. Incidentally, Jessop also built Shee or Scow (Skew) Bridge on the Grand Canal a little west of Robertstown in the early 1790s.

Jessop having started them off, the committee were content to leave construction to resident engineers. Nevertheless, from time to time they asked Jessop back to report on progress.

His first was made to the committee on 22 January 1796 and repeated to the shareholders' meeting in May.[55] He had found no material error,

And, considering the very great progress which has been made in many of the most difficult, and expensive parts of the work, I must, in justice to the conductors of it, say that, in my opinion, the works of Masonry are in general sound and substantial, and that upon the whole there appears to have been good management in the conduct of the work, and economy in the expenditure.

Late in 1796 William Crosley died, and was succeeded by the experienced Thomas Bradley from the Calder & Hebble, and Thomas Townshend. Bradley returned to the Calder & Hebble in 1801, and for a year Townshend carried on. Then he left, and William Crosley junior, himself to become a sound canal engineer, succeeded him and opened the canal in 1804.

In 1797 Jessop came back again to report, on 19 April, to the shareholders' meeting in early May.[56] Progress had been good. The two biggest aqueducts, Hebden Bridge with four 25ft arches, and Todmorden with two of 21ft, were well forward, the deep cutting at the summit was half done, the Slack's Valley embankment about one-third built.

The masonry works from Sowerby Bridge to Rochdale, he thought, could be finished that summer. Then the only obstacle to opening to Rochdale would be the Dean Head deep cutting on the summit, where he repeated his advice to cut deep back drains as the best way of preventing slips.

He recommended a small reservoir in the Chelburn Valley

near the Canal . . . to serve as a regulating Reservoir, at all Seasons, and in Winter, or other rainy Seasons, it may totally supply the summit, without having resort to the large Reservoir . . . .

This reservoir, Lower Chelburn, was built and opened in 1798, along with the bigger Hollingsworth and Blackstonedge. Then he went on to comment on the Slack's Valley embankment, 'the Work which will longest delay the Opening of the Canal to Manchester', and to give us his ideas on embankment building:

I must take this opportunity of observing that the Embankment at present is not forming exactly in the way that it ought; the most proper way is to form the external Slopes first, and to fill up the middle afterwards, in order that in its settlement it may form itself into Concave Laminae instead of Convex, which is the unavoidable consequence of having the middle part condensed first, leaving the Banks and Slopes to settle afterwards; I must therefore recommend that Men be immediately employed in taking the Earth from under the Stage, as it falls from the Waggons, and therewith forming the external Slopes, so as at least to carry up the whole together on a uniform level.

When the Bank shall thus have been raised within two or three feet of the Bottom-Level, the lumps of Clay should be chopped into smaller pieces, and be regularly trimmed; and then, instead of using Water to puddle the bottom, it should be trampled, layer after layer, by heavy Horses; this I have experienced as a safe and cheap mode of forming a Canal on an embankment of slippery Clay or Marl; after having seen, near the place where this was done, another Embankment, which was puddled in the common way with Water, continue to slip until it had formed its own Slope, at an inclination of about 5 feet horizontally to one foot perpendicular.

When the bottom is thus secured, so as to prevent Water from getting into the body of the Embankment; the Side-Banks may be formed without hazard, in any way that may be most convenient.

On 24 August 1798 the canal opened from Sowerby Bridge to Todmorden, and on 21 December of that year over the summit past Dean Head cutting to Rochdale.

Of Jessop's final report on April 1802, we only have a paragraph quoted in the company's printed report to shareholders of 9 June 1803,[57] in which he takes the familiar line that the quicker the line is finished, the sooner will tolls come in, and therefore shareholders should subscribe what is necessary as quickly as possible.

On 21 December 1804 the canal was finished. Not far away, Jessop's partner at Butterley, Benjamin Outram, was struggling with his great Standedge Tunnel on the narrow-lock Huddersfield, not to be completed until 1811, by which time the Rochdale was carrying some 200,000 tons a year, which by 1829 had risen to half a million. And so, within three months of one another, in December 1804 for the Rochdale, and March 1805 for the Grand Junction, Jessop saw two of his greatest works completed.

Let us end this chapter with a glance at a third, less important than these, but nevertheless, one that was to have a long and profitable life, the Barnsley Canal.

Barnsley Canal

Jessop learned and first practised his trade in Yorkshire. He was summoned back, when in August 1792 the Aire & Calder Company launched the Barnsley Canal project to run from their line near

133

Wakefield past Barnsley to Barnby Bridge near the Silkstone coalfield, and wanted Jessop to survey and report on it, working with their own engineer Elias Wright and superintendent William Martin. Jessop came in September to confirm the survey Wright and Martin, now with John Gott junior's help, had made, and report that it would 'be a very eligible Line to be Adopted.[58] Whereupon the four were asked to 'prepare a Plan and make an Estimate . . . . .'

The final Barnsley line[59] was 15 miles long from its entrance lock; thence the canal ran by two more at Agbrigg and a flight of twelve at Walton to a pound level to the junction with the Dearne & Dove Canal outside Barnsley, and then on to Barugh, where a flight of five more took it to the coal-loading terminal basin at Barnby. Five colliery railways from the section above Barnby were included in the Bill. Locks took craft of 58ft × 14ft 10in: those in the Barugh flight were of 8ft fall, those at Walton and Agbrigg of 7ft 6in. Jessop appeared with Elias Wright on the Bill in 1793, and the Act was passed on 3 June, Jessop then being paid £189 19s for what he had so far done.

To build the canal, Jessop went to two old contacts: John Pinkerton as contractor, and Samuel Hartley as resident engineer. It proved an unhappy arrangement, which was to land Jessop in sad trouble.

A minute book entry of 17 October 1793 throws light on Jessop's way of working out a contract price:

It being represented to this Meeting that Mr. Jessop .. preferred making such Estimate and Value upon a Section of the Line of the Canal and part of the said Work being already done and other part in a progressive state, Ordered that the Surveyor do make such Section as soon as possible in Order that the same may be sent to Mr Jessop and procure such proposed Estimate with all due Diligence, both for what is Executed and may be Executed, during such time as the same can be procured, and that Mr. Pinkerton do in the mean time proceed in the works.

Whereupon follows:

I do hereby agree to proceed in the Execution of the Works and to Abide by the Estimate of the said Mr. Jessop,

signed by John Pinkerton. So great was the pressure of work that it was eight months later that Jessop's report and estimate was received,[60] whereupon the company approved it and ordered a draft agreement with Pinkerton to be prepared and cleared with Jessop.

One section of this report read:

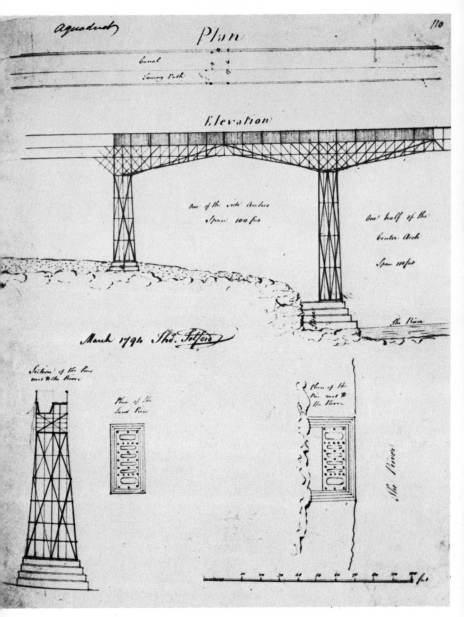

Drawing signed by Telford, dated March 1794, for an iron aqueduct

(*above*) Pontcysyllte Aqueduct as shown in a contemporary print
(*below*) Caledonian Canal: one of Jessop's sections, dated August 1804

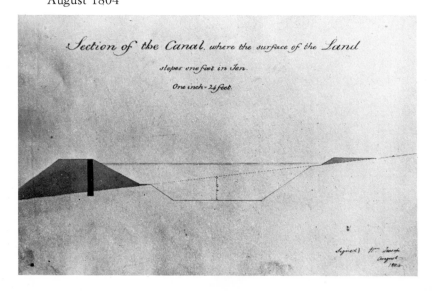

Section of the Canal, where the surface of the Land slopes one foot in Ten.

One inch–24 feet.

Signed Wm Jessop
August
1804

On observing that the ground on each side of the Dearne valley is chiefly Rock I have reason to believe that an Aqueduct of Masonry will be done at less Expence than an Embankment and I have accordingly drawn a Design for it and Computed it ... to cost £3,000.

This aqueduct of five 30ft arches—sadly now demolished—replaced Jessop's earlier idea of an embankment and a single 30ft arch.

Jessop reported on the works in January and November 1796, and again in July 1798,[61] when he supported Pinkerton's claim to extra-to-contract payments. The canal was opened from the Aire & Calder to Barnsley on 8 June 1799; the upper part followed early in 1802, soon after Jessop had again reported. It had been completed by other contractors, Pinkerton having left it with most of the work done. Jessop was present again in March 1803 upon talks about water supply.

Pinkerton had lost on the contract through unforeseen difficulties in the work itself, rising prices, and what he claimed to be unreasonable interference by Hartley, and Jessop sympathised with him. He claimed £5,000 above the contract, and also £2,000 he had been advanced by the company in 1796. Sadly, though arbitration was several times suggested to the company, they persisted to the end in 1812, when they were awarded their £2,000 with accrued interest.

In the course of the quarrel, Pinkerton in 1805 brought a Chancery action against the company. The Master of the Rolls then proposed arbitration, but was critical of Jessop's conduct in 1793 and 1794.

Given that Pinkerton had, as we have seen, agreed in advance to accept Jessop's figures, the Master considered that Jessop's position was that of an arbitrator and that these should have been chosen as equally fair to the company and to Pinkerton. Instead of which:

Mr Jessop because he was the Engineer employed by this Canal Company supposed he was their Servant also in fixing the prices at which this work was to be done & that he was to act in their behalf as against ... Mr. Pinkerton.

The Master went on:

There is not in this case the least ground for impeaching Mr Jessop's professional skill or his moral character but he unfortunately has fallen into a mistake with respect to the nature of the Situation in which he was placed ....

Jessop seems to have thought that his prices should be on the safe side as regards the company, for if the contractor should suffer too severely the company could compensate him. The Master did not think much of 'This notion of Mr Jessop's that the Company would set all to rights by that liberal Discretion which he took it for granted they would at all times exercise.[62]

One cannot help feeling that Jessop had been unwise in trusting the canal company to act liberally by their contractor, and so had behaved unfairly to an old friend and colleague; that Pinkerton had been most unwise in agreeing to prices he had not seen, and then in agreeing to those he did see without clear provision for extra costs; and that the company behaved harshly in refusing arbitration over and over again, and sticking to the letter of their contract in spite of inflation. Pinkerton comes best out of an episode that must have given Jessop much pain.

7

JESSOP AND TELFORD:
THE ELLESMERE AND CALEDONIAN CANALS
AND ABERDEEN HARBOUR

Jessop worked with Telford from 1793 till 1812, first on the Ellesmere, then with some overlap of time on the Caledonian and on Aberdeen Harbour. In this chapter, more than anywhere else, do we regret the loss of Jessop's personal papers, for the interaction of two great engineers offers problems, solutions to which can only be guessed at.

Ellesmere Canal

For nearly two years from 1789 a group of promoters, working with three local men, John Duncombe and Joseph and William Turner, had planned, surveyed and estimated alternative lines to link the Mersey by what was later to become Ellesmere Port to the Dee at Chester and the Severn at Shrewsbury, and at the same time to generate considerable internal traffic. Between Chester and Shrewsbury, rival groups pressed the merits of alternative lines.

One proposed a hilly, difficult line to serve the Wrexham collieries, the Bersham-Brymbo ironworks complex, and the Ruabon and Chirk coal lands. It would then cross the valleys of the Dee and Ceiriog to reach Shrewsbury, with a branch to the Llanymynech limestone quarries. A second group wanted[1] a trunk east of the Dee, perhaps using the Chester Canal for part of the way, to Ellesmere and Shrewsbury, with a branch to Ruabon and Bersham and others to Whitchurch, Prees and Llanymynech. Such a line left the Wrexham and Chirk collieries unserved, but avoided the hills and river crossings of the western route.

The promoters now wanted 'an Engineer of approved Character and Experience'[2] to decide between the rival lines, and prepare the way for a Bill. They chose Jessop on 7 November 1791. He accepted. It was his first offer of a major trunk canal, and maybe he hoped that it would help forward his earlier plans for canalising the Severn. When, some five years later, he realised that a Severn junction had been lost in the

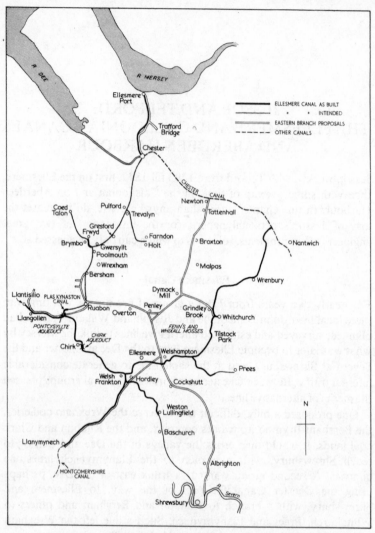

Fig 16   The Ellesmere Canal as planned and built

proprietors' anxiety to develop specialised local trades, Jessop seems to
have turned away from the Ellesmere to more important work.

He put in a preliminary report in January 1792,[3] and a fuller one in
August.[4] It said that to combine an eastern line with serving the
collieries that were to supply Chester and Shrewsbury was not possible;
therefore he favoured the western route. Basing himself on Duncombe's

earlier survey, he proposed a line across the Wirral from the Mersey to the Dee, and thence east of Pulford and Trevalyn to Wrexham, Bersham, by a 4,607yd tunnel to Ruabon to cross the Dee at Pontcysyllte, then by a 1,235yd tunnel at Chirk to cross the Ceiriog at Pontfaen (some $\frac{1}{2}$ mile to the west of the final line), and so by Frankton, Weston and a 476yd tunnel to the Severn at Shrewsbury. The rise from Chester would be 303ft, the fall to Shrewsbury 150ft.

Jessop drew attention to what were likely to prove the two greatest engineering difficulties, the long tunnel at the level of the Dee crossing, and that crossing itself. He explained that to cross the river at the canal's summit level would cost £35,000 and require an aqueduct 970ft[5] long and 126ft high (almost exactly Pontcysyllte's final dimensions). Were it to be lowered 24ft, using three locks down and up again and then pumping back by 'an Engine to be worked by the River Dee', the cost would fall to £21,286. Were no tunnelling involved, he went on, he would have liked a canal wide enough for river boats. But as internal conveyance was the great object, he proposed that the Mersey-Chester section, and possibly the extension to Wrexham, should be built broad, the rest to take 70ft × 7ft narrow boats. His main line, excluding branches, was 53¾ miles long, and his estimate included the cheaper alternative at Pontcysyllte.

On 10 September most of those present accepted Jessop's report, though a minority preferred the eastern line. On the 26th the committee asked Jessop, with Turner and Duncombe to help him, to reconsider the line at Ruabon to avoid a tunnel if possible. This he did by planning a higher summit level and more locks. And so the Act was passed on 30 April 1793 on the same day as that for the Grand Junction, Jessop appearing before the Lords committee. Because the supporters of the eastern and western lines had now amalgamated, the Act included a clause permitting a junction between the Prees branch and the Chester Canal.

Jessop, now owning ten shares in the company, had three assistants in laying out the line, Thomas Dadford junior, William Turner and John Duncombe, the last having Thomas Denson working for him. But Jessop, in the middle of the canal mania, could not supervise construction. An engineer to manage the undertaking was needed, and on 19 August the committee decided to advertise for one, on the same day that they ordered William Turner to prepare plans and estimates for the aqueducts at Pontcysyllte and Pontfaen.

William Turner expected to get the job, and was bitterly disappointed when on 23 September Thomas Telford[6] was appointed 'General Agent, Surveyor, Engineer, Architect and Overlooker of the Works', with Turner and Duncombe as his assistants. He was

> to make Reports to superintend the cutting forming and making the Canal and taking up and seeing to the due observance of the Levels thereof to make the Drawings and to submit such Drawings to the Consideration and Correction of Mr William Jessop ... His Engagement to extend to all Architecture and Engineering Business to the Drawing forming and directing the making of Bridges, Aqueducts Tunnels Locks Buildings Reservoirs Wharfs and other works ...[7]

Telford's was a part-time appointment, for he continued to hold his post as Surveyor of Public Works for Shropshire that he had occupied since 1788. For his work on the canal he received a salary of £300pa.

In trying to assess as accurately as possible the achievements of both Jessop and Telford on the Ellesmere Canal, and especially their parts in building the great aqueducts, let us note that Jessop had laid out the line and in 1794 provided the first working drawings;[8] had in his report of 23 August 1792 envisaged an aqueduct at Pontcysyllte very similar in length and height to that later built (though proposing a lesser one on grounds of expense) and another at Chirk; and had been the principal engineering witness in Parliament. Now he, rising 49, the most experienced civil engineer of his generation, was to work with Telford, aged 36, also to become a great civil engineer and an inspired bridge and road builder, but at that time a man unacquainted with canal construction, whose work had been mainly in the erection of county buildings and bridges.

A committee meeting on 17 January 1794, with Jessop and Telford both present, agreed to start the Wirral Canal and the branch past Llanymynech to Carreghofa, especially because of the projected Bill to extend it to Newtown as the Montgomeryshire Canal. They also agreed to begin 'the building of the great Aqueduct over the River Dee'. For it,

> the plan of the Aqueduct at Pontcy sylltee with three arches as prepared by Mr William Turner of Whitchurch, Architect, shall be adopted by this Committee with such Alterations therein as Mr Jessop shall communicate to Mr Telford, and that Mr Telford do prepare a specification and proper sections and working drawings, to enable workmen to give in estimates for erecting the said Aqueduct,

after which tenders were to be sought. At another meeting on 31 January,

Mr Telford having stated to this Committee that he is not sufficiently prepared to enable him to advertize for proposals for erecting the Aqueduct at Pontcysyltee And that he wishes to consult Mr Jessop upon various points relating to it It is Ordered that the advertizement be postponed until such time as Mr Telford shall have consulted Mr Jessop upon the Subject And that Mr Telford have Credit on Messrs Eyton and Company the Bankers for One hundred pounds to enable him to prosecute the said work at Pontcysylltee.

And at a meeting two months later on 31 March it was

Ordered that the Plans, Drawings and Sections of the intended Aqueduct at Pont cy sylltee produced to this Committee by Mr Telford and which have been settled and approved by Mr Jessop be adopted And that Mr Telford do forthwith prepare a particular Description and Specification for the erection of the said Aqueduct and that Advertisements be inserted . . .

Contractors were then sought for this 'very extensive Aqueduct' by advertisements published on 7 April.[9]

A drawing by John Duncombe dated April 1794, preserved in Reynolds' collection,[10] shows that the possibility of building a full-height (125ft) masonry aqueduct was considered, at least unofficially, at this stage. It had two tiers of arches rather like Pont du Gard. But probably a height of 76ft as then envisaged was thought to be sufficiently bold without risking the construction of what would have been a very expensive and unprecedented structure. More puzzling is another drawing in the same collection (see p 135). Bearing Telford's signature and the date March 1794 (these not written at the same time as the lettering on the drawing) it depicts an aqueduct carried about 95ft above a river on trussed girders supported on trestle piers. The river span is 110ft, the side spans 100ft, and we assume the structural material is cast-iron.

L T C Rolt in his book on Telford takes this drawing to be the basis of the design approved by Jessop and accepted by the committee on 31 March. But even if intended for Pontcysyllte,* we cannot believe that an iron aqueduct, let alone this hair-raising structure, can have been implied when no mention is made in the minutes of such a revolutionary concept, when iron is nowhere mentioned in the advertisement, when no approach to ironmasters is made, and when, as happened on 26 May,

---

* And, oddly enough, the measurements are almost exactly those of Marple Aqueduct.

'James Varley of Colne . . . Mason, having proposed to undertake the building of the Aqueduct at Pontcysyltee upon more reasonable terms than any other person . . .' the committee accepted his tender. All the evidence indicates that Varley had agreed to build the lower level masonry aqueduct designed by Turner and detailed by Telford. Appointed, Varley started to cut and dress stone.

Meanwhile, on 21 February 1794, Matthew Davidson of Shrewsbury was appointed Inspector of Works at Pontcysyllte and along the Llanymynech line. A good man had come. Later, in August, Telford proposed a modified route for the canal between Pontcysyllte and Chester, which was agreed subject to Jessop's opinion.

Early in 1795 Varley seems to have got behind with his contract, for on 21 March the Committee 'Ordered that an accurate account shall be taken . . . of the stone raised and work done by James Varley the contractor for building the aqueduct at Pontcysyltte'. However, all must have been well, for on Saturday 25 July 1795 the foundation stone was laid and the *Salopian Journal*, reporting the event, says 'it is expected that the work will go on with much expedition, as a great part of the materials are already provided'.[11] No doubt the inscription to be fixed on one of the piers was composed at this time, though the plaque itself appears not to have been made until the end of 1796.[12]

Telford having done further work on the revised line between Pontcysyllte and Chester, on 14 July 1795 Jessop from Shrewsbury wrote a report[13] to the chairman of the committee which approved, except in one place, Telford's resurveyed line. He recommended that the flight of locks down from Plas Kynaston quarry to Pontcysyllte shoud be 'gradual and be disposed in regular distances to near that Aqueduct', and that a branch should be built to near the Acrefair collieries. He also proposed to raise Bala Lake 6in as a source of water additional to the Dee until the aqueduct could carry supplies from his intended summit reservoir (he had not yet planned an intake at Llantisilio above Llangollen). As for the proposed Whitchurch Branch-Chester Canal link, this he thought had better wait until construction on the main line and branch had made water available. So soon had the old eastern line reinstated itself; it was to grow quickly in importance.

Then, in the same report, Jessop went on to make historic proposals for the great aqueducts:

It had been proposed to save expense in the Aqueduct at Pontcysylte to reduce the height 50 feet and descend and ascend by Locks, but in

144

due consideration I must now recommend to the Committee to make this saving by adopting an Iron Aqueduct at the full height originally intended which on correcting the Levels appears to be 125 feet above the surface of the water of the River Dee.

The advantages that will attend the preservation of this Level are too obvious to need explanation. The arches or rather openings of the Aqueduct may be seven of 50 feet each the remainder may be raised by an embankment, and this embankment will be formed by Earth to be boated from the Cutting between the Dee and the Chirk valley—as few Hands can be employed in this mode of Working, and it will of course take much time in the Execution, no time should be lost in beginning it.

It was originally proposed to cross the Chirk Valley a little above Chirk Bridge but from an objection by the owner of the land, the Line was altered to cross at Pontfain. It would still be very desirable to adopt the first Idea, and if instead of an embankment of Earth, which would shut up a view of the valley, it be crossed by an Iron Aqueduct I should hope the objection might be removed and instead of an obstruction it would be a romantic feature in the view and avoid damage to much of the Meadows and the Plantations on the Banks of the valley, and miss a very expensive and hazardous part of the line on the steep Banks on the South side.

Meeting on 10 August, a fortnight after the foundation stone had been laid, the committee accepted these Pontcysyllte and Chirk proposals as they stood, and ended their minute:

It is ordered that the recommendation of Mr Jessop in that respect shall be adopted and the General Surveyor and Agent to the Company is hereby directed to proceed in the said works conformably thereto.

This fundamental revision of the aqueduct plans took place during a period of intense activity in the development of iron structures. The proposal by Reynolds and Telford for an iron aqueduct at Longdon on the Shrewsbury Canal was accepted in March 1795;[14] an iron trough 186ft long in four spans supported at a height of 16ft above the river Tern on cast-iron pillars. Next month a contract was awarded to the Coalbrookdale Company for building an iron bridge over the Severn at Buildwas to Telford's design.[15] On 11 June the Derby Canal Company authorised a cut across the Holmes, which implies that Benjamin Outram, the canal's engineer, had designed his single-span (c35ft) iron trough aqueduct a little before this date. All three structures reached completion in 1796, as did the impressive 236ft span arch of the iron bridge at Sunderland which had been under construction by Thomas Wilson since 1793.

Meanwhile, in February 1795, the Peak Forest Canal Company, whose engineer was also Outram, had decided to build their great Marple aqueduct over the River Goyt in stone. Then, on 22 April, the American engineer Robert Fulton, one of their contractors, proposed 'substituting Cast Iron instead of Stone Arches for the Aqueduct'.[16] It was to have been 90ft high and 200ft long (so a contemporary newspaper reported, but probably a misprint for 300ft, for the present aqueduct is 309ft long, and it is difficult to see how another 100ft of embankment could have been built), presumably in three spans. No other details are known, but Fulton's intentions may have been as indicated by the engraving published on 1 March 1796 as Plate 13 in his *Treatise on the Improvement of Canal Navigation*, which shows an iron trough carried on iron arch ribs in a manner foreshadowing Pontcysyllte as built.

Now there is no doubt that each of the engineers in this tightly knit circle knew what the others were doing, Jessop, acquainted with Reynolds since 1788, was working with Outram and Telford; Outram with Fulton, and Reynolds with Telford. Outram visited Reynolds soon after 23 April 1795 on Peak Forest Canal business.[17] Fulton greatly admired Reynolds' inclined planes, and put Jessop's name at the head of the engineers to whom he submitted some ideas on small canals in July 1795,[18] while among the drawings listed in Telford's possession[19] was one endorsed 'Details of an Iron Bridge by Robt Fulton 14 March 1795'.

Whoever may have suggested that the Pontcysyllte aqueduct could be carried at the high level in an iron trough on masonry piers (and it might well be Telford), the idea emerged from the thoughts and work of this group. But it was Jessop, in his report of 14 July 1795, who put the full weight of his professional authority, and his responsibility as principal engineer of the Ellesmere Canal, behind it.

The discussions which had been taking place in Shrewsbury were continued by letter after Jessop's return to London when, on 26 July, he wrote to Telford:

In looking forward to the time when we shall be laying the Iron Trough on the Piers I foresee some difficulties that appear to me formidable—In the first place I see the men giddy and terrifyed in laying stones with such an immense depth underneath them with only a space of 6 feet wide & 10 feet long to stand upon and the same want of room will hardly allow space for the Beams and scaffolding while the Iron work is putting together—

I therefore think in the first, that in order to reduce the weight of the Iron, or the parts of it—it will be better to have the openings narrow by adding another Pier, so as to have 8 openings of 52 feet from Centre to Centre instead of 60 feet.

In the next place I would have the Piers 7 feet wide at the Top instead of 6 feet, and make them about 2 feet more in the other dimensions.

I hope you will not have proceeded with the other Foundations till you received this.

And I begin to think it may be better to have the Canal 9 feet wide & 5 feet deep, as was first intended . . .[20]

As regards the remark about foundations, it seems likely that, until Jessop's report could be considered by the committee, no official change could be made. Therefore the foundation stone of the masonry aqueduct had had to be laid the day before this letter was written, even though the two engineers were redesigning the whole structure.

The proposals accepted in August 1795 were for much more embanking and a much shorter aqueduct—perhaps some 500ft in all, against 1,007ft as built. But Jessop's dimensions for the height (125ft) and clear span (45ft) are those finally adopted.

The same meeting of 10 August told the surveyors, Davies and Jebb, (or failing them, Duncombe) to prepare

a drawing and section of that part of the line of the said Canal which is intended to cross the Chirk Valley a little above Chirk Bridge, and of the improvement proposed by Mr Jessop in passing the said Valley by means of an iron aqueduct . . .

They also approved the resurveyed line from Chester to Pontcysyllte (subject to Telford asking Jessop for clarification upon the water supply to the summit) and for the Whitchurch branch, and finally ordered parliamentary notices to be published preparatory to a Bill.

In October William Turner, who since the beginning of the year had been no more than a shareholder, issued a statement criticising the revised route to Chester, and suggesting alternatives. He and Jessop having then gone over the line again, the latter reported hurriedly from London on 8 December 1795.[21]

Two canal Acts resulted in 1796. The first abandoned the old Whitchurch branch, and substituted a new one, with branches from it to

Prees and Ellesmere. It also required the Ellesmere Company within two years to seek an Act to join the Chester. The second authorised the revised route from Pontcysyllte to Chester, with branches to Acrefair and Talwern collieries. Jessop appeared in Parliament on both, supported on the first by Denson, on the second by Telford and Denson, this being Telford's first appearance before a Lords committee.

No work was thereafter done on the Pontcysyllte-Chester section except to build $2\frac{1}{3}$ miles of the Ffrwd colliery branch, begun in 1796, though various ideas, including using inclined planes or substituting a railway, were afterwards aired. The lack of drive behind it may have been, partly at any rate, the result of the internal explosions in the Wilkinson empire around this time. It was formally interred in Jessop's report of 24 January 1800.

By now it had become clear that the true future of the company lay in the development of its central coal-limestone-lime exchange, and in the prospective link with the Chester Canal. The branch from Frankton past Llanymynech to Carreghofa was opened in 1796, to be extended in 1797 for $16\frac{1}{4}$ miles to Garthmyl when the first part of the Montgomeryshire opened. It was followed by Frankton-Weston in 1797. In February of that year work also began on the realigned branch towards Whitchurch and the Chester. That, and the completion of the Frankton-Chirk collieries line, were now priorities, with access to the Ruabon collieries over Pontcysyllte coming next. By 1801 the Whitchurch line had reached past Ellesmere to Bettisfield, and two miles of the cut through Whixall Moss had been opened to drain it. In 1801, also, the Chester Canal junction at Hurleston had been authorised; it was to be completed in 1805.

Let us now follow the story of the aqueducts on from where we left it at 10 August 1795. On 9 September the committee was told that John Simpson was to join Varley as co-partner of the Pontcysyllte work, a new contract to be drawn up. So far Varley had been paid £2,002, so he must have prepared and cut a good deal of stone. In October, Telford reported that 'the Aqueduct at Pontcysyltee is carrying on with all the dispatch that a work of that magnitude will admit of,[22] and on 26 November it was

Ordered that the Embankment at the south end of the Aqueduct at Pontcysyltee and the cutting along the adjoining Bank and towards Chirk valley which is necessary to form the said Embankment shall be carried on under the direction of Mr Telford and agreeable to the directions in Mr Jessop's report...

By the opening of the year 1796 wartime inflation was beginning to bite, money was coming in more slowly, and costs had begun to rise. These factors influenced action upon major projects like the two big aqueducts.

On 20 January contractors had been appointed for Chirk: John Simpson again, with William Davies and also William Hazledine, the ironmaster of Shrewsbury, this to be finished by 1 October 1798. In February Outram's iron trough at the Holmes was ready, in March that at Longdon. Nevertheless, it took Hazledine and Telford less than a month to conclude that the difficulties of giving Chirk an iron trough were too great, for on 15 February Telford, writing to Matthew Davidson, said: 'I have seen Mr Jessop as to the Aqueduct at Chirk, and he agrees as to the general principle of the adopting Brick or Rubble Arches instead of an Iron Trough . . .'[23] Maybe Longdon and his Buildwas road bridge had taught Telford how much was still to be learned about iron. He was not the only one. On the Peak Forest the proposed iron aqueduct at Marple was scrapped after Fulton left in September 1795; instead, Outram built the fine masonry structure we have today.

Work at Chirk was delayed while the aqueduct was redesigned. It seems first to have been planned as a plain masonry work.[24] Only later was it decided to build the spandrels of the arches with longitudinal walls, and then to lay a cast-iron bottom for the water channel across them, the sides being made up of ashlar masonry backed by bricks. In his report of 27 November 1799 Telford tells us that its arches had been completed, and that 'proposals for the Iron Plates, which are to form the bottom, have been received, and they will be provided and laid early next summer.[25] Two days later, Hazledine of Shrewsbury's proposals for 'furnishing plates and screws' for Chirk was agreed. Jessop then had a look at it, and in January 1800[26] wrote:

> The masonry of Chirk Aqueduct is very perfect. I have seen no reason to recommend any deviation from the design . . .

Chirk, opened at the end of 1801, is 696ft long and 70ft high; it has 10 arches of 40ft span, a navigable width of 11ft, a width of masonry each side of 5ft 6in, and a water depth of 5ft.

As for Pontcysyllte, little was done for several years. On 10 February 1797 the committee minuted to enquire 'upon what terms Mr. John Wilkinson and Mr William Reynolds will either jointly or individually agree to furnish the Iron Work for Pont cy syltee and fix

149

up and compleat the same'—an interesting minute, for by excluding Hazledine it suggests that his Plas Kynaston foundry near the aqueduct's north end, which was to be the key to success, was not yet available.[27] The responses must have been discouraging, for on 28 June the committee ordered that proposals should be advertised, though we have not traced any such advertisement. And then work was suspended to expedite that at Chirk. Not until 27 November 1799 did the committee order the remaining mason's work at Pontcysyllte to be advertised.

In his report of 24 January 1800, Jessop tried to deal with the problem of how to get coal from Ruabon on to the southern canal lines across Pontcysyllte, now that the main line to Chester had been abandoned. He proposes a railway from the collieries to the aqueduct, and then puts alternatives: should the railway 'be continued over the columns intended for the Aqueduct, or whether the Aqueduct should be completed to communicate with the Railway on the north side of the river'. He inclines towards bringing the railway over the piers, and goes on:

In the execution of the columns, I would recommend, that, in what remains to be done, they should be built hollow, and be composed of stones well worked to two feet in bed, and be connected one side with the other, at every six feet in height, by two pieces of oak (dovetailed a little on the underside) principally for the purpose of internal scaffolding. The courses thus put together, will be less liable to false bearings than if they were solid; it will save five or six hundred pounds in the expence; and what to me appears most material, it will afford safety to the workmen.

Instead of wing walls connected with the abutments at the ends of the embankments, it will save some expence, and perhaps have a better appearance, if the abutment, built of rough masonry, and connected by bond timbers, with a counterfort about 12 feet in length, and 7 feet in thickness, be buried in the slope of the earth, terminating the embankment; the earth, so sloping, will bury near a half of the next column, which half may, of course, be built of rough masonry. The whole of the sides of the embankment should be planted, which in time, would become not only ornamental, but profitable.

I cannot leave Pont Cysylte without saying that the columns, without any exception, are executed in a more masterly manner than any thing of the kind that I have before seen,

These structural recommendations seem all to have been carried out.

The piers, 20ft × 12ft at base tapering to 13ft × 7ft 6in at the top, were built hollow above 70ft, but using cross-walls instead of cross-timbers. The embankment was brought forward, and the abutment has very short wing walls with the counterforts extending right down to the base of the foundation. The decision to extend the aqueduct to its full eighteen piers and to shorten the approach embankments (though leaving a 500yd embankment on the south side) must have been taken before Jessop wrote, and probably in the light of comparative estimates for the cost of bridging or embanking,[28] for immediately after his report, on 5 February 1800, the committee accepted John Simpson's tender to complete the piers and abutments.

Jessop's suggestion[29] that the piers might be used for a railway instead of a canal was considered, but on 25 November 1801 the committee decided in favour of a canal, Telford then being told to prepare drawings and specifications for it. By that time a good deal of work had been done, for in his report of 25 November 1801, Telford wrote:

> During the last year and a half, five Piers have been built from the foundations up to the level of one hundred and ten feet from the common surface of the river Dee. Nine other Piers have been raised twenty-three feet in height, which has brought them up to the same level; there are five other Piers which require twenty-three feet each to raise them to the before-mentioned level.*

It was probably only now that, in consultation with Hazledine, the final design for the trough was settled on. On 17 March 1802 his tender for executing and erecting the cast-iron work was accepted, this to be supplied from his Plas Kynaston foundry. Meanwhile, William Davies was building the southern embankment, the maximum height of which is 75ft.

In 1803 decisions were taken to build a coal-carrying railway from Ruabon to Pontcysyllte, and to seek an Act for a water feeder up the valley past Llangollen to an intake from the Dee at Llantisilio. In October of that year the committee asked Jessop to survey and report on the whole line, especially on the progress of the Chester Canal connection, the proposed Shrewsbury connection, Pontcysyllte, and water supply. There is no record of his doing so, other than the evidence he gave on the 1804 Bill, when he proved the preamble and produced the estimates, while Telford gave evidence on the

* In fact, the aqueduct has eighteen, not nineteen, piers.

151

financial position of the company.

Telford's report of 1804 says:

The Iron work of the Trough-part of the Aqueduct of Pontcysylte over nine Arches is now put up, being nearly one half of the whole Length; many Plates being now cast and brought to the Bank at the North-end of the Aqueduct—The Workmen being familiar with the operations of putting the Plates together—and the operations at the Foundry being in a very regular Train, and well supplied with Metal, there is reason to expect that the whole of the Trough-part will be completed about Midsummer next. Timber has been provided for a part of the Towing Path, whch will be put up early in the Spring, as well as the Iron Rail to protect it.

The Earthen Embankment and Lining for the Canal, is carrying on by means of three Iron Railways; and it is proposed to have this Part finished at the same Time as the Aqueduct.[30]

The cutting of the navigable feeder upwards from Pontcysyllte to Llantisilio was authorised in 1804 and practically finished in 1806. Meanwhile, on 26 November 1805, the aqueduct had been opened with much ceremony.

Rowland Hunt, who had been on the committee since the beginning, and was currently chairman, gave the oration. In it he said:[31]

Here . . . we will mention, as concerned in the scientific and practical construction of the works, our General Agent, Mr Telford; who, with the advice and judgment of our eminent and much respected Engineer, Mr Jessop, invented, and with unabated diligence carried the whole into execution.

He then goes on to mention Hazledine, Simpson, Davies and Davidson; and, regarding the canal, Duncombe and Denson. In his covering letter sending the oration to the Earl of Bridgewater he says the opening of Pontcysyllte was

a just acknowledgment to Mr Telford, to whom it was deservedly a proud day; and who had . . . constructed the wonderful Edifice that supported us.

Just how much the aqueduct in particular and the canal in general owed to Jessop's 'advice and judgment' we hope to have shown; and we cannot help remarking that Telford, in his autobiography, does less than justice to his senior colleague.[32] Beyond all discussion of origins and credits, however, stands Pontcysyllte itself; 1007ft long and the loftiest aqueduct ever built, to our knowledge, anywhere in the world. Though today it carries pleasure cruisers and not coal boats, it still serves its purpose, perhaps the finest single achievement of all the Industrial Revolution.[33]

Caledonian Canal

In 1801 Telford was asked by the government to report upon what public works in the Highlands might help to discourage emigration. Telford was chosen, probably because, as surveyor and engineer to the British Fisheries Society, he had reported on the North West as long ago as 1790. One of the subjects Telford was told to examine was the often suggested canal[34] through the Great Glen from the east to the west coast that, at 10ft depth, had been surveyed by James Watt in 1773. His first[35] report, written in October 1801, said:

> I am convinced that a navigation may be formed from Inverness to Fort William of the description that is wanted. The line is very direct, and I have observed no serious obstacle in any part of it. The whole rise between the shores is trifling, and on the summit there is an inexhaustible supply of water. The Entrances from the Navigation into the Sea, are immediately in deep water, good anchoring ground, and in places of perfect safety at Inverness and Fort William.

He was here working on a canal of 50ft bottom and 100ft top width, and 20ft depth. His locks would have an 8ft rise, and these he thought might be turf-sided and cost £5,000 each, there being plenty of water.

Sent back to the Highlands in 1802, he reported fully on 15 March 1803[36] on five subjects, the canal among them. In a question he put to the Highland Society of Scotland he says: 'I have for the sake of distinction, named this Navigation "the Caledonian Canal" '. Finally, he writes: 'My Estimate of the Expence of forming this Navigation is nearly £350,000, and the time required to complete it would probably be about seven years'.

The government committee concerned then examined a number of expert witnesses, among them Rennie and Jessop.[37] Rennie said firmly that the locks should be lined with stone, and estimated them at £14,000 each, and the whole canal—perspicaciously—at £600,000–£700,000 'at least'. Jessop put his locks, also of masonry, at £10,000 each on average, but in a letter to Telford subjoined to the report said that the figure was calculated to be on the safe side.

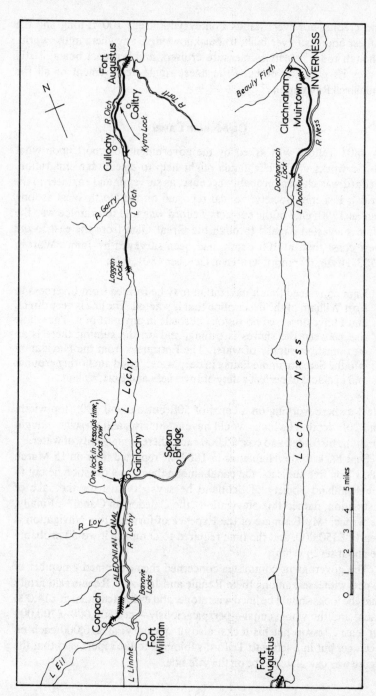

Fig 17 The Caledonian Canal

Using this figure, when asked whether he could estimate the canal's likely cost if it were for craft drawing 18ft, he replied:

Under the favourable circumstances of ground tolerably even, and the soil moderately good, I should suppose it might cost about £22,000 a mile, including the Locks, Bridges and Canal, and other necessary works, but making no allowance for any extra works. I am also supposing that you have the opportunity of chusing your ground, so that with about 15 feet cutting, you may make Banks that will retain 20 feet water.

This estimate, also, did not of course include land purchase costs. The committee reported that they were 'convinced of the practicability, as of the importance, of the work'. Their report convinced Parliament, and a preliminary Bill for this great state canal went rapidly through both Houses without opposition in July 1803.

The Act had named commissioners, of the nature of an executive committee, who moved quickly. Early in August they met Telford to draw up his instructions. He was to go to Scotland

to make the necessary Surveys, and set out the Line of a Canal . . . examining the navigation of the several Lochs or Lakes, and making proper trials of the intermediate ground through which the Canal was intended to pass; and also to expedite the Plans and Notices required by the Standing Orders of the House of Commons, in order to the making application for a regular Canal Act in the present Session . . .

He was also to begin the excavation of the two entrance basins, open quarries, order materials and machinery, and draw up plans for financial control, accounting and correspondence.

Telford then left for Scotland, where he stayed till the middle of October. However the committee,

Thinking it our duty, in the prospect of so important an Undertaking, to omit no means of enabling ourselves to form an accurate judgment as to the practicability of the proposed Work, and the probable expence of executing it, We took measures as early as the 4th of August, for obtaining the opinion and assistance of Mr. William Jessop, another eminent and experienced Engineer . . .[38]

We do not know why Jessop was chosen. The commissioners may have liked the way he had given his earlier evidence, and the fact that his estimate and Telford's agreed, whereas Rennie's might have suggested extravagance. Or possibly because of his surveys of the only navigation in the British Isles that already combined lakes, canal sections and a river—the Shannon.

It had been intended that Jessop should be present at the briefing sessions in early August, but the commissioners' letter of 4 August 1803 found him away from home. When he replied, he did not seem to know the major part he was destined to play, for he said:

When my humble Services may in any way be useful to the Commissioners, I shall be happy in receiving their Commands and in obeying them, so far as I can consistent with prior Engagements.[39]

The Commissioners then tried again, but Jessop was away from home. Meanwhile, on 27 September, Telford, already in Scotland, wrote to John Rickman, secretary to the Commissioners:

As the idea of Mr. Jessop being consulted was suggested before I left London I was in hopes, if his coming down had been considered necessary, that he would have been here by this time, in which case he would have accompanied me along the whole Line from this place to Fort William, for which place I sett out tomorrow morning.

It is now late in the season for him to examine the Line, and I am obliged to be in Shropshire by the middle of October. But it is possible that Mr. Jessop may not judge it absolutely necessary to view the Line. I can shew him a correct Map of the Line of the Canal, with a section of the Ground; I can describe the nature of the Soil in each District with the situation and quality of the material for Building. He can examine Mr. Simpson an Eminent and reputable Builder, who has examined these matters very carefully, and with whom Mr. Jessop has been acquainted for many years, he can also examine Mr. Howell who took the levels and made the surveys for me, and Mr. Jessop is likewise acquainted with him. If after all this, Mr. Jessop should think it necessary to view the ground, the doing this early in the spring would be more advisable after we have opened some quarries and proved the ground near the entrance to the sea. But if the Commission and Mr. Jessop determine upon his coming North immediately, he will be shown the ground by Mr. Wilson, who will be either at Fort William or Inverness.[40]

Whereupon the Commission wrote again to ask Jessop to meet them, and again he could not:

I have been peculiarly unlucky in being two or three times

156

disappointed of the honor of attending at the meeting of the Commissioners; and it coming now to my turn to serve the office of Mayor of this Borough for the ensuing Year—and the 4th of October happening to be the Day fixed for holding the Sessions for the Borough I cannot be in Town till after that Day.[41]

However, he was free 'after next week', so Rickman was told to write to tell Jessop to go to Scotland to examine the line himself, 'and that whether he meet with Mr. Thomas Telford or not he proceed immediately to survey the proposed Line of the Canal and also the proposed Basins at each end of it'.[42] He met Telford in mid-October, and proceeded on his survey. On 25 November the Commissioners had a letter from Jessop, as a result of which they told Telford to send him at Newark

the Section of the Line of the Canal and such accts as he may have received of trials which may have been made by Boring in several parts of the Line, since he left Scotland.[43]

This Telford did, and on 14 December the two engineers met the Commissioners to report orally. After they had 'stated generally that upon the result of the trials and observations which they had made ... no material objection or difficulty occurred to prevent its execution', they were asked to make a final report before February 1804.

On 25 January 1804 Telford had written to Rickman that 'Tomorrow I set off on purpose to have an interview with Mr. Jessop, and prepare the report to the Board'.[44] However, the report was dated from Newark on 30 January, a little after Jessop's fifty-ninth birthday, and was signed by him alone. It was central to the enterprise, for his was the estimate upon which it went ahead.[45] His figure was £474,531 excluding the cost of land, for a canal of 50ft bottom width and 90ft at top (this last figure being later changed to 110ft). Locks, now thought to be 23, would average £7,449 'exclusive of digging the Foundation and backing it with Earth'; this cost was later taken at £288, making £7,737 per lock. He had in mind masonry locks, each to be built separately, for he is maintaining his dislike of staircases, though later he had to give way for economy reasons. The locks were to be 152ft × 38ft, and the canal 20ft deep.

Jessop sent his report to Telford, who on 2 February wrote a covering letter. Both then went to Rickman for the Commissioners' meeting on the 6th. In his report Telford, explaining that trial borings had been made and pits sunk along the line and at each end, went on:

The particulars of these experiments have been regularly communicated to Mr. Jessop, as well as every information which appeared to be useful; and I have likewise had frequent Interviews with him in order to explain matters more fully:—Under the circumstances he has made out the Report and Estimate which I have here inclosed.

On the west the canal would start with a sea-lock at Corpach, then rise by a flight of eight at Banavie and run by several aqueducts to Loch Lochy, which was to be entered by the old bed of the Lochy, this river being given a new channel. The level of the loch was to be raised 12ft, to reduce the height of the deep cutting that was still necessary at Laggan to bring the canal in level with the bed of Loch Oich, which would itself need deepening. A weir was to be built to allow the loch water to discharge into the Spean.

From Loch Oich the line would follow, and in part use, the bed of the River Oich to Fort Augustus, where there would be problems in building locks because of the porous soil of gravel and sand, and in constructing the lowest of them 24ft below summer level in Loch Ness. It would need, said Jessop, 'the cutting a new Channel for the River through Rocky Ground at Fort Augustus, and making a Coffer Dam there for inclosing the Lock Pit'. At the loch's eastern end the River Ness would have to be dredged at its entrance to Loch Dochfour, which would itself have to be kept at the same level as Loch Ness. Thence a canal would be built to Muirtown, where four locks would take it to a huge basin to be built to serve Inverness. Thence the line would continue to the eastern entrance (at first to be at Kessock, then switched to Clachnaharry), where a coffer-dam would be needed to build the sea-lock. The canal was to be cut from each end, so that completed sections and locks could be used for transport when building the line further inland.

For their work so far Telford was now paid £667 18s 2d, and 'William Jessop, for his Survey, Report and Estimate, and for his Travelling Expences', £209 15s, his rate being still 5 guineas a day.

On 9 February the Commissioners met again, and minuted:

The report and Estimate signed by Mr. Jessop, being considered as a sufficient foundation for the intended application to Parliament for further Grant and Powers, the Board proceeded to consider a draft of the petition . . . . the draft of the proposed Bill, and the alterations therein proposed by Messrs. Jessop and Telford having been examined by the Board, it is referred to Mr. Mundell to insert the necessary corrections . . .

Jessop and Telford were then asked to prepare a joint statement of the financial grants that would be needed from year to year 'to complete the Canal as expeditiously as possible'.[46] On the 18th they provided an estimate of the current year's probable expenditure.

On 14 June 1804, Jessop appeared before the Lords committee on the second and principal Caledonian Bill:

> Mr. William Jessop, Engineer, proves the Estimate of the Expence of the Undertaking, and that it amounts to £474,531. Mr. Thomas Telford, Surveyor, proves the Estimate of the Expence of the Land necessary to be purchased, and that it amounts to £15,000. Mr. Telford proves the other allegations of the Preamble.

The engineering estimate is signed by Jessop only, that for land by Telford.

A little earlier, just before a Commissioners' meeting on 7 June, Telford had written to Rickman:

> ... in a business of the magnitude of the Caledonian Canal, in order, as much as possible to ensure success, and avoid blame, it is prudent and adviseable to have every matter considered with great care before it is entered upon. And the Nature of the Soil, and the quality of the materials having now been sufficiently proved for the purpose of determining the precise situation, forms dimensions and values of each sort of work; It would be a great satisfaction to my mind, as well as an additional evidence to the Board, to have the assistance and advice of Mr Jessop, while in Scotland determining the above measures.[47]

On 7 June 1804, therefore, the Commissioners resolved

> that Mr Jessop should again visit the Line of the intended Navigation in concert with our Engineer, Mr Telford, in order that they might jointly inspect the progress of the works already commenced, and reexamine all the particulars of their former Survey; that they might determine the proper situation of each Lock on the whole Line of the Canal, and as far as possible fix the situation, dimensions and construction of the Bridges, Culverts, and other necessary works; and also that they might take into particular consideration the manner in which it would be most convenient to connect the Line of the Canal with the several Lochs or Lakes forming part of the intended navigation, and also settle the price of labour, and the mode

in which the several works would be most advantageously lett in Lots to the Workmen, or otherwise executed in the best and safest manner.

The following day Telford proposed the appointment of resident staff and addressed a formal letter to Jessop putting forward names and duties of men 'as have to my own and your knowledge, for ten years past, been employed upon Works of a similar nature'; in fact, men from the Ellesmere Canal works. Matthew Davidson was to superintend the Clachnaharry end, John Telford (no known relation) the Corpach end. Jessop is then asked whether the salaries previously mentioned of 150 guineas each, plus a house and travelling expenses, were adequate for the superintendents, Jessop's reply[48] agrees to the appointments, and suggests £200pa each for the superintendents. As for John Simpson, proposed in charge of construction, 'I know Mr Simpson well'.

On 11 June a paper, 'Propositions to the Board by Messrs William Jessop and Thomas Telford'[49] was sent in, setting out seven points that would need attention, to all of which the Commissioners agreed. Meanwhile, the two engineers were to consider the difference in cost of building varying sizes of lock to accommodate different-sized frigates and merchant ships. On the 14th, their statement was considered.

In his estimate annexed to their first report, Jessop had taken the lock size as 152ft × 38ft,

these dimensions having been deemed amply sufficient for the reception and passage of West-India and Baltic ships, and for Frigates not exceeding Twenty-eight Guns in force.

They now reported that at very small additional cost, the popular-sized 32-gun frigates could be accommodated. The Board therefore decided that the locks should be increased to 170ft × 40ft, canal dimensions remaining as before at 110ft wide at top, 50ft at bottom, and 20ft deep. Jessop's estimated lock cost of some £7,737 was now increased to £8,088.

At their meeting on the 18th, the Board set out their 'Instructions to be observed by Messrs. Jessop and Telford; respecting their Proceedings in determining upon the different Works . . .' These were an enlarged version of the 'Propositions' they had themselves submitted, and included everything concerned with setting out the line of canal, settling lock sites, wharves, turning places, bridges, culverts, weirs, the number and size of steam engines required, the method of letting contracts and their prices, and rules for the superintendents' conduct. In fact, all policy decisions were to be matters of joint decision and report. Separate instructions were set out for Telford alone in Appendix E of their second report, authorising the appointment of agreed staff, details of contract methods, and providing for monthly reports.[50]

Jessop, rising 60, and Telford went to Scotland together in August 1804. While there, Jessop wrote 'Instructions from Mr Wm Jessop Civil Engineer to Mr John Telford, for marking out the Caledonian Canal 1804'. A notebook, presumably John Telford's, survives,[51] with six sectional drawings of the proposed canal: three (see p 136) are signed by Jessop in August 1804, three are unsigned. Accompanying them are detailed instructions[52] for marking out the line. Since a structural drawing of this date also survives, 'Culvert for the River Loy',[53] we can assume that Jessop also provided others.

John Telford's notebook also contains those drawings of railway waggons that are reproduced in the *Atlas* accompanying Telford's *Life*. As partner in Butterley (itself to supply railway material for the canal) with Benjamin Outram, the greatest railway builder of the day, and himself engaged at this time on the Surrey Iron Railway, Jessop may well have supplied the drawings. The double-jib crane shown on Plate 19 of the *Atlas*, and captioned 'This Crane was used on the Rochdale Canal', seems likely also to have been of Jessop's providing. Simpson seems to have specified the locks, and Jessop to have approved them.

On 6 November Telford wrote to Rickman: 'I have made out a draft of Report Jessop and self and shall transmit it to him for examination and signature after which it shall with some papers annexed be sent to you.'[54] This report of 29 November went in considerable detail into the state of construction, the financial arrangements they had made, and wage and price levels. As agreed the previous year, Telford was also to visit the works every spring and autumn for a thorough financial check. The report goes on to say that Telford was placing contracts for timber and ironwork, including railways, with 'Iron-masters in Denbighshire, Derbyshire and Aberdeenshire',[55] and buying materials-carrying sloops and steam engines. Their report included a decision to build most locks 'in clusters, so as to make a considerable saving in the expence of erection' (ie to build staircases), and a consequential decision to lengthen such locks to 180ft.

On their autumn 1804 inspection Jessop and Telford had had to postpone consideration of some points. Telford had also written to Rickman from Corpach on 26 April 1805:

I shall be able to state pretty fully on the head of Prices, but I could do it more profitably after my return to England, and it would be more satisfactory to me, to have shewn my statements to, and taken Mr. Jessop's experience and assistance upon a point where he is materially concerned ... I have made an arrangement with Mr. Jessop to examine the whole of the works in August or September next.[56]

The Board agreed.

On 15 September, Telford writes to Rickman from Clachnaharry that 'Mr. Jessop is .... arrived, and I have with him examined the works at this place, they are going on well'.[57] They now altered the line at the eastern end, deciding to divert the River Ness by an embankment into a newly-dug channel in order to use part of its old bed for the canal, and so get rid of the difficulty of the Ness's current in flood-time. On 27 September Telford wrote again to Rickman:

Mr. Jessop and I have been at Corpach, and we have carefully examined the Western portion of the Canal ... we are now engaged in making arrangements respecting the Works between Loch Beauly and Loch Ness.[58]

They reported in November 1805. A barge had been built to carry 'the Dredging Machine and Steam Engine' to deepen Lochs Oich and Dochfour, the machine itself having been designed by Jessop and built, along with the steam engine, at Butterley and shipped at Hull for Inverness. It was intended to start work in the spring of 1806. Butterley also provided considerable lengths of contractors' railways and waggon wheels: £4,687 had been spent on them by 1807.

As regards bridges,

On the Caledonian Canal it is intended to construct Bridges similar to those at the West-India Docks, and which have been imitated in Cast-Iron at the London Docks; they swing horizontally to each side of the Canal or Lock.

Jessop being engineer of the West India Docks at the time must have suggested the design,[59] which originated with Ralph Walker, his resident engineer there.

After his spring 1806 visit, Telford reported that the first lock to be completed (except for its gates), that next above the sea-lock at Clachnaharry, had been built within Jessop's estimate.[60] For his work from the inception of the canal to the end of 1805, the canal's birth years, Jessop was paid £635 5s in all, including travelling expenses.

Jessop and Telford met again at Inverness on 19 September 1806, and their report[61] details the progress made. The Commissioners' spring report added that the two Corpach locks above the sea-lock had been built for under Jessop's price, but that single locks in future were likely to run at about £500 above, presumably because of the rise in the masonry price. It is perhaps worth noting, as we watch the various aqueducts being built along the line, that at no time were any in iron suggested: they are always of stone.

Next autumn the two engineers met again to review progress, as they did again a little later in the year 1808.[62] On this occasion they began their survey at Corpach on 1 November, and completed it in a fortnight. They now changed their minds on an important matter. They had intended to build both sea-locks by carrying rubble from excavations inland to form two projecting piers. Within the space between they intended to erect cofferdams, and then build the sea-locks inside them. This method succeeded (though only after great damage by storms) at Corpach, but not at Clachnaharry. They reported:

On the shore at Clachnaharry, both the Mounds have been advanced so far as to embrace a portion of the space which was to have been occupied by a Coffer-dam; but as the weight of the earth employed has caused these Mounds to sink considerably into the mud, it has suggested to us the idea of covering the whole space between them with earth and the rubbish from the neighbouring Quarry, so as to form it into an artificial Peninsula, for the purpose of so compressing or squeezing out the mud as to make it a firm foundation for a Lock, and thus to save a considerable portion of the expence of a Coffer-dam.

In their covering report the Commissioners paid Telford a tribute:

The steady progress .... has evinced the prudence and foresight of the arrangements which were at first established by our Engineer Mr Telford, and the punctual observance of his Regulations by the Superintendants employed under him ....

On 27 May 1809 the Commissioners,

taking notice of the considerable degree of forwardness of the several works on the Canal near Clachnaharry and Corpach, and that the Expenditure now approaches to a Moiety of William Jessop's estimate of 1803–04, direct him and Telford to compare what has been done with the estimate, allowing for the larger locks and the Clachnaharry sea mound and other alterations, and to do a new estimate of the cost of completing the canal.[63]

Jessop and Telford met again on 8 October 1809, and spent ten days together on the line.[64] Their change of plan at Clachnaharry was going well:

> As we have discovered by boring, that the Side-banks [of the Mound . . .] have settled about eleven feet into the mud, we have directed that upon the middle space where the Lock itself will be placed . . . . . the Earth shall be raised some height above the Level of the Side-banks, in order, by this additional weight, the more speedily and effectually to consolidate the Mud.

This very early example of pre-consolidation, coupled with pre-loading, proved to be brilliantly successful, and the lock was finished in 1812.

With £250,000 spent by 1809 the two engineers now estimated[65] a further £300,000 would be needed to complete the canal plus the cost of land for the middle district—in spite of the need to increase some wages, still not much above Jessop's original figure of just under £500,000. The Commissioners were pleased, and wrote:

> we think that praise is justly due to Messrs Jessop and Telford for the accuracy of their Calculations, and likewise to the Superintendents and other Persons employed by Mr Telford, for their judicious arrangements, and faithful execution of their various duties.

For the years 1803–9 inclusive, Telford had been paid £1,858 10s, and Jessop £1,329 15s.

His and Telford's report of October 1810[66] records straightforward progress. Copies also survive of two instructions, each of this date, one to Matthew Davidson, the other to Alexander Easton and his subordinates.[67] They are lists of things the engineers were to attend to over the following year, and each is signed first by Jessop and then by Telford. They show, perhaps, that although the detail is probably Telford's, Jessop is taking a major share of responsibility as first signatory, and that Telford is willing that he should do so.

A year later, in 1811,[68] Clachnaharry Lock is standing firm, and 'justifies the mode which was adopted to consolidate the soft Mud upon that Shore'. The engineers were now beginning to plan the works of the middle district:

We have carefully examined the ground near Fort-Augustus, and have given directions for workmen to be employed in making Trial-pits and bore holes, to enable us to determine the precise site of the Locks . . .

Butterley was now supplying lock ironwork, for on 10 December 1811 Alexander Easton wrote to Telford: 'I have had notice from Mr. Jessop that part of the Iron work for the gates was sent to Liverpool'[69]

In 1812 an employee accused Easton, who has succeeded John Telford as superintendent at Corpach, of fraud and collusion with master workmen in measuring work. Rickman wanted Jessop to take part in an enquiry, and wrote to James Hope, law agent at Edinburgh,

He (Telford) is not without hope that Mr Jessop may be prevailed upon to travel northwards, and today I wrote to him . . . to urge the matter . . . as much as possible . . . this matter resting rather on the *Reputation* of the Judges, and especially *Highland Reputation*, than on any qualities however excellent if not recognised by all.[70]

From which we may take it that Jessop had such a reputation with the men working on the canal. On 17 October Hope wrote to Rickman: 'Mr. Telford has heard from W. Jessop who is to set off to Corpach and meet him there on the 25th October.[71]

A formal enquiry with two magistrates took place on 27 October. The report, signed by the magistrates and Jessop, completely exonerated Easton. Jessop and Telford also signed a joint report on the canal, but as it is dated October, it is probably mainly Telford's work.

In this year's cumulative accounts, we may notice the following:

Thomas Telford, for general Superintendence and Management, 1803–1813—£2,464 7s
William Jessop, for Attendance on the Business of the Caledonian Canal, 1803–1812—£2,057 3s

By this time the sea-lock at Clachnaharry, the next lock to it, the four at Muirtown, and most of the canal to Loch Ness had been finished. Then nothing at Fort Augustus and little in the middle district. A good deal from Loch Lochy, including much of the deep cutting, and most aqueduct work. Banavie Locks were finished,[72] and so was the line thence to Corpach and the sea.

Jessop had made his last visit to the Caledonian, for he had little longer to live. Telford was now on his own, though in his report of 1813 he makes one more mention of his colleague: 'Mr Jessop and I have settled for cast-iron bridges at Muirtown and elsewhere.' Cast-iron they were to be instead of wood as had been first intended: one such bridge can still be seen on the canal.

Samuel Hughes[73] reported a great puddling controversy, but we fear that he both misreported the facts and exaggerated the consequences. However, with Hughes' summing up we can indeed agree:

> My own opinion, derived from the information of several gentlemen whom I have consulted, as being the most impartial of those possessing any knowledge of this subject, is this, that although Mr Jessop did originally design the works, and settle the principal points, yet in the execution of these works, which were afterwards much varied from the original intentions, these two engineers are entitled to share alike in all the merits and defects which belong to them. It will add to the weight of this opinion to state, that it coincides with that of Mr. George May, of Inverness, the present talented engineer of the Caledonian Canal Commissioners.

This conforms to a near contemporary statement, that published in 1817 in Vol XI of the *Edinburgh Encyclopaedia*, which contained a biography of Jessop:

> For several years, previous to his death, he acted jointly with Mr. Telford in conducting the great Caledonian Canal in the north of Scotland, and that engineer embraced every opportunity of acknowledging, in the warmest manner, the advantages and satisfaction he derived from the able, upright, and liberal conduct of his enlightened colleague and friend,

a remark we have seen to be true from Telford's correspondence.

Let us accept these two assessments, pass by Telford's autobiography which, in its account of the Caledonian, makes no mention at all of Jessop, and give Telford all the credit he deserves for continuing and completing this great canal.

Aberdeen Harbour

Jessop acted as consulting engineer to the Aberdeen Harbour Commissioners for improvements carried out under Telford's direction. He also reported briefly on another of Telford's harbour jobs at Ardrossan.[74] Visits to these sites were of course arranged to take place during his trips to Scotland in connection with the canal and the

166

Kilmarnock-Troon Railway (see Chapter 8).

The harbour at Aberdeen was effectively created by works executed under an Act of 1773 to Smeaton's designs, the principal feature being a masonry pier 1200ft long on the north side of the mouth of the River Dee. Plans for further improvements came from Rennie in 1797 and Telford in 1802. The latter's ideas were amplified in a report by Jessop and Telford in 1805, including the important recommendation that a steam dredger should be used for deepening the harbour and its entrance.[75]

Jessop drew up plans for the dredger in 1806.[76] John Gibb arrived as resident engineer in 1809; later that year Telford reported again; Jessop and Telford produced estimates in April 1810;[77] an Act was obtained soon afterwards, and in October they delivered in a large scale plan and sections of the proposed extension of the pier.[78]

The dredger, with engine and machinery from Butterley, began work in the autumn of 1811. The north pier had then been built out some 300ft with such obviously beneficial results that the two engineers in a report of October 1811 recommended a further extension of 500ft.[79] Plans for a breakwater on the south side of the entrance were discussed and agreed in 1812. On Jessop's last visit to Aberdeen in November 1812 he and Telford were able to report that a 4ft extra depth of water had already been achieved.[80] The new works were successfully completed in 1816 at a cost around £100,000.

8
IRON RAILWAYS

The development of iron railways in the pre-locomotive era is a fascinating story in which Jessop and his Butterley partner, Benjamin Outram, played leading parts. Outram did more than any one to promote the plate railway, and Jessop was engineer to the Surrey Iron Railway, the most famous of these early lines. He also engineered the first public railway in Scotland, the Kilmarnock & Troon.

A point of particular interest, requiring examination, is the long established tradition that Jessop introduced the first iron edge-rails, on the Loughborough to Coleorton branch of the Leicester Navigation; a tradition supported by a rail in the Science Museum attributed to this line and dated 1789 by its donor.

The Forest Line

The Forest Line of the Leicester Navigation (see Chapter 3) was built as a railway from Loughborough to Nanpantan, thence as a canal to Thringstone, and thence again as a railway to Coleorton, the whole being opened in October 1794. The total length of track was $4\frac{3}{4}$ miles. Jessop and Christopher Staveley produced the plan in 1790; the railway contract was let in February 1792, and by March 1793 everything had been made ready for laying the rails. These were supplied by Joseph Butler of Wingerworth and Ebeneezer Smith of Chesterfield; payments recorded in the minute books run from April 1793 to May 1794, the price being £11 10s per ton.[1]

The 1789 date for the Loughborough rails is therefore inaccurate, as Abbot proved in 1955,[2] and this error coupled with the paucity of contemporary descriptions has thrown doubt on the whole tradition of the 'Jessop rail' as expounded in standard works on early railways by Dendy Marshall[3] and Lee[4] and, though of course with revised dating, in the recent book by Lewis.[5] Moreover, in view of Jessop's consistent use of plate rails subsequently, scepticism has gone so far as to question the very existence of edge-rails at Loughborough.

Such an extreme opinion, however, ignores the evidence. In the first

(*above*) Surrey Iron Railway: Wandsworth Basin as shown in an
early nineteenth-century painting
(*below*) Croydon, Merstham & Godstone Iron Railway:
embankment and arch over the Chipstead Valley Road.
Watercolour of 1823 by G. B. Wollaston

(above) The City Canal: an engraving of 1824 by Henry Moses

(below) The West India Import Dock: an engraving by
W Cooke after Samuel Owen, 1811

place, there were by the mid-eighteenth century many railways (from collieries, ironworks and quarries to navigable rivers and canals) on which waggons, with flanged wheels, ran on wooden edge-rails supported by cross sleepers.[6] In addition, a step towards iron edge-rails had been made so long ago as 1767, at Coalbrookdale, by placing an iron strip on top of wooden rails. More than 20 miles of such railways had been laid by 1785 in the Dale works alone and they were copied elsewhere.[7]

The rails laid in 1791 from Dowlais ironworks to the Glamorganshire Canal were probably of the Coalbrookdale type,[8] but when Thomas Dadford junior began building the Beaufort and Blaenavon lines to the Monmouthshire Canal he adopted cast-iron edge-rails of rectangular section having a width of $2\frac{1}{2}$in (chamfered at the top) and a depth of 3in. The decision to order these rails, which were 4ft in length, dates from August 1792 and substantial payments to several local ironworks had been made by May 1793.[9]

Thus there is no reason why edge-rails should not have been used at Loughborough. Further, John Farey saw the Forest Line in 1807 and said 'The Railways ... are single, and have bars flat at top and the wheels are cast with flanches, inside, for keeping the trams upon them'.[10] No clearer description of an edge-rail is needed; but for corroboration we have a letter from William Jessop junior, written in 1821, which speaks of the line built by his father between Coleorton and Loughborough as an 'edge Rail Way'.[11] And it was in 1824 that Robert Stevenson launched the tradition by referring to the railway at Loughborough instituted

in the year 1789, under the direction of the late Mr William Jessop. Here this eminent engineer introduced the Edge-rail, the upper surface of which was of an elliptical figure, with flanges upon the wheels to guide them upon the tracks....[12]

He goes on to say that some years later 'Mr Benjamin Outram, an engineer of acknowleged ingenuity and merit' constructed the railway at Little Eaton in Derbyshire where 'the plate-rail was adopted, with the flanges cast upon the rails, for the direction of the waggons, instead of having them upon the wheels as is the case in the edge-railway'.

The question of edge-rails having been settled, consideration can now be given to their shape. From various statements in the Leicester minute books we know or can deduce that the rails were of cast-iron, 3ft in length, weighing about 30lb and with a bearing surface rather more than 2in wide; and they were carried on wooden supports on timber sleepers.[13] Three hypotheses may be examined:

1 The iron used was in the form of rectangular strips on wooden rails, in the Coalbrookdale style. This is a perfectly feasible solution, but subject to the difficulty of seeing why Farey did not describe the rails in such terms and how some 2,000 of them could be sold in 1825 as rails (not scrap iron) at 10 guineas per ton.[13]
2 Rectangular bars without a supporting wooden rail. With a top width of, say, $2\frac{1}{2}$in rectangular rails weighing 30lb per yard would be about $1\frac{1}{4}$in deep, and their strength would be quite inadequate.
3 The same amount of metal disposed in the form of a T-section. Assuming the head was $2\frac{1}{2}$in wide and $\frac{1}{2}$in thick, and the vertical rib or web had a thickness of $\frac{1}{2}$in, the average depth of the rail would be about 4in. This gives sufficient strength, and the T-section seems to us to be the most likely form of the Loughborough rails.

To go further and suggest that the rib was deeper at mid-span than at the ends (ie the rails were 'fish bellied') is to push speculation too far; though rails of just such a shape were certainly used by Thomas Barnes in 1798 at Walker Colliery near Newcastle, and they even had a rounded upper surface reminiscent of Stevenson's 'elliptical figure',[14] while the Science Museum has a similar T-section fish-belly rail of unknown provenance which is thought to date from around 1800.[15]

For a given weight of cast-iron a still stronger rail can be made by providing a bottom flange; that is, by adopting an I-section. The earliest rails of this type that can be dated accurately are those supplied in 1813–15 by the Butterley Company for a railway from the Grantham Canal to Belvoir Castle. Several of these rails are in the Science Museum; they are 3ft long, weighing 40lb and have a bearing surface 1in wide.[16] The rail presented in 1892 by Mr Stretton as having come from Jessop's Loughborough-Nanpantan line of 1789 is almost identical to the Belvoir rails.[17] The date is in any case a little too early, but for reasons which are apparent we believe the attribution is probably erroneous.

Now the Belvoir rails may well have been designed under the direction of William Jessop junior or his brother Josias, and Josias undoubtedly used rails of this kind (with a slightly heavier section) for the Mansfield & Pinxton Railway in 1817–19.[18] Hence it is appropriate to refer to these as 'Jessop rails' and to consider them as being a development from T-section rails possibly used for the first time by William Jessop senior at Loughborough in 1793–4.

The cast-iron rails patented by Losh and Stephenson in 1816 were of the 'Jessop' type. But a new era began in 1820 with the introduction by John Birkinshaw of rolled wrought-iron rails; ten years later the use of cast-iron had become an anachronism, and plate-rails were a thing of the past.

Early Iron Plate Railways

Plate-rails are L-shaped with the vertical flange on the inner edge of the rail, not on the wheel. The waggons can thus be led off the railway on to ordinary roads or paving wherever suitable arrangements are made. This was reckoned to be so advantageous that plate-rails came to dominate the railway scene, except on Tyneside, for about twenty years despite the fact that, in respect of strength per unit weight and the difficulty of keeping them free from dirt, they were inferior to edge-rails.

It is not certain whether flanged iron plates on wooden rails were used, about 1779, on the railway from Caldon Low lime quarries to the Trent and Mersey Canal,[19] but in December 1790 such plates were ordered, and then laid on massive timber rails for the inclines of the Shropshire Canal.[20] Meanwhile, John Curr had introduced all-iron plate-rails of uniform section throughout their length, on wooden cross sleepers, at Sheffield Park Mine in 1776, 1778 or 1787. The date is in dispute[21] though no one doubts these were the earliest of their kind, or that similar rails were employed above ground at Butler's Wingerworth Ironworks near Chesterfield about 1788. The latter rails, 4ft long and weighing 24lb per yard run, were laid to a 20in gauge.[22]

It is probable that the next use of iron plate-rails can be claimed for the Butterley Company in a line, just over a mile in length, built for their own use from Bullbridge Wharf on the Cromford Canal to lime quarries at Crich.[23] The date is 1793 and the gauge 3ft 6in but no other details are known.[24]

Almost simultaneously work began on the Little Eaton railway extension from the Derby Canal. As we have seen in Chapter 3, this line was proposed by Jessop in a report dated 3 November 1792; the first batch of rails was ordered from Joseph Butler in December 1793, at £10 10s per ton;[25] and the Little Eaton Gangway, to give its local name, reached completion under Outram's direction in May 1795. It had a single track of 3ft 6in gauge,[24] with passing places, and the rails of 3ft length weighed 28lb.[26] The *Lincoln & Stamford Mercury* for 16 August 1793 carried an advertisement for oak sleepers 4ft 6in long to be squared at each end for 9in in length.

173

Concerning the rails, Jessop simply said they should be of cast-iron, though he implies the use of plates by suggesting that the waggons 'may be so constructed as to be carried into the Town without unloading'. In fact, transferable waggons were not adopted and it seems that Outram, in following Butler's precedent for demountable boxes (see Chapter 3), also copied the Wingerworth rails with only minor modifications.

Next comes Outram's $5\frac{1}{2}$ mile railway from the Peak Forest Canal to lime quarries near Buxton. The rails were ordered from the Butterley Company in December 1794,[27] probably its first order of any size, and the railway was completed in August 1796.

The gauge may have been 4ft 2in which virtually became standardised after the construction in 1796–7 of a line from the Cromford Canal to Joseph Wilkes' colliery at New Brinsley. The rails here, supplied by Butterley, were 3ft long weighing 33lb and laid at the 4ft 2in gauge, carrying waggons with an all-up weight of $2\frac{1}{4}$ tons.[28]

Before the end of 1799 work had started on three notable railways, all of this type: the Ashby Canal lines totalling $12\frac{1}{2}$ miles in length, of which 4 miles were double track, built by Outram with 37lb rails on stone blocks;[29] the Penydarren line with $9\frac{1}{2}$ miles of single track from the ironworks near Merthyr to the Glamorganshire Canal at Abercynon, engineered by George Overton;[30] and the Blisworth Hill Railway on the Grand Junction Canal. Fortunately we have a considerable amount of information on this line which is no doubt typical of the best practice of the period. Its history will be found in Chapter 6. Here we need only say that Jessop was the consulting engineer and Outram, as contractor, completed the work in October 1800 using Butterley rails. The double-track line had a length of 3.4 miles from Blisworth to a point south of Stoke Bruerne. Specifications, dated October 1799, call for a 24ft width of properly drained ground on the central 18ft of which is to be placed a bed of small stones, gravel and broken brick to a depth of 12in. Stone blocks of not less than 112lb for the sleepers are to be obtained from local quarries and the cast-iron rails, 3ft long and weighing 37lb, are to be spiked into octagonal oak plugs set in the stone blocks.[31] Recent field investigations have proved the gauge to be 4ft 2in[32] and rails preserved in the Stoke Bruerne Museum are similar to those of the Surrey Iron Railway (Fig 18) except that the small strengthening rib on the underside is near the middle rather than at the outside edge.

In 1799 two canal schemes were under consideration for linking the northern parts of Surrey to the Thames. One of these materialised as the Croydon Canal, opened in 1809 and falling through no less than 28 locks in a distance of 9 miles, where it joined a short length of the Grand Surrey Canal, with an entrance lock and basin at Rotherhithe;[33] the other envisaged a canal from Croydon passing along the busy Wandle Valley to the Thames at Wandsworth.[34] Jessop received a request to examine the latter project, and his report is dated 9 December 1799.[35]

He found a canal to be altogether impracticable as 'strong objections would arise to taking water from the streams that feed the River Wandle, the works on which are perhaps more valuable than any others within an equal compass in the kingdom', and there was no economical alternative source of supply. But there is, he says,

> another way of obtaining the object in view; if not quite as effectually as by a Canal, it will, under all circumstances, be not much inferior to it; this is by the adoption of an Iron Railway. Railways of wood or iron have many years been in use in the northern parts of England, chiefly among the coal mines; it is but lately that they have been brought to the degree of perfection, which now recommends them as substitute for Canals; and in many cases they are much more eligible and useful.

He suggests that the railway, 8 miles in length from Croydon to Wandsworth, would cost about £24,000.

The committee of subscribers, meeting at the Wheatsheaf in Tooting on 12 December, under the chairmanship of John Hilbert, received this report and decided to send a deputation to view some existing iron railways.[36] The logistics of the visit took some time to sort out, but eventually four committee members met Jessop at Nottingham on 8 July 1800. They spent the next week with him seeing a recently completed railway at Beggarlee Colliery near Langley Bridge, on the Cromford Canal, then going to Crich and finally to the Peak Forest line.[37] The deputation having presented a favourable report at a general meeting, it was agreed to apply in the next session for leave to bring in a Bill under the name and style of *The Surrey Iron Railway Company.*[38]

Eight gentlemen formed a management committee with Jessop as their engineer and John Foakes and George Wildgoose as land surveyors. More surveys were then carried out and Jessop proposed that a dock basin, with an entrance lock from the Thames, should be constructed at Wandsworth. On 10 December 1800 he presented a second report detailing the route from Wandsworth to Croydon, and also a branch line to Hackbridge near Carshalton, and firmly recommending the Wandsworth Basin.[39] The total length of railway now envisaged (and actually built) was $9\frac{1}{4}$ miles, and the cost as given in Jessop's estimate came to £33,000.[40]

In the course of this report Jessop refers to the Blisworth and Ashby Railways as examples additional to those seen by the deputation in July, and expresses his belief that

> The utility of Railways is no longer a question of speculative opinion; the more they became known, the more generally they will be accepted, and will very soon be marked as a distinguished feature among the national improvements which facilitate and promote the commerce and agriculture of the country.

Fortified by such sentiments and Jessop's clear-cut plans and estimates the subscribers to what was about to become the world's first independent public railway, submitted their petition to Parliment in February 1801. Jessop, the two surveyors and Mr Luttly, a solicitor and clerk to the company, gave evidence; and with an amendment specifying that the rail flange should not exceed 1in in height at road crossings, the Act (41 Geo III, c.33) received the Royal Assent on 21 May 1801. The full title of this historic document is

> An Act for making and maintaining a Railway from the Town of Wandsworth to the Town of Croydon, with a Collateral Branch into the Parish of Carshalton, and a Navigable Communication between the River Thames and the Railway at Wandsworth, all in the County of Surrey.

An engraved plan of the line was deposited in the House of Lords on 21 April 1801.[41]

At a meeting held on 4 June 1801 it was resolved to confirm Jessop, Foakes, Wildgoose and Luttly in their posts and to advertise for tenders for carrying out the works.[42] Construction must have proceeded with great expedition, as the *Monthly Magazine* in February 1802 reported that

> The locks, canal and basin, from which the Surrey Iron Railway is to commence at Wandsworth, have lately been opened, and the water admitted from the Thames. The first barge entered the lock, amidst a

176

vast concourse of spectators, who rejoiced in the completion of this part of the important and useful work. The ground is laid for the railway, with some few intervals, all the way up to Croydon, and the [contractors] wait only for the approach of permanent open weather to lay down the iron.

In the same journal's issue for August 1802 we read

The Surrey Iron Railway is now completed over the high road through Wandsworth town. On Wednesday, June 8 [this should be June 9] several carriages, of all descriptions, passed over the iron rails, without meeting with the least obstacle.

And finally, in the *European Magazine* for August 1803 appears an item stating that on 26 July 'The Surrey Iron Railway from Wandsworth to Croydon was opened to the public for the conveyance of goods'. The Carshalton Branch, $1\frac{1}{4}$ miles in length, may have been opened a little later.

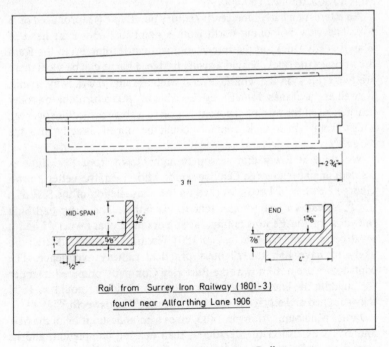

Rail from Surrey Iron Railway (1801-3)
found near Allfarthing Lane 1906

Fig 18   A rail from the Surrey Iron Railway

177

Technically, the railway differed in no essential respects from the Blisworth line: double track throughout with cross-over points[43] and 38lb plate-rails. A broken, discarded rail was found in 1906, after being buried for perhaps a century, and is now in the Science Museum (Inv No 1913–483). Dimensions derived from this fragment, shown in Fig 18, closely resemble those in a sketch by Josias Jessop of the 38lb rails ordered in 1804 for Bristol Docks. Stone-block sleepers, of which many examples survive, are roughly 14in square by 9in thick. After crossing Wandsworth High Street the railway was carried over the Wandle on two timber bridges,[44] but along the rest of the line only minor earthworks were required and the cost of the track, amounting to £2,950 per mile,[45] is only slightly higher than Jessop's estimate. The Wandsworth Dock, however, was made substantially larger than proposed in the original plans, with a capacity for containing up to thirty vessels from the 'west country' Thames barges down to small lighters and passenger boats.[44] This, added to inflationary advances in the price of labour and materials, probably explains the increase in authorised capital which, after a further Act had been obtained in March 1805, totalled £60,000.

An interesting early nineteenth-century painting[46] is reproduced on p 169. The view is looking north from a point just above the head of Wandsworth Dock; in the foreground is a cut leading up to the Ram Brewery. In the dock, behind a swing bridge, a barge can be seen; there are two cranes on the wharf, several waggons and the railway tracks. As well as the cranes, John Farey describes in 1805 a turntable on roller bearings used for turning the waggons on to a stage projecting over the wharf from which their contents could be tipped directly into the barges.[43]

We think it likely that Jessop brought down from Yorkshire as resident engineer George Leather senior whose son, the better known George Leather of Leeds, worked on the construction of the SIR as a boy,[47] perhaps a trainee-assistant to his father. The latter had built railways for the Fenton family, large Yorkshire coal owners[48] and it must be remembered that before 1801 few in the London district are likely to have had the slightest practical railway experience. The contractors are not known; the Butterley Company prepared a tender for building the line[49] but were not successful bidders, though in 1803 they supplied and erected two weighbridges at Wandsworth.[50]

James Malcolm, writing in 1805, gives a good description of the SIR and of its extension to Merstham, then nearing completion, and he quotes an optimistic appraisal by the company of its financial future.[44]

But over the years those hopes were not fulfilled; tolls charged on all goods carried by the railway just about balanced maintenance and running costs; dividends were small and paid at irregular intervals.[42]

So great was the enthusiasm in the initial stages, however, that the extension just mentioned was conceived, quite seriously, as forming part of a railway running all the way to Portsmouth.[51] This idea came up for consideration at a meeting held in the Spread Eagle, Wandsworth, on 3 June 1802 when the decision was taken to have a survey made, as a first step, from Croydon to Reigate by Jessop, Samuel Jones and George Wildgoose.[52] The preliminary work was completed by September[53] and Jessop presented his report on 7 October 1802.[54]

The proposed line ran from the end of the SIR at Croydon to Merstham and on to Reigate with a branch to Godstone. Jessop remarks it is fortunate that the line passes by the quarries at Merstham which yield a useful building stone and also a hydraulic lime 'apparently superior in Quality to either that of Guildford or Dorking'. The probably consumption of this lime in London will be great, he predicts, 'for it may be sold there as cheap as the common Chalk-lime, as One Horse will draw 10 tons of it to Wandsworth in Four Hours'.

At a meeting held on the same day, with George Tritton as chairman, the committee for 'the Extension of the Surrey Iron Railway' decided to go ahead and appointed 'Mr William Jessop and Mr Josias Jessop, Engineers, with such Assistants as they may engage' to prepare plans and sections.[55] This they did; the petition went to Parliament on 13 December 1802, Jessop prepared the estimates,[56] Josias gave evidence together with Jones, Wildgoose and Luttly, and after some arguments with the subscribers to a rival scheme for a London-Portsmouth canal, the Act (43 Geo III, c.35) became law on 17 May 1803. The proprietors, many of whom held shares in the SIR were incorporated as *The Croydon, Merstham & Godstone Iron Railway Company*.

Jessop's estimate, including £5,600 for land purchase, came to £52,350.[56] But by the time the Bill went to the House of Lords only £43,600 had been subscribed, out of which the legal and surveying charges were owing. Construction of the whole length of line therefore could not be contemplated at this stage, so specifications were drawn up and tenders invited for building the railway from Croydon to Merstham. The Butterley Company won the contract with a bid of £36,350.[57] The first invoice for rails dates from August 1803 and for stone blocks in March 1804. By that time £1,700 had been paid to workmen and by the end of the year a total of nearly £9,000. The last invoices for rails and blocks are dated July 1805.[58]

179

This is an early example of a single firm acting as general contractor on a large job. From the surviving accounts it is clear that Butterley supplied all materials, equipment and labour and built the bridges, cuttings and embankments as well as laying the track. Outram personally directed the contract, his fees and expenses (paid by Butterley) amounting to £285. He died in May 1805 shortly before the work reached completion.

Before going to Bristol in February 1804 Josias Jessop, as assistant engineer to the clients, set out the line;[59] young George Leather, then in his late 'teens, checked the levels of the track as it was being laid,[47] and there is every reason to suppose that Jessop himself visited the site from time to time. Certainly he would have been involved in several variations which had to be made to the contract during construction.

The ruling gradient of 1:144 entailed moderately heavy works including a 30ft cutting north of Merstham and a 20ft embankment with an archway through it for the Chipstead Valley road to pass under the railway at Smitham Bottom near the Red Lion.[60] This arch, depicted on p 169, was designed and built with ten reinforcing iron ribs[61] but was constructed in masonry, not brick as originally specified. Whether due to inaccuracies in the preliminary surveys or alterations in the route, a considerable amount of earthwork additional to the quantities specified had to be carried out. It was also decided to extend the main line 250yd beyond the contract length and to build a branch line to some gravel pits. These and other items increased the engineering costs to £41,800 by completion of works in August 1805.[57]

The main line, $8\frac{3}{4}$ miles in length, was double throughout with tracks laid at a 4ft 2in gauge, which of course must apply to the SIR.[62] The rails, weighing not less than 40lbs, cost £12 per ton and the stone blocks, mostly sent from Cromford and Little Eaton, were charged at 2s each delivered on site. The waggons had a gross weight of 3 tons and were normally drawn in a train of 5 by a single horse.

In October 1805 when the accounts were drawn up the company still owed Butterley £2,580. By an Act obtained in July 1806 the proprietors could raise more capital, but it seems they only succeeded in paying their debts and making minor improvements. Extensions to Godstone and Reigate never materialised. The total expenditure on construction, land purchase and so on came to approximately £50,000.

The Croydon Railway enjoyed slightly better financial returns than the SIR; dividends, probably of 2 per cent, were paid in all but two years from 1809 to 1820 and thereafter at irregular intervals.[63] But, if disappointing as an investment, these pioneer lines were the first of a whole series of public, horse-drawn railways of which some 350 miles had been built in Britain before the opening of the Liverpool & Manchester Railway in 1830.[64]

Railways in Scotland

Among the earliest iron railways in Scotland were those used by the contractors building the Caledonian Canal, for earth moving and carrying stone from the quarries. Invoices in the Butterley ledger for rails, waggon wheels and axles supplied to the canal begin in September 1804.[65] The rails, weighing 38lb, cost 11 guineas per ton delivered at Hull, whence they were shipped to Inverness. At about the same time other, smaller deliveries came from a Denbighshire foundry via Chester to Fort William and also from a firm at Aberdeen, and later from Inverness itself. Annual reports by Jessop and Telford and the canal Commissioners from 1805 to 1811 contain many references to the railways.[66] The expenditure during this period came to rather more than £12,000. This sum included about £8,600 for iron and £3,500 for labour costs incurred by the contractors Simpson & Cargill at the eastern end and by Simpson & Wilson at the western end of the canal works. Additional sums, not explicitly recorded, would have been spent on building the waggons[67] and for timber sleepers which were adopted to facilitate shifting the track as construction proceeded. The gauge was 3ft 10in.

During the period in which he was engaged on the Caledonian Canal, Jessop carried out several other commissions in Scotland. His consulting work at Aberdeen and Ardrossan Harbours, in conjunction with Telford, is briefly mentioned in Chapter 7. He was also called upon for an opinion on the ambitious project of building a railway from Glasgow to Berwick in 1810.[68] Of greater interest, however, is the railway from Kilmarnock to Troon and the associated Troon Harbour.

Robert Stevenson in 1818 refers to 'the late Mr Jessop' as 'the first engineer of eminence who seems to have introduced railways in the South', and goes on to say 'He was also the engineer for the magnificent works for his Grace the Duke of Portland in Scotland, connected with which there is a double railway from Kilmarnock to Troon, which is ten miles in length'.[69]

The idea of building this railway is mentioned in a letter from the Duke to the Earl of Eglinton, in April 1806,[70] and the proposed line is shown in a map by John Wilson dating from 1807.[71] We suppose that Jessop had already been consulted; certainly he prepared the estimates and, with Wilson, gave evidence on the Bills before Parliament both for the harbour and the railway. The Railway Act (48 Geo. III, c.46) received the Royal Assent on 27 May 1808; it was the first for a public railway in Scotland. The Harbour Act (48 Geo. III, c.47) also passed on the same day.

With Thomas Hollis as resident engineer, under Jessop's direction, work began later in 1808, chiefly using direct labour, though Mr Simpson (probably John Simpson, one of the Caledonian Canal contractors) undertook construction on the River Irwine bridge.[72] Butterley supplied rails and wheels in the early stages but the main rail contract went to the local Glenbuck iron works in July 1809.

In June 1811, the *Ayr Advertiser* records that the harbour is 'in a great forwardness and will be completed in the course of the autumn', and the same journal in September of that year says that the railway is opened and coals are now exporting from Troon Harbour. By-laws regulating use of the line are dated 4 October 1811.

The harbour consisted of a wet dock about 6 acres in extent opening off an outer tidal basin protected by a breakwater pier.[71] The railway ran alongside the dock and then for $9\frac{3}{4}$ miles to Kilmarnock, the greater part of the first 2 miles being on an embankment up to 10 or 12ft in height, then, further along the line, crossing a peat bog about 1 mile in width, followed by a masonry bridge of 4 arches (each of 40ft span) rising 25ft above the River Irwine, and finally up a gentle incline to Kilmarnock.[73] The original rails, 3ft long and weighing 40lb, were laid to a 4ft gauge in the form of a double track[74] with cross-overs and frequent 'turnouts' for the waggons to leave or enter the railway. The company imposed a weight limit of $2\frac{1}{2}$ tons gross for waggons using the line. Each waggon had to have its weight, and the owner's name, painted on it.

The engineering works of the railway cost about £42,000, compared with Jessop's estimate of £38,167, in addition to another £3,000 for legal and parliamentary charges. Tolls charged on coal, the main commodity carried (at 2d per ton per mile), and on other goods and also on passengers, brought in very adequate returns; annual dividends of 5 or $7\frac{1}{2}$ per cent and occasionally 10 or 15 per cent were paid up to 1839 when the Glasgow, Paisley, Kilmarnock & Ayr Railway leased the line. Throughout this period the Kilmarnock & Troon Railway was horse-operated, though it seems that an unsuccessful experiment with steam locomotion took place around 1817.

Note

Several published works, as Robert E. Carlson's *The Liverpool & Manchester Railway Project, 1821–1831* (1969), refer to surveys made between 1796 and 1798 by both Jessop and Outram for a railway between Liverpool and Manchester. Extensive searches through newspaper files and local history collections have yielded nothing: we have been unable to trace the story further back than the fertile historical pen of C E Stretton, in 1901.[75]

9
THE PORT OF LONDON

In planning the docks and other improvements in the Port of London, Jessop acted as consulting engineer to the City Corporation from 1796 to 1799. He then took on one of the biggest jobs of his career, as engineer to the West India Dock Company (Chapter 10), but during the same period he was also engineer to the City for a ship canal across the Isle of Dogs (1799–1805) and for the removal of an outcrop of rock in the bed of the Thames at Blackwall (1804–6).

Planning London's Docks

By the standards of the mid-eighteenth century and earlier times the Thames provided an excellent natural harbour and port. As many as 500 vessels could safely lie afloat along the river banks in the Pool of London, leaving a wide central channel for navigation.[1] About half this number, consisting of coasting and other vessels up to 200 tons burden, moored in the Upper Pool (Fig 19); some larger vessels were accommodated in the Middle Station near Wapping, and about 200 ships including most of the colliers and West Indiamen not exceeding 400 tons burden could moor in the Lower Pool. In addition, ships bringing timber from Baltic ports had moorings a little downstream of Limehouse; there was room at Deptford for about 30 merchant ships up to 500 tons burden; and the big East Indiamen, requiring a depth of at least 20ft, moored at Blackwall. The sea-going ships were unloaded into river barges or lighters either for direct delivery or, in the case of cargoes attracting duty, for Customs examination at the Legal Quays or at various authorised wharfs (the so-called Sufferance Wharfs). The goods were then taken by road to the warehouses. For exports, the process of course worked in reverse order.

A surprisingly large volume of trade could be handled by this system. Thus in 1750 about 8,000 ships entered the port and their tonnage amounted to nearly three-quarters of a million tons.[2]

The Thames near London also provided accommodation for the biggest concentration of shipbuilding activities in the country.[3] The

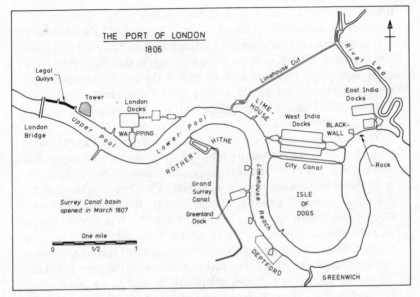

Fig 19

Navy had its great establishments at Deptford and Woolwich; a dozen important building yards existed along the river from Blackwall to Limehouse, and there were several wet docks for the fitting-out and repair of merchant ships. These included the Old Dock at Blackwall, mentioned by Pepys in his diary, the Howland (later renamed the Greenland) Dock at Rotherhithe, opened in 1699, the dock of Messrs Wells nearby, and the Lower Wet Dock at Deptford which is shown on Rocque's map of 1746. To these was added in 1790 the Brunswick Dock of Messrs Perry at Blackwall.

But there were no commercial wet docks on the Thames before 1800; all loading and unloading took place while the ships rode at moorings. Nevertheless, in the days before overcrowding and delays became serious problems, the port worked with reasonable efficiency. Apart from the Customs, with their headquarters on the Legal Quays, the Corporation of London had overall authority for the port and dealt with such matters as tonnage duty, moorings and wharfs, while Trinity House looked after navigation and the dredging of ballast.

However, by the end of the century conditions had changed very much for the worse due to a large increase in trade. Official statistics show that between 1750 and 1795 ships entering the port nearly doubled in numbers and the tonnage increased about two and a half times.[2] Additional moorings had been provided but even so they became seriously overcrowded. A count in August 1794 showed nearly 800 vessels crammed into the Pool, instead of about 550 for which there was proper space, and at some of the moorings in the Lower Pool large ships were lying 12 or even 16 abreast in the tiers.[1] The quays and wharfs were now hopelessly inadequate for the rapid handling of cargoes, and losses by smuggling and by plundering had reached intolerable proportions.

The merchants suffered most from these evils and it was they who took the initial steps towards reform by establishing, in September 1793, a committee to consider ways and means of overcoming the problems. Their leading figure was William Vaughan, a public-spirited individual and a director of the Royal Exchange Assurance Corporation,[4] who wrote his historic *Treatise on Wet Docks, Quays and Warehouses for the Port of London* in December 1793. Here, for the first time, conclusive arguments were presented showing the need for spacious docks with associated warehouses in the port. He could foresee the possibility of docks at Rotherhithe and on the Isle of Dogs but preferred a site at Wapping, close to the City yet with access to water of an adequate depth for all but the largest vessels.

Vaughan's ideas quickly gained support. John Powsey, who had been engineer for Brunswick Dock, was employed to make a feasibility study. He reported favourably in August 1794; whereupon the group, following the advice of Vaughan and Capt Joseph Huddart, commissioned a detailed survey by Daniel Alexander.[4] Before the end of that year Alexander produced a plan for a pair of docks at Wapping, already called the 'London Docks', with an entrance basin and locks from the river and linked by a ship canal $2\frac{3}{4}$ miles long to the Thames at Blackwall, just east of Brunswick Dock.[5]

In March 1795 the committee resolved to adopt this scheme; Rennie was engaged to estimate the engineering costs, and by February 1796 the merchants had raised enough money for a Bill to obtain powers to build the docks.[6]

These proposals attracted considerable attention. Various individuals started preparing their own schemes and the Corporation of London appointed a committee in 1794 to consider what should be done for the better accommodation in the port.[7] Initially the Port Committee seems to have been content with plans for improvements at the Legal Quays, and the most promising of these was submitted to Jessop, Rennie and John Foulds for comment.[8] But from the beginning of January 1796 the problems were tackled far more seriously. By this time it was becoming obvious that major works would be required, involving unprecedented capital expenditure and affecting a large amount of exisiting property. Parliament, the City, Trinity House, the Commissioners of Customs and Excise, the wharfingers and lightermen, all were concerned, so it is not surprising that the period of planning, negotiation and parliamentary enquiries lasted a long time; though no one perhaps could have foreseen that three and a half years would pass before the first of the necessary Acts received the Royal Assent. However, it must be acknowledged that the planning proved to be highly effective; seven years after the first Act the Port of London possessed the finest and the most extensive dock system in the world.

Throughout the period 1796 to 1799 the Corporation of London properly played a leading role. George Dance, the City's surveyor, directed operations, attended by his engineer assitant John Foulds and other members of the Guildhall staff, with Jessop as consulting engineer.[9] Dance and Jessop worked together very harmoniously and were soon on terms of friendship. Dance, a Royal Academician, made the excellent portrait drawing of Jessop in 1796 (p 34); in 1798 he was elected to the Smeatonian Society on the proposal of Jessop, seconded by Matthew Boulton and Robert Mylne;[10] and Joseph Farington, the landscape artist, notes in his dairy on several occasions that he dined with Dance and 'Jessop the engineer' at his own or Dance's house.[11]

By May 1796 Jessop and Dance had drawn up four alternative proposals for providing greatly increased accommodation at the Legal Quays and wharfs, together with plans for docks on the Isle of Dogs and at Rotherhithe. But even by mid-February the Port Committee was able to communicate its preliminary recommendations to the Chancellor of the Exchequer,[12] and within a few weeks a parliamentary committee was set up to examine the whole question. It sat for twenty-five days, hearing evidence from all interested parties and receiving details of no less than eight different schemes.[1]

The Committee's report, published in May 1796, wisely makes no specific recommendations, as none of the projects could yet be considered as having reached finality, but it comes out strongly in favour of the principle of building docks and accepts beyond question the absolute necessity of improving the port facilities. Of the various schemes submitted it is sufficient here to mention only five.

First, there is the merchants' plan as drawn up by Alexander and Rennie. This differed in no essentials from the original project of 1794. The two docks at Wapping were planned to have water areas of 25 and 10 acres, with warehouses surrounding the larger one.

The City's proposals, as submitted to the Committee, were based on rather different principles: (1) to extend the Legal Quays and wharfs and provide ample warehouse accommodation on both banks of the Upper Pool, and (2) to remove timber ships and/or colliers from the river, by means of docks. Jessop and Dance presented their main evidence on 7 April 1796. Under heading (1) they described two of the alternatives already under consideration by the City. The Quays could be enlarged by the construction of wide jetties projecting in front of the existing river wall to create five small docks for lighters, or the present Quays could be widened and at the same time a new range of wharfs would be built along the south bank downstream of London Bridge. In both variants large warehouses were to be erected together with road improvements to reduce traffic congestion. In the second part of the City's project Jessop proposed a 100 acre dock for colliers at Rotherhithe, with two entrance basins and, as an optional extra, a barge canal from the dock to Vauxhall; and a dock of similar size for timber ships, also with two entrance basins, to be built across the Isle of Dogs. No warehouses would be required for the trade at either of the docks. The cost of the engineering works he estimated at a little under £300,000 for each dock, but the total cost of the warehouses and improvements of the Quays, as estimated by Dance's surveyor, James Peacock, came to well over £1 million.

Of the schemes submitted by individuals the proposals by Ralph Walker take pride of place. He had been captain of a West India ship and subsequently became a Jamaica planter. His interest in navigation led to studies in magnetic variation and the design of an improved mariner's compass. In 1793, at the age of 45, he settled in London and devoted himself to these matters with such success that he received a premium from the Board of Longitude, and the Navy Board adopted his compass.[13] He also made tidal observations in the Thames. Then, on his own initiative and without previous engineering experience, Walker prepared plans for docks at Wapping which in some respects were preferable to the 'official project'. Those he presented to the Committee in April 1796 together with a recommendation for constructing a ship canal across the Isle of Dogs in place of the canal from Wapping to Blackwall. The City had already contemplated the possibility of an Isle of Dogs canal, though it formed no part of Jessop's evidence to the Committee, and Walker's plan may be taken as the effective origin of this element of the port improvements. He suggested a depth of 21ft and a width of 120ft.

Finally, we note that the engineer-architect Samuel Wyatt also submitted plans for large docks in the Isle of Dogs, and Joseph Hodskinson presented a logical development of the existing system; dredging a deep channel in the river from Deptford up to the bridge, with a much increased number of mooring chains from Wapping to Limehouse, and enlarging the quays and warehouse facilities further upstream.

Encouraged by the parliamentary report, the merchants submitted a new petition to the Commons in November 1796, this time without a canal,[14] while in February 1797 the City introduced its own Bill for extending the Legal Quays and for 'making a navigable cut across the Isle of Dogs to which may be added docks for the reception of as many ships as may be necessary to relieve the navigation of the river'.[15] This plan combines Jessop's Isle of Dogs (though not Rotherhithe) docks with Walker's canal. The latter, by substituting a cut $\frac{3}{4}$ mile in length for the 3 mile loop in the river past Deptford seemed obviously to provide an improved navigation up to Wapping and the Pool. The docks were advantageous in removing moored ships from the tideway, but the question of their finance had yet to be resolved.

However, some influential West India merchants led by George Hibbert, a City alderman, now realised that the Isle of Dogs might prove a better site for their purpose than Wapping. Admittedly it was much further away but land could be purchased at a lower cost, deeper water existed at Blackwall, there was room to build very large docks with extensive warehouse capacity and, not least, the City would regard such a plan with favour.[16] The West India trade would have the exclusive use of docks capable of handling their biggest ships and a vast quantity of cargo, privileges for which the merchants were prepared to advance substantial sums, and, in so doing, they would contribute towards the City's objective of reducing the number of ships in the river, at a point of great benefit to navigation.

To examine this scheme in detail the West India merchants employed Ralph Walker and the City again called on Jessop. The investigations began in July 1797. George Dance acted as co-ordinator, with John Foulds making the first sketch plans and taking levels and soundings, and Walker supervised the borings.[9] On 29 August 1797 Jessop, Dance and Walker produced a joint report and estimates for two linked docks of 21 and 10 acres, with an entrance basin of 5 acres at Blackwall and a lock at Limehouse, and also for a canal having a depth of 23ft and a water surface width of 176ft. The larger of the docks was to have 8 stacks of warehouses along its north quay and 2 at the ends, the whole to be enclosed by a wall 30ft high. The smaller dock, for outward-bound ships, had rigging houses and sail lofts alongside. The sills of the entrance locks to the canal and to the Blackwall basin would be 6ft below LWST giving a 24ft depth at high-water springs.[17] The total cost worked out at £524,000. Their plan was issued from the Surveyors Office, Guildhall, in September.[18] Though several important changes were later made, the 1797 plan includes many of the essential features of the docks, warehouses and canal as actually constructed.

The scheme was approved by a general meeting of West India merchants and planters in December, and by Common Council in January 1798.[19] A joint petition for leave to bring in a Bill went to Parliament in February. After examination by the Commissioners of Customs and Excise, the loading and unloading docks were reversed in position, for security reasons, and on further thought the engineers increased the water areas to 15 and 28 acres respectively.[20] Revised estimates were prepared by Jessop and Walker in November 1798 as follows:[21]

Docks and entrance basin	£270,000
Warehouses	242,000
Canal	64,000 (as in 1797)
	£576,000

An engraved plan with the new arrangement, signed by Dance, Jessop and Walker, appeared soon afterwards[22] and accompanied the next petition to Parliament submitted by the City and the West India merchants in December 1798.

All now appeared to be settled. There was nothing to stop the London merchants going ahead with their free-trade Wapping scheme, which they certainly intended to do, and the City's canal would of course be beneficial to them. The West India merchants were able to raise the money for their own docks, the City proposed to finance the canal from an increased tonnage duty, and the owners of the Legal Quays would receive adequate compensation from parliamentary funds for loss of trade. The Bill went to committee during February, March and April, when some interesting evidence emerged and Hibbert, Jessop and Walker spoke on the proposals.[23] But just after the committee stage had been completed, yet another scheme emerged. This had originated a few months earlier in a pamphlet by Ralph Dodd, advocating that London Bridge should be rebuilt to provide sufficient headroom and the river deepened up to Blackfriars Bridge for ships of

500 tons.[24] Within days of the pamphlet's publication Dance, again with Jessop and Foulds, began investigations to show the impracticability of Dodd's plan,[9] but it nevertheless found support and reached the Commons on 2 May 1799. Fortunately, a Select Committee had just been appointed to make final recommendations on the docks, so the new scheme was referred to them. They reported, with commendable speed, in June 1799[25] advising that whatever merit there might be in rebuilding London Bridge (and this proved to be the source of another marathon enquiry)[26] the case so far as the Port of London was concerned admitted no doubts: the river above London Bridge could never be suitable for large ships, the docks at Wapping should be built, and there were overwhelming reasons for constructing the canal and docks on the Isle of Dogs without delay.

This recommendation prompted immediate action. With some changes in the manner of financing the canal, from the Consolidated Fund, and with a requirement that the loading and unloading docks must each have their separate entrances, to meet a further point by the Customs authorities, the Act (39 Geo III c.69) for the West India Docks and the City Canal received the Royal Assent on 12 July 1799. William Vaughan and his group had to wait for the next session, but their Bill for the London Docks at Wapping passed without difficulty in June 1800. Moreover, the East India Company followed suit with an Act for building docks at Blackwall, which they obtained in July 1803. All three docks schemes and the canal were completed by 1806. The main dimensions of the entrance locks (length between gates × clear width × depth on sills at HWST) and the water areas, excluding entrance basins, are:

West India Docks	54 acres, lock 193 × 45 × 24ft
City Canal	15 acres, lock 193 × 45 × 24ft
London Docks	20 acres, lock 150 × 40 × 23ft
East India Docks	26 acres, lock 210 × 47 × 25ft

The extent to which Jessop had been engaged as planning engineer to the City of London can be deduced from his bills. For consultations, designs and attendance at Parliament from January to May 1796 he charged £145, at a daily rate of 5 guineas plus expenses, and for the whole period up to July 1799 a total of £420. As his expenses for subsistence and travelling typically came to £1 per day he must have devoted at least 65 days to this work.[27] The cost of obtaining the 1799 Act amounted to £17,600.[28]

191

The Act of 12 July 1799 did not mark the end of planning activities for the West India Docks and the City Canal. The requirement that the loading and unloading docks were to have separate entrances meant that they had to be arranged in parallel, rather than in series, and, as there was no room for expansion to the north, owing to the existence of Poplar Street and its adjoining houses, the canal had to be relocated further south. Also the West India Dock Company, immediately after its formation in July, decided to make the docks somewhat larger than proposed in the 1798 plan.

A short but hectic period of work ensued. Dance engaged a surveyor, John Manwell, to produce an accurate map of the area. Before the end of July Dance and Jessop, with Manwell's assistance, had staked out a provisional line of the canal and on 9 August Dance attended Trinity House with the revised plan. Meanwhile Ralph Walker, soon to have his appointment confirmed as resident engineer to the Dock Company, was drawing up the new dock scheme in consultation with Jessop. On 16 August a further revision took place, regarding the canal entrance at Limehouse. Six days later a joint deputation from the Port Committee and the Company, attended by Dance, Jessop and Walker, visited Trinity House to seek acceptance of the new canal line. By 29 August the exact and final position of the canal had been staked out, and next day a sketch plan of the docks was approved by the Directors of the Company.[29]

The subsequent history of the West India Docks is given in Chapter 10.

The City Canal

Construction of the ship canal across the Isle of Dogs, commonly called the City Canal, came under the administrative direction of George Dance on behalf of the Port Committee of the Corporation of London. His department at Guildhall also handled the purchase of all lands and property required for the West India Docks and the canal. The entire undertaking was financed by a government loan to the City, totalling £182,000 from the Consolidated Fund. This slightly exceeded the total expenditure up to the opening of the canal on 9 December 1805, but some further works during 1806 used up the balance and an additional £5,000 advanced by the Corporation.[30]

Jessop held the position of engineer from July 1799 to December

1805. John Foulds acted as assistant engineer to March 1802 at a salary of £225pa. He seems to have been concerned chiefly with the mechanical engineering aspects: mortar mills, pumping machinery for dewatering the excavations, and so on. There was no resident engineer, in the usual sense of that term, but cash accounts of the work done by direct labour and by contract were kept throughout the job by James Mountague, one of Dance's assistants. After Jessop left, Mountague took over as 'Surveyor and Superintendent of the Canal' at a salary of £400pa with free rent of a house at Blackwall. It is probable that Daniel Vaux was employed as engineering assistant in this later stage, and perhaps from 1804, but the records are not clear on this point.

Unfortunately the minutes of the Port Committee cannot now be traced,[31] so none of Jessop's letters and progress reports are available. From the arrangements just outlined it is obvious, nevertheless, that Jessop had full responsibility for the civil engineering works. This is confirmed by his fees which, in the absence of other information, are worth quoting to show the extent to which he was involved in design and construction (Table 3). There can be no doubt that he prepared the drawings and dealt with technical aspects of the specifications and contracts, as well as spending much time on site.

Table 3 City Canal: Jessop's Fees

Period		Fees and Expenses	Approximate number of days per month
Dates	Months		
July 1799–July 1800	12	£418	6
July 1800–Sept 1801	14	£388	4
Sept 1801–March 1803	18	£316	3
March 1803–March 1804	12	£369	5
March 1804–March 1805	12	£329	4
March 1805–Dec 1805	9	£346	6
Total		£2,166	

No changes were made in the basic dimensions of the canal from those in the original plan of August 1797: a top-water width of 176ft and a depth of 23ft. However, instead of the first idea of having a single pair of mitre gates at each end, together with a pair of floodgates pointing outwards, Jessop decided to build two locks.[32] These had a clear width of 45ft, a length between gates of 193ft and sills laid 6ft below LWST, providing a depth ranging from 20 to 24ft at high water of ordinary neap and spring tides respectively, and thus permitting the entry of ships up to 500 tons burden. The distance between the locks was 3,710ft, giving an area of impounded water equal very nearly to 15 acres.[33]

As the land in the Isle of Dogs lay about 6ft below HWST, and therefore the same distance below normal top-water level, the canal had to be embanked. The banks, formed of gravel taken from the excavations, with a puddle clay core, were built 12ft high to a level of 6ft above top water, in order to ensure a safe freeboard against exceptional high tides or surges. A general fill was placed to the same height between the north bank and the boundary wall of the docks, and also for a width of 50ft adjoining the south bank. Materials for the general fill came from dredging operations to deepen the river at Blackwall and at the canal entrances. Protection from flooding during construction was, of course, provided by the existing river embankments and by cofferdams erected in front of each entrance.

The ground consisted of 4ft of brick-earth followed by 2ft of clay overlying at least 24ft of gravel.[34] The gravel proved to be an excellent bearing stratum for the lock walls. The sides of the canal were cut at slopes of 2:1 to the full depth of 17ft below ground, leaving a bottom width of 76ft.

Drainage of the excavations was effected by means of a 15hp Boulton & Watt steam engine[35] pumping from a well sunk into the gravel and located 200ft south of Blackwall lock (see Fig 20). A cast-iron pipe, laid in a tunnel, led water from the excavations to the well.

Details of the construction procedures and progress are given in the canal account books[30] and the Port Committee contracts.[36] The first contract, awarded to John Clark and Thomas Thatcher, is dated 24 October 1799 and relates to excavation of the top 6ft down to groundwater level. They began work in January 1800 and completed in July. Meanwhile, construction had started on the tunnel, well and engine house. The engine arrived from Birmingham in December and the iron pipes from Butterley soon afterwards. Rennie supervised erection of the engine, according to what seems to have been a usual arrangement with Boulton & Watt for their work in London.

John Dyson* had the main contract for excavating the lower part of the canal, and the lock pits, and for building the banks. He started in

---

* John Dyson the younger of Newington near Bawtry, probably the son or nephew of John Dyson who had been Jessop's resident engineer on Everton, Gringley & Misterton Drainage (Chapter 4) and contractor for the Sleaford Navigation (Chapter 3).

March 1801. Brick kilns had already been built for the production of 2 million bricks, using the brick-earth dug out by Clark & Thatcher. The bricks would be required for the lock walls and floors. In addition, the walls were to have masonry facings, copings and quoins. The stone began arriving on site in August 1802 together with Dantzig timber for the piled foundations and elm for the platforms. John Fentiman of Kennington contracted to build the Blackwall lock and John Dyson, still busily engaged on the excavations, took on the Limehouse lock contract. The mason's work at both locks went to William Brown of Smithfield.

The locks had walls with a curved vertical profile and an inverted arch floor. The walls were built in brickwork 6ft thick backed by counterforts and faced with stone. The mortar consisted of 1 part Dorking or Guildford (hydraulic) lime to 4 parts sand, and the counterforts were bonded into the walls by flat iron strips placed every 3ft apart in height.

Up to the summer of 1802 drainage of the excavations, both at the canal and at the West India Import Dock, had benefited mutually from the pumping carried out at each site (see Chapter 10). But after completion of the dock the canal engine would have to cope alone,[37] and at a time when the canal excavations were reaching their maximum depth, especially at the lock pits. The engine was therefore increased in power by converting it from single to double acting and a larger boiler was obtained.[35] The conversion had been achieved by April 1803. Work on the lock foundations began two months later and both structures were completed by May 1805. Meanwhile, oak timber for the gates arrived in June 1804 and a contract for supplying ironwork for the gates, and also for swing bridges to be built over the locks, was awarded in April 1804 to William Bailey, James Ward and William Crawshay.

The gates were 28ft high and slightly curved in plan, a pair forming a pointed arch of 45ft span. They ran on rollers bearing on iron 'sweeps' and were operated by chains and capstans. The swing bridges were built in timber, each leaf being supported on twenty iron rollers working between upper and lower centre plates.

James Spedding of Poplar contracted to build both cofferdams, which he completed in April 1805. By this time Dyson had finished all the excavation work. William Stewart then began building the wing walls at the entrances, and John Hughes started removing the river banks behind the cofferdams. At the same time the great timber beams arrived for the 'preventer dams', that is, the temporary wooden walls made by lowering the beams one on top of another with their ends in vertical slots in the masonry outside the lock gates.

So far the works had proceeded as planned with no interruptions other than a slip in the sides of the canal cut in February 1802. But at high tide on 24 July 1805, just three weeks before the formal opening of the canal was due to take place, the Blackwall cofferdam failed by underseepage.[38] Fortunately no lives were lost, but the cost of remedial works amounted to £9,000 and the opening was delayed by four months.[39] However, by Monday 9 December 1805 all had been made ready and a West Indian ship, *Duchess of York*, was ceremoniously towed through the canal.

Jessop's connection with the work then ceased. James Mountague carried on as surveyor and under his direction, during 1806, the wing walls were extended and capstans and mooring posts installed to facilitate the passage of ships through the locks.

Up to the opening of the canal in December 1805 construction costs amounted to £117,000.[30] Part of the increase over the 1797 estimates can be attributed to inflation, at about 15 per cent, and to the extra cost of building locks instead of single gates, reckoned by Jessop at £6,500,[37] as well as the £9,000 spent on remedial works. But even so, the job took considerably longer and construction costs were about £40,000 higher than expected. Total expenditure to December 1806, by which time the bills had been settled, came to £187,600[30] plus £5,900 for that part of the 1799 Act chargeable to the canal.[28]

In the first twelve months of operation rather more than 1600 ships passed through the canal.[39] After 1810 traffic declined, but the canal was increasingly used as a dock for laying up; ships were ranged along practically the full length of the north bank (see p 170). However, the income rarely exceeded £4,000pa which just about paid for maintenance and wages, so the canal could not be considered a financial success.

Perhaps the main reason for the loss of transit business can be attributed to the opening of the Commercial Docks system on the Surrey side, carried out in four stages between 1809 and 1815. By the 1820s the docks were accommodating 350 to 500 ships a year, mostly in the timber trade,[40] and with the entrance at the rebuilt Greenland Dock none of these vessels needed to use the canal. No doubt other factors were involved, including the advent of steam dredgers to deepen the river channel, and eventually in 1829 the canal was sold to the West India Dock Co. Renamed the South Dock, it was later enlarged by constructing a timber-pond, still with Jessop's entrance locks, and finally rebuilt in its modern form around 1870. Even then, the Limehouse lock was retained, as being in good condition and of adequate size for barges and small ships.

Blackwall Rock

In addition to planning improvements in the Port of London and building the City Canal, Jessop's third job for the Corporation of London was the removal of a rock outcrop in the bed of the Thames at Blackwall.

The outcrop, known as Blackwall Rock, lay on the north side of the river about half way between the entrances to the West India and East India Docks (Fig 19). It was described by the geologist William Smith, in November 1804, as a mass of siliceous 'pudding stone' about 300ft in length, 150ft wide and not more than $2\frac{1}{2}$ft under low water at spring tides.[41] Obviously it constituted a hazard to navigation, but no one seems to have been able to face the problem of removing it until the autumn of 1802 when the Port Committee, strongly pressed by Trinity House, decided that action of some sort could no longer be delayed. At the same time the opportunity would be taken of deepening the river for new East India moorings, immediately downstream of the rock.[42]

Dredging began at the moorings early in 1803. Except that the ground was harder than usual there were no special difficulties in obtaining a moderate depth, and Trinity House started work using the traditional hand-operated 'bag and spoon' technique. By this somewhat primitive but economical method between 20 and 50 tons, depending on the depth and nature of the bed materials, could be raised in a tide's work. Trinity House had six dredging barges at Blackwall and charged the Port Committee for their services. John Mills also had a contract for removing in his lighters all material unfit for ballast.

Other methods, of course, had to be devised for removing the rock, which was likely to prove a very expensive undertaking; and as the large volume of dredging required at the moorings would also be costly, the City obtained an Act (in July 1803) for a loan of £100,000 from the Consolidated Fund. Preliminary surveys and soundings were made under the direction of Robert Mylne.

At the outset, attempts were made to break up the rock by underwater blasting. J M Warren supervised the operations which involved boring holes about 6ft deep and blowing the rock by means of cartridges enclosed in tin. Little success could be achieved, however, owing to the presence of sand layers interbedded in the rock which 'destroyed the effect of the Powder'.[41] In January 1804 it was therefore decided jointly by the Port Committee and Trinity House to seek advice from several of 'the most scientific Civil Engineers'.[42] As a result, reports were received in March and April from Ralph Walker, Jessop, Mylne and William Chapman. The nature of their proposals is not known, but on 6 June 1804 the Port Committee resolved that Mr Jessop be appointed as 'consulting Engineer' and that Warren should be engaged as the 'resident and executive Engineer under Mr Jessop' at a salary of £5 per week.[43]

Work soon got under way driving piles and fixing booms around the site, to enclose the operations of removal of Blackwall Rock, and in November 1804 Jessop submitted a further report on his plan of action.[44]

Briefly, he proposed to break up the rock by means of a heavy steel chisel, then to sink an iron cylinder which could be pumped out to allow miners to excavate the broken rock, working at and around low tide both day and night. The chisel was attached to a cast iron ram operated from a barge carrying apparatus rather like a conventional pile engine. The cylinder had some form of 'skirt', perhaps made of leather, to provide a seal to minimise the inflow of water, and it could be handled from a floating stage or pontoon fitted with lifting tackle and pumps.

During the winter two copper-barrelled pumps were purchased, the barge and pontoon were fitted out, and in March 1805 the cylinder arrived from Butterley.[45] Meanwhile, in August 1804, the Trinity House men had started dredging mud and gravel adjacent to the rock and they continued to do so, except for the winter months, until the end of 1805.

Few details are available on the progress of the work, but regular payments of wages are entered in the account book for workmen at the Rock; Jessop spent about forty-five days on site during the summer of 1805; pipes were purchased in September for 'lengthening the pumps for the cylinder employed at Blackwall', and there are several references to a doctor attending the miners. The miners, who came from Cornwall, were provided with special jackets and trousers and living accommodation on a barge converted for the purpose.

Up to the end of 1805 the job was carried out by direct labour. But now the method had proved effective the work could be let on contract. The choice fell on James Spedding who, with two partners, signed a contract on 16 January 1806 to lower the rock surface and the surrounding gravel to a depth of 18ft below low-water springs, and to deliver the excavated materials as fill adjoining the south bank of the

City Canal. He had the use of the Port Committee's barge *John*, equipped for breaking the rock; the pontoon with its lifting gear and pumps; and the barge *Elizabeth* as living quarters for the men.[46] Another change took place at this time: James Mountague, who had been acting as Dance's deputy, took over as surveyor in charge of operations from Christmas 1805, and soon afterwards Daniel Vaux became engineering assistant. Jessop, however, stayed on as consulting engineer until September 1806 and visited the site occasionally.

Spedding successfully executed his contract by March 1808 and thus completed the business of removing Blackwall Rock. The cost of the work amounted to about £42,000, of which sum Jessop's fees and expenses came to £505.[47]

This is not quite the end of the Blackwall story. Dredging at the new East India moorings continued until September 1807, using the *Brunswick* steam dredger in the last eight months. The cost of deepening the river at the moorings amounted to £52,000 bringing the total expenditure on the works at Blackwall to about £94,000, plus £3,800 for parliamentary and legal charges.[47]

10

BUILDING THE WEST INDIA DOCKS

The plan depicted in Fig 20 shows the Import and Export Docks, the entrance basins and locks, and the warehouses, as built between 1800 and 1806 on the reclaimed marshes of the Isle of Dogs.[1] The strata comprised 5 or 6ft of sandy clay over at least 24ft of gravel, and original ground level, protected by the river embankments, lay about 6ft below mean high water of spring tides.[2] Gravel from the excavations was used as a general fill to raise the ground adjacent to the docks and basins by 12ft; that is, to a level 6ft above mean HWST and just above the highest known tide.

Description of the Docks

Construction started in February 1800 on the Import Dock, 2,600ft long by 510ft wide, with an area of 30 acres, and 23ft deep below normal top water. The quays were 6ft above this level, so the walls rose to a height of 29ft above dock bottom. They had a curved vertical profile and were built in brickwork 6ft thick at the top, with counterforts bonded into the wall by iron reinforcement, and massive coping stones. The walls were backed with puddle clay, and a layer of clay about 1ft in thickness blanketed the dock bottom. These measures greatly reduced the loss of water by seepage through the gravel stratum. Moreover, the volume of water in the dock was so large, as compared with the loss by lockage, that the water level remained almost constant, just below HWST. The embankment surrounding Blackwall Basin was also puddled.

From the east end of the dock a lock led into the Blackwall Basin, excavated to the same depth, with an area of 6 acres and sloping earth sides.[3] Access to the basin from the river was gained through the Blackwall entrance lock. This had a clear width of 45ft, a length of 193ft between gates, and sills laid 6ft below low water giving a 24ft depth at high-water springs or 20ft at high-water neaps.[4] The lock gates, built in oak, were 28ft high and slightly curved in plan so that a

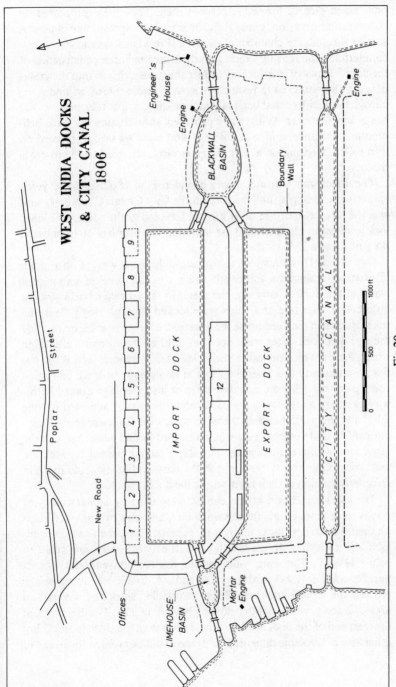

WEST INDIA DOCKS
& CITY CANAL
1806

Fig 20

pair, when closed, formed a pointed arch. They were supported on rollers running on iron 'sweeps' and operated by capstans and chains. A section through the chamber of the lock (Fig 21) shows the walls, their counterforts and masonry facing, and the inverted arch construction of the floor.[5] Rows of interlocking timber sheet piles, driven into the gravel beneath the gates, gave protection against internal erosion under the considerable differential head of water existing, at low tide, between the basin and the river. Wing walls provided an exceptionally wide bell-mouthed entrance, and a double-leaf timber swing bridge, pivoted on iron rollers working on a 12ft diameter circle, enabled traffic to cross the lock.[6]

The Blackwall entrance lock, completed in 1802, is three years earlier than Jessop's similar locks on the City Canal (Chapter 9), and was the largest structure of its kind in England at that date. The inner lock leading into the dock had the same depth, a length of 162ft between the gates, and a 38ft width.

Operation of the inner lock took place in the usual way, as on a canal, in order to maintain a full depth and a constant level of impounded water in the dock. Generally, the water in the entrance basin stood a little below high tide and ships were locked through singly from the river. But when the need arose for a number of ships to enter on one tide the entrance lock gates were not shut until an hour or two after high water, during which period the basin level fell by several feet. When the tide rose again to this level the gates automatically opened, and ships could pass through from that time up to or just after high water.[7] In this way as many as twelve ships could conveniently be admitted on one tide;[8] and the width between the wing walls gave sufficient room for an outward-bound vessel to pass out, an inward-bound vessel being at the same time within the entrance. The ships, having passed through the lock, moored at one of the buoys in the basin until they could move in an orderly fashion to their berth within the dock.

The locks and basin at Limehouse were used by lighters carrying goods to or from points further upstream, and also by unloaded ships on their way to dry docks up river for repairs. The Limehouse entrance lock had a width of 36ft, a length of 155ft between gates, and sills 22ft below HWST. The wing walls formed a more conventional, almost parallel-sided entrance with rounded ends. A double-leaf swing bridge crossed the lock. Limehouse Basin had walled sides and covered an area of 2 acres, with a depth below high water of 21ft. The inner lock at the west end of the dock was slightly shorter than the entrance lock, but otherwise of the same dimensions.[9] It too could be crossed by means of

(*above*) Bristol Floating Harbour, the entrance to Cumberland Basin; an engraving by S Bradshaw after W H Bartlett, *c* 1835

(*below*) Iron bridge over the New Cut at Bristol, from Charles Hutton, 1812

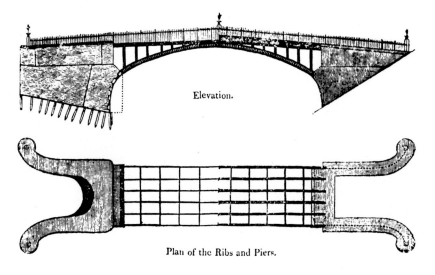

Elevation.

Plan of the Ribs and Piers.

(*above*) Sunderland Harbour: aquatint by and after William Daniell, 1822

(*below*) Model of Selby Bridge, probably made in 1791

a swing bridge, providing access to the south quay.

Six warehouses, 222ft long and 126ft wide and five storeys high, plus a basement and attic, were built along the north quay 60ft back from the coping (Nos 2, 3, 4, 6, 7, and 8 in Fig 20). They had external brick walls and timber columns and beams supporting wooden floors. Internal brick walls, with iron doors, divided each warehouse into three divisions to prevent the spreading of fire, and strict safety regulations were enforced to minimise fire risk throughout the docks, as well as on board the ships. These large warehouses, which feature so prominently in views of the dock (p 170) were used for the storage of sugar and coffee. In addition, three single-storey warehouses (Nos 1, 5, and 9) provided extra space for sugar, and casks of rum were stored in their basements. An open timber-framed transit shed ran along the length of the north quay. On the south quay there were two extensive single-storey warehouses for rum and another for cotton (No 12) while cargoes of mahogany and other imported timber could be handled at both ends of this quay.

The official opening of the Import Dock took place on Friday, 27 August 1802.[10] By that time the dock, the Blackwall Basin and its two locks, the inner Limehouse Lock and three large warehouses on the north quay had been completed. The Limehouse Basin and entrance lock and the other north quay warehouses reached completion about July 1803.

In October 1803 the second stage of construction began with excavations for the Export Dock. This was 2,600ft long and 400ft wide, covering an area of 24 acres. Like the Import Dock it had a 23ft depth and the same type of walls. No warehouses were required as cargoes went directly into the outward-bound ships from lighters or, if the goods were sent down by land for shipment, from the north quay via transit sheds. The locks leading from the two basins into the dock had practically the same dimensions as those into the Import Dock, and the western lock could be crossed by a swing bridge.

The formal opening of the Export Dock occurred on Saturday, 12 July 1806.[11] By that date all the works described above had been finished, including the south quay of the Import Dock with its three warehouses and timber wharfs.

Nothing on this majestic scale had been seen before in the history of dock construction in England or any other country.

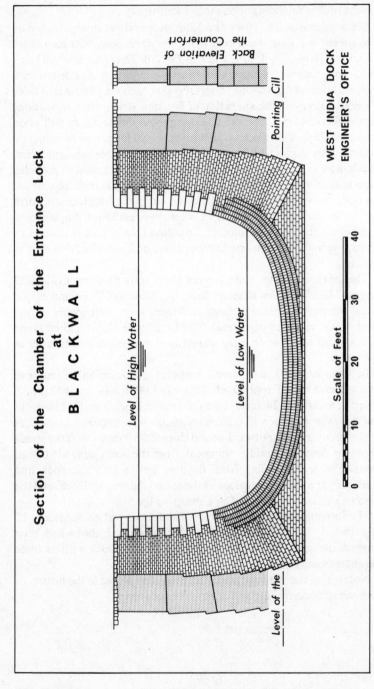

Section of the Chamber of the Entrance Lock
at
B L A C K W A L L

Back Elevation of
the Counterfort

Pointing Cill

Level of High Water

Level of Low Water

Level of the

Scale of Feet

0   10   20   30   40

WEST INDIA DOCK
ENGINEER'S OFFICE

Fig 21

Organisation

The docks were financed and operated by the West India Dock Company under the administration of a court of twenty-one Directors, eight representing the Corporation of London, under the chairmanship of George Hibbert. On the engineering side, Jessop was appointed 'Civil Engineer' on 14 February 1800, initially with fees of £500pa, but from October 1802 at 5 guineas per day. He held this post until November 1804, and then was retained for several months as consulting engineer. From February 1801 to February 1803 he had as an assistant his son Josias, who received £100pa. Ralph Walker's appointment as resident engineer dates from 14 August 1799, at a salary of £850pa with a house at Blackwall; but from this sum he paid about £250pa to an assistant and a draughtsman. Walker resigned on 19 October 1802. Jessop then carried on in sole charge of the engineering department for rather more than a year, with Daniel Vaux as deputy and an extra assistant, until the appointment of Thomas Morris as resident engineer on 12 December 1803. Morris, who had been dock engineer at Liverpool, received £840pa with the house at Blackwall and remained at the docks until he retired in 1811; his assistant, William Pilgrim, was paid £157pa by the company. Rennie became consulting engineer in 1809 at an annual retainer of 100 guineas.

George Gwilt and his son George Gwilt junior were appointed jointly as architects and surveyors in February 1800 with fees of £1,050pa out of which they had to pay their assistants and all expenses. They left in May 1804, after which date Morris took on the added responsibility of directing the building work.

Construction of the docks and warehouses was undertaken mostly by contract. Supervision and measurement of the engineering contractors' work came under the resident engineer who had craftsmen as superintendents of masonry, carpentry, brickwork and excavation; and similar arrangements applied in the building department.

Changes in Design, September 1799–December 1800

After two major alterations from the first scheme proposed in 1797, a sketch plan showing the docks approximately in their final form was approved by the Court of Directors on 30 August 1799. The evolution of the designs up to this date has been outlined in Chapter 9.

Ralph Walker then settled down to produce a detailed plan and report with estimates. These he submitted on 15 November 1799.[12]

Rennie had been consulted on the exact position of the entrances at Blackwall and Limehouse (report dated 23 September 1799) and Thomas Morris was asked for general comments on the scheme. He reported (8 November 1799) in favour of supplying the docks with fresh water, either from the canal at Paddington or from the River Lea, and recommended a long lock with three pairs of gates at each entrance, but otherwise approved highly of the plans. Jessop, in a brief report dated 26 November 1799, quietly dismissed the arguments regarding the need for a fresh water supply:[13] Thames water could be used, and any silt brought in from the river would be deposited in the entrance basins from which it could be removed economically by the occasional use of dredgers.

This view had already been accepted by Walker, presumably after discussions with Jessop, but for the time being he retained single pairs of gates at the entrances.

During the next three months several design modifications were made:

1 The Export Dock south quay and the quay between the docks were reduced in width, without changing the position of the City Canal or the south boundary wall.
2 Blackwall Basin was increased in size.
3 Locks, with two pairs of gates, were substituted for the single pairs of gates at the Blackwall and Limehouse entrances.
4 A single warehouse, instead of a pair, was to be built at each end of the Import Dock.

These alterations are incorporated in a large engraved plan published by John Fairburn in May 1800.[14] Two further modifications should be noted:

5 It was agreed in April 1800 to build nine, instead of ten, warehouses on the north quay of the Import Dock.
6 The widths of the locks as finally fixed by Walker and Jessop were approved in December 1800.

At the time of Jessop's appointment, in February 1800, the Directors refer to the fact that he had 'already been consulted frequently on the Works', and by his own account he had spent a total of eight days 'settling the general Plan with Mr. Walker, making Sketches of Designs and making Estimates.'[15]

Clearly, then, the planning of the West India Docks was a joint effort. But Walker had been employed full-time on this work since August 1799 and, especially in view of his very comprehensive report presented in November 1799, the fairest summary would be to say that the detailed plans of the docks and the mode of carrying out the construction were drawn up by Walker, with Jessop's advice. However, from February 1800, Jessop undertook the design of all engineering works (dock walls, lock structures, cofferdams, etc) and had overall control of construction. Walker, from that date, acted as resident engineer for the Import Dock and Basins, just as Morris acted as resident engineer for the Export Dock from December 1803.

Progress of the Work, 1800–3

The contractors John Holmes and William Bough of Poplar began excavating on 3 February 1800. They were joined shortly afterwards by three smaller firms, but these lasted only a few months. By August 700 men were working on the site.

From June 1800 drainage of the excavations was accomplished by leading the water through cast-iron pipes beneath the river bank to a sluice at low-tide level. The drain from this outlet had been brought up to the west end of the dock by October.

Meanwhile, two steam engines were ordered from Boulton & Watt: a single-acting engine of 28hp, with a 36in diameter cylinder and 8ft stroke, for draining the excavations below low-water level, and a 20hp engine for grinding mortar. The latter was set up near the site of the Limehouse entrance, together with six lime kilns.

The pumping engine and its well were located 150ft north of Blackwall entrance lock. Work on the well and engine house began in August 1800. The engine parts arrived from Birmingham in September. Rennie supervised their erection, but there were delays and not until April 1801 was the deep drain from the well brought up through the south side of the dock. A second pumping engine was ordered in case extra power should be required for draining the lock pit excavation, but experience proved it to be unnecessary and this stand-by engine was sold in 1802 to the Kennet & Avon Canal Co.

As soon as the Blackwall engine came into operation excavations to the final depth could be started. They were completed as follows: dock wall foundations June 1801, Blackwall entrance lock July 1801, inner lock at the east end of the dock September 1801, and the main excavation February 1802.

Excavation of the Limehouse Basin and lock was let on a separate contract to John Dyson. His men started digging in February 1801 and completed the work in September. Drainage of the excavations at the Limehouse end of the site was also accomplished by the Blackwall pumping engine.

Bricks for building the warehouses were brought down river from Brentford and unloaded from barges at Limehouse. A light railway ran from the Limehouse wharf along the north side of the dock. William Adam and the brothers Daniel and Alex Robertson signed a contract for building the six large warehouses on 26 May 1800. Pile driving began a week or so later and the first stone of the foundation was laid on 12 July 1800. Warehouses Nos 2, 4 and 8 were completed in August 1802 and Nos 3, 6 and 7 in February 1803, having been the responsibility of the architects George Gwilt and his son.

For building the walls of the dock and Limehouse Basin and the lock structures the same contractors, Adam & Robertsons, agreed in September 1800 to make 20 million bricks, using clay from the excavations. Another 10 million were ordered later. Also in September Jessop gave orders for the supply of 50 tons of hoop iron for reinforcement of the walls. In December a contract was agreed for 6,000 tons of Dorking (hydraulic) limestone and Jessop wrote detailed specifications for the hollow and 'common' quoins and ashlar masonry for the locks and for the coping stones of the dock and locks. The stone, dressed at the quarries, was supplied by James Mylne and shipped to Blackwall from Dundee.

Jessop's designs for the dock and lock walls were approved by the Directors in January 1801. Adam & Robertsons then submitted a successful tender for building the walls and lock structures. The first brick of the Import Dock wall was laid on 16 June 1801. In July Walker reported that 'Messrs Adam & Robertsons are going on with very great Spirit upon the Dock Wall' and already had sixty bricklayers at work. Except for the stone coping the dock walls were finished by April 1802.

From a report by Jessop dated 3 October 1800 it is clear that he had by this time made drawings for the Blackwall Lock foundations. He says:

The first foundation ready for building on will be the Entrance Lock at Blackwall and this must first be attended to, because the Piling and Carpenters work may be done before the Weather will be proper for Brickwork in the Spring. Mr. Walker, from the Plans, will specify what is to be done, and it will be sufficient in an Advertisement (for the Carpentry Contract) to refer to him for information. It will chiefly consist of preparing and grooving the Sheet piles, and framing the Timbers for the Platforms.

He drafted the advertisement in November. Tenders were received at the beginning of January 1801 and the contract went to John Bunn a fortnight later. The Dock Company had to supply the timber; the contract was for preparing and driving beech wood piles and sheet piles and for preparing and fixing beech planking and fir for framing the platforms of the gates and oak for the pointing sills.

However, things did not go according to plan. Excavation of the Blackwall Lock pit was not completed until July 1801 and long delays were encountered in obtaining the beech, which had to come from Ashridge in Hertfordshire. On 5 July 1801 Jessop wrote that

> Mr. Bunn gives me the strongest Assurances (tho' not occular demonstration) that he will have everything ready in due time for the Foundations of the Lock and that he would immediately learn where the Timber is stopt which he has for a week past expected at Blackwall.

Four days later Bunn had indeed started driving piles for the platform of the outer gates, and early in August he was ready to lay down the planking and pointing sills, and had started piling for the inner gates.

But the Directors were now becoming impatient with what they considered to be the slow progress of the engineering works, and forced Bunn to resign his contract. This brought a protest from Jessop, who wrote on 14 August 1801 as follows:

> If Messrs Adam & Robertsons undertake the carpentry ... I trust they will forward it with Alacrity but if they do not undertake it I am afraid it may be retarded and I should then wish the Directors had not parted with Mr. Bunn as I think Poverty was the source of all his Sins, and if they would advance him Money even at a little risque he might be made to do very well as he now knows how it must be done. He has done his Pile driving well.

In fact, a new contractor was found, Thomas Clark of Woolwich. He finished the carpentry work at Blackwall and in September began piling at the inner lock. Also in September he contracted for the piles and planking, etc of the two Limehouse locks. Next month he personally visited Ashridge, as there were still serious delays in the delivery of timber, and found that the Grand Junction Canal was practically out of action owing to works on Lord Clarendon's bridge near Watford and disputes with the millers over the use of water. He therefore arranged for the timber to be sent down to the Isle of Dogs by road, at great expense, using teams of six horses.

Meanwhile, at the Blackwall entrance Walker reported on 7 August 1801 that the spandrels for the inverted arch beyond the outer pair of gates had been raised to the level of the platform and work had started on the arch; and before the end of September construction of the side walls had started. The number of bricklayers employed on the dock walls and locks now totalled 107. Stone was arriving regularly at site in readiness for its use at the locks but, even so, the quantities were judged to be insufficient in view of the furious rate of construction envisaged by the Directors to fulfil their plan of opening the dock in July 1802. A stern letter was therefore dispatched to Dundee.

Jessop now began designs for the lock gates and for two bridges, over the Blackwall and Limehouse entrance locks. At first he contemplated building the traditional type of canal drawbridges, but on 1 October 1801 he wrote to the chairman, saying:

I should have laid before you tomorrow a specification and advertisement for the Drawbridges but I beg leave to postpone it as Mr. Walker showed me last Evening a Sketch for a design which he is preparing for a turning Bridge which I like much better than my own if, consistent with facility of opening and shutting, it is capable of having a firm abutment—the only point that I am doubtful.

This almost certainly refers to an adaptation of the cast-iron swing bridge illustrated in an engraving entitled:

Plan of a Double Turning Arch Bridge invented by Ralph Walker, Civil Engineer, 1800.

Rennie, who received one of the engravings from Walker,[16] later introduced bridges of very similar design at the London Docks. But for the West India Docks, although it was decided to use bridges of the same basic form, timber not iron was used in their construction.

Plans and specifications for the bridges were approved on 6 November 1801, and advertisements prepared by Jessop for tenders for making eight pairs of lock gates and for the timber and workmanship of two swing bridges were issued in December. Specifications for the ironwork of the gates and bridges followed in January 1802. Contracts for the carpentry and for the ironwork went to Messrs John Morris & Benjamin Paine and to Allan McFarlane respectively. The shipwrights Perry & Wells agreed in February 1802 to supply the oak timber required.

The Blackwall entrance lock and bridge and the lock leading from the basin into the dock were completed in August 1802. The two Limehouse locks, except for their coping, were finished shortly afterwards. Adam & Robertsons built the swing bridge over the Limehouse entrance lock.

At the Blackwall entrance, in order to build the wing walls, the foundations of which went 7ft below low-tide level, a cofferdam had to be constructed. Jessop wrote the specifications in September 1801. The cofferdam consisted of two segments each about 120ft in length, one from the north bank to an old wharf situated roughly in the middle of what was to be the entrance to the Blackwall Lock, and the other from the wharf to the south bank. Two rows of 6in planks, grooved and with iron shoes, were driven 10ft apart to a depth of 12ft below the river bed, the last 7ft being in hard gravel. This sheet piling projected 16ft above the bed, to a height of 3ft above HWST. To guard against exceptional tides an extra 4ft height was provided by horizontal planks. The sheeting was supported by two double lines of horizontal walings bolted to the principal or 'gauge' piles. The latter were 14in square and 36ft long, driven to the same depth as the sheeting, at 15ft centres. The walings were tied together across the dam by $1\frac{1}{4}$in iron bars and the space between the sheeting piles was filled with well compacted earth. On the inside the dam was supported by heavy timber shoring.[17]

William Bough and Thomas Clark joined forces to undertake construction of the cofferdam. In November 1801 they began preparing the timber and assembling their horse pile engines. Most of the gauge piles had been driven by January 1802, the sheet piling was driven in February and the whole job completed about a month later. Work then started on the wing wall foundations.

By April the pressure on Jessop and Walker to bring the works to a state that would enable the dock to be opened in mid-July was becoming intense. From the beginning of January Jessop had been spending seventeen days a month on site; in May he missed only three weekdays, while throughout the whole of June and July he worked six or sometimes seven days a week on dock business. In a report dated 30 April 1802 he said:

Upon the whole I have a lively hope that from the arrangements now

213

made and from a continuance of that exertion which is now completely awake (among the contractors) it will, if the opening at Blackwall may be effected, be found possible to bring ships into the dock on the 12th day of July.

Jessop knew that the coping of the dock wall could not be finished in time; but this caused no real concern. The major problem was opening the Blackwall entrance. To speed this operation he advised, perhaps against his better judgement, that dredging outside the cofferdams should be commenced as soon as possible, 'taking care not to approach so near the Coffre Dams as to cause much oozing of the water through the gravel when the skin of mud is bared from it.' Under normal conditions this operation, a lengthy and tedious affair, would be left until after dismantling the cofferdam.

But worse was to follow. By the beginning of July it became obvious that the formal opening would have to be postponed, and 29 July was fixed as the date. Again in an attempt to save time Bough's workmen, who had been digging away the earth behind the cofferdam, were allowed to take their excavation close up to the dam itself. Admittedly, care was taken to decrease the depth of digging as the piles were approached, but nevertheless by 20 July the men were working 3 or 4ft below low-tide level over a length of 30 or 40ft. This left only the bottom 4ft of the piles in the gravel. There were still no signs of underseepage, so the work continued; and dredging also continued outside in the river. Then, at 7 o'clock in the evening of 22 July, at high water, a section of the dam gave way and water rushed in through the gap to fill, in a very short time, the space between the cofferdam and the 'preventer dam' of stop logs in front of the outer lock gates. About thirty men were working there. On the alarm being given most of them escaped, but six lost their lives: Richard Bough, who was superintending the work, four labourers and a boy. The families received financial compensation from the Dock Company.

In their report on the failure Jessop and Walker attribute the collapse to a pile having been broken in driving. But this is supposition; more probably, the collapse resulted from piping or internal erosion in the gravel. The newspapers naturally managed to find someone who had issued warnings which were neglected by the engineers. Without in any way attempting to shed their responsibility, Jessop and Walker repudiated this particular charge and their point is supported by William Bough, who wrote to the editor of the *Gentlemans Magazine*, on 26 July, saying:[18]

I did not in the least doubt the stability of the coffre-dam; I was myself close upon the spot, within the distance of three yards from my brother (Richard), who unfortunately fell, and was overwhelmed in an instant.

As the cofferdam was due in any case to be dismantled a week or two later, no great delays ensued; and, as the preventer dam resisted the flood, no damage occurred in the entrance lock. The Directors again urged the engineers 'to press every person in their Department to use every possible exertion to have the works in as complete a state as possible' before the end of August. Adam & Robertsons finished the ashlar work on the Blackwall locks by the middle of the month, and Jessop made arrangements to begin filling the dock on 23 August. He wrote a set of instructions for operating the locks.

The formal opening on 27 August 1802 had the air of a national celebration. Various estimates reported in the press record between 10,000 and 30,000 as the number of people present. There were bands playing and a salute of 21 guns as the first West Indiaman, decorated with flags, moored opposite warehouse No 8.

A good account of the opening, with a well informed description of the docks, is given in the *European Magazine*. It comments that:

Whoever has enjoyed the satisfaction of visiting and viewing the work in its present state, must be astonished at the stupendousness of its scale, and the extent of human wisdom, skill, and industry, which has begun, carried on, and so far completed, in the course of five and twenty months, an 'imperial work', the proof of past and pledge of future prosperity.
... Nothing can be conceived more beautiful than the dock. The water is of the necessary depth; its surface, as smooth as a mirror, presents to the eye a haven secure from storms ... The warehouses are the grandest, the most commodious, and spacious, that we have ever seen.[19]

Commercial activity soon got under way but a good deal remained to be done to complete the first phase of development. Already in February 1802 Jessop had decided that the Limehouse entrance wing walls could be built with their foundations at low-water level, on timber piles; and as construction would in that case be carried out in 'tide work' no cofferdam had to be used. This meant that the opening of the entrance could be accomplished shortly after the locks were completed. He produced plans for the walls in August; Holmes & Bough started cutting through the river bank in September, and the opening was achieved in the first week of October 1802. From that time the dock became fully operative. The wing wall foundations were prepared by November and bricklaying began after the winter frosts. Building the walls proceeded without interference to the passage of lighters. They were finished about May 1803.

On 13 October 1802, shortly after opening the Limehouse entrance, another failure occurred, this time involving the south wall of the Limehouse Basin. The wall had not yet been brought up to its full height when an exceptionally high tide lapped over and percolated into the gravel backing. No harm would have resulted had someone not opened by mistake the sluice paddles in the lock gates after the turn of the tide. This allowed the water level to fall in the basin, but owing to the puddle clay lining behind the wall the water level in the gravel backing remained practically unchanged. As a result of the unbalanced pressures part of the wall fell into the basin.

This accident, following so soon after the cofferdam disaster, and at a time when both Jessop and Walker were suffering the effects of severe overwork, led to recriminations between them. Moreover, a few weeks earlier Jessop had quite rightly put forward a method of lining the dock bottom with clay which differed explicitly from a rather silly suggestion by Walker, and when Jessop not so correctly laid part of the blame on Walker for the wall collapse it was too much for the former sea captain. One of the Directors reported that 'some very improper language had passed in his presence from Mr. Walker to Mr. Jessop respecting the Accident and other Works at the Isle of Dogs'. It was thereupon resolved on 19 October 1802:

> That as no cordiality can hereafter be expected to subsist between Mr Jessop and Mr Walker in the carrying on the Company's Works and as Mr Jessop being in course preferred, That Mr. Walker be informed he is at liberty to resign his Situation.

This he immediately did, with feelings probably not unmixed with relief.

Walker undoubtedly had considerable talents and the ambition of becoming a consulting engineer. His work and constant association with Jessop at the docks gave him the experience he needed, and he went on to a successful career.

Rebuilding the south wall presented few problems. Rennie was called in for advice,[20] but he and Jessop had no difficulty in agreeing what should be done, except for a couple of details. Jessop made arrangements with William Bough to start clearing away the fallen wall and preparing the new foundations, and then, at the end of November, took a fortnight's leave of absence having left instructions with his recently appointed deputy engineer, Daniel Vaux, and plans for a transit shed to be built on the north quay of the Import Dock.

While at home in Newark, Jessop wrote a long letter to the chairman, dated 9 December 1802,[15] relating that before his appointment as engineer he was asked on what terms he would furnish designs for the works and hold himself responsible for their success.

I replyed that I was willing to be engaged at the same rate of Compensation, as I had many years been in the Habit of receiving from all my other Employers; which was Five Guineas pr day, and my Expences when from home. I was then told that it would be more satisfactory to the Directors to engage me under a fixed Salary, which I was desired to name. I understood that Mr Walker was then engaged as Resident Engineer whose province it was to see my Designs, or those of any other Person who might have been in my Place, properly carried into Execution.

I thus conceived myself placed in the same relative Situation that I had stood in on other Works where I had been previously employed, and taking for granted Mr Walker's abilities ... I estimated that £600 pr annum would pay me for the time necessary for me to devote to the Business, and for my Expences. The Directors, probably having a still higher opinion of Mr Walker's Sufficiency thought this too much and submitting to their better judgment, as I thought, I accepted of £500 pr annum.

I need not say that both the Directors and myself made an erroneous Estimate.

Having been accustomed to keep a Journal of the time which I have spent in my various Employments I take the liberty of stating the time that I had been under the necessity of devoting to the West India Docks, which if not so occupied I should probably have been paid for by other Employers, and the Directors will not think this Inference unfair, if they will believe me when I say, that for many years before I have never asked for employment in any one instance; but have been pressed to accept of more Business than I could undertake to engage in.

Jessop then gives a detailed account of his time at the Docks, which may be summarised as follows:

1800 February–December	112 days	= 10 days/month
1801 January–December	120 „	= 10 „
1802 January–April	69 „	= 17 „
1802 May–July	80 „	= 27 „
1802 August –November	81 „	= 20 „

Total   462 days

At 5 guineas per day, plus expenses which he put very reasonably at 15s per day and travelling expenses amounting to £108, the corresponding total amounted to £2,880—a sum more than double his payment to date.

To this letter the Directors gave a cool reply: Jessop had complete responsibility for the engineering works and if he required extra assistance he should have said so at the proper time. Nevertheless, the Court later agreed to pay him 5 guineas per day retrospectively from 19 October 1802, and in July 1803 resolved that a gratuity of 1,000 guineas be granted in consideration of 'his extra attendance and Services during the time he was on Salary'.

Meanwhile, the rebuilding of the Limehouse Basin wall and construction of the wing walls, as well as numerous relatively minor works, proceeded without trouble and on 7 July 1803 Jessop was able to write to the chairman, saying:

> I have now the satisfaction of reporting to you that the whole of the Works of the Inward bound Dock with all its appurtances which have been under my department are now complete, except part of the coping of the South Wall of the Dock and a little at the East End; as a sufficient quantity of Stone is now delivered it will be laid on in about three Weeks.

And by this time all six large warehouses and the three single-storey warehouses had been finished.

Thus, in their annual Memorial to the Treasury, dated 12 August 1803, the Directors could report the completion of all essential works on the Import Dock.

Progress of the Works, 1803–6

In his report of 7 July 1803, after announcing completion of the Import Dock, Jessop goes on to say that work should now start as soon as possible on the wall foundations for the Export Dock in order to have them finished before the City Canal is filled with water. A fortnight later he was given authority to draw up the plans; his report, drawings and detailed specifications are dated 25 August 1803.

The first contract, for the wall excavations, went to John Dyson on 13 September 1803 and contracts for the carpentry, brickmaking and stone supply were awarded on 22 November to Thomas Clark, John Fentiman and James Mylne respectively. Next month Thomas Morris arrived at Blackwall to take up his appointment as resident engineer and William Pilgrim, recently appointed as deputy engineer, became his assistant.

For draining the dock excavations Jessop proposed making arrangements to use the pumping engine of the City Canal works, which had recently been increased in power to 30hp (Chapter 9). It began work for the dock in December, and enabled Dyson to proceed with the excavation below ground-water level; but he seems to have made rather slow progress and in February Morris was directed 'to write a stimulating letter to Mr Dyson pressing him to forward the excavation as far as possible'. This must have had the desired effect since only a few weeks later the contract for building the walls was let to Aslat & Stewart of Poplar. The contract for masons' work went to Thomas and William Crawford.

Cofferdams, required to protect the locks during construction, started in February 1804 with Thomas Clark as contractor. Tenders were invited for the main excavation of the dock in April, and a contract with William Bough was made on 18 August 1804.

Bough, in partnership then or a little later with John Hughes, completed the 650,000 cubic yards of excavation for the dock in October 1805* and it is a matter of considerable interest that they used a steam engine, perhaps for the first time in excavating work, to haul upwards of 2,000 tons of gravel daily on an inclined plane.[21] This was the engine subsequently employed in the steam dredger *Brunswick* on the East India moorings job (Chapter 9).

One of Morris' early commissions had been to build, under his own direction and using direct labour, the swing bridge over the west lock of the Import Dock. After the Gwilts left in May 1804 Morris took on the design and supervision of the building works, and in June he submitted plans for the two single-storey warehouses on the south quay. They were under construction by October 1804. Work began on the central

---

* Volume of excavation on the entire West India Docks job amounted to about 1.8 million cubic yards.

warehouse (No 12) in April 1805 and all three had been brought into use by September of that year.

Meanwhile, once Bough & Hughes had taken over the main excavation contract, work on the Export Dock proceeded smoothly; so much so that in November 1804 the Directors questioned 'how far it may be necessary to continue Mr Jessop's services on the same plan or whether it would be better to apply to him occasionally as he may be wanted'. In other words, the Directors were now seeking a polite way of dismissing Jessop as engineer and transforming his function to that of a consultant, as they had more ruthlessly dispensed with the services of George Gwilt and his son, a few months earlier, as soon as the big building programme had been completed and Morris was available to carry on. Jessop had plenty to do elsewhere, especially with the enormous project at Bristol (Chapter 11), but he was naturally rather upset at this offhand treatment, and said so. Once again he received a cool reply:

> Mr. Jessop is to be reminded that the resolution was meant to save him unnessary trouble and the Company needless expence . . . and this Court is sorry that a resolution so reasonable should have occasioned anything like dissatisfaction.

Jessop's last fees were paid in June 1805, and there is no evidence of any further services. Indeed, from June 1805 the minutes refer to Morris as 'the Engineer' and he was clearly then in full charge of the engineering and building departments.

It is a remarkable fact that in just under six years, from July 1799 to June 1805, Jessop had worked for about 650 days at the West India Docks. During this period his fees and expenses totalled £3,300.

There is little more to record. The cofferdams were removed in April 1806. Morris erected two transit sheds on the north quay, and the south boundary wall was completed. The Export Dock came into operation on 7 July and the formal opening ceremony took place five days later.

Costs

The costs involved in building the West India Docks up to 1806 were as follows:[22]

	£
Purchase of lands	94,000
Interest payments	34,000
Construction of Import Dock and Basins	310,000
Construction of Export Dock	205,000
Warehouses, quays, roads	557,000
Miscellaneous works	27,000
	£1,227,000

From February 1808, after the first full financial year of operation, the annual income rarely fell below £200,000. Dividends often rose to the 10 per cent maximum permitted by the Act, and ample sums were provided for maintenance and improvements. The West India Docks had been an immediate success.

11
BRISTOL FLOATING HARBOUR

The position enjoyed by Bristol as a major port in the nineteenth century was due in large part to the very remarkable improvements in dock facilities achieved under Jessop's direction during the years 1804–9. His involvement in the planning stages took him to Bristol in the period 1788–93 and again in 1801–3, while the design and supervision of the works demanded and received much of his time and effort.

Comparable in scale with the West India Docks, the Bristol job was one of Jessop's outstanding achievements, and these two works place him among the foremost dock engineers of all time. A point of added interest is that his son Josias held the post of resident engineer at Bristol throughout the period of construction.

Planning

The Act of 1803 for 'improving and rendering more commodious the Port and Harbour of Bristol' marked the culmination of a lengthy and complex series of studies.[1] The story begins with a scheme put forward by Smeaton in January 1765 on behalf of the Society of Merchant Venturers.[2] He proposed to construct a dam across the mouth of the Frome, near letter K in Fig 22, and also a weir across the branch of this river where it enters the Avon above Bristol Bridge, and to make a cut across Canon's Marsh with an entrance lock (38ft wide) situated near a bend in the river $\frac{1}{2}$ mile downstream of the dam. In this way ships at the Frome quays, from the dam up to Stone Bridge, would remain always afloat at the level of high tides, instead of being grounded at every low tide, as hitherto.

Smeaton's scheme was entirely practicable but open to two objections: the quays on the Avon at the Grove (see Fig 22) were left in tidal water, and the entrance lay too far upstream for ships to lock through at neap tides.

A more radical proposal appeared in January 1767 from William ·

222

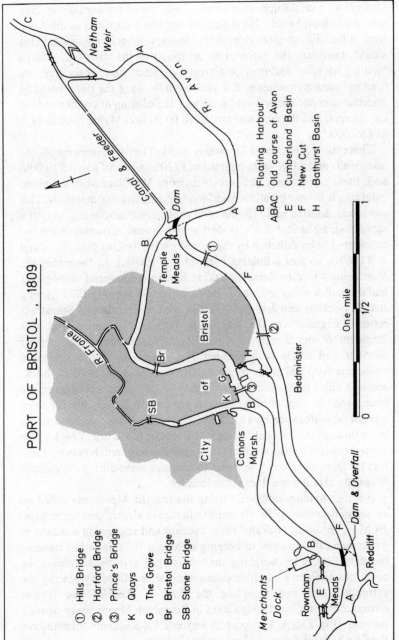

PORT OF BRISTOL, 1809

① Hills Bridge
② Harford Bridge
③ Prince's Bridge
K Quays
G The Grove
Br Bristol Bridge
SB Stone Bridge

B Floating Harbour
ABAC Old course of Avon
E Cumberland Basin
F New Cut
H Bathurst Basin

Netham Weir
R. Avon
Canal & Feeder
Dam
Temple Meads
Bristol
R. Frome
City
of
Canons Marsh
Bedminster
Rownham
Merchants Dock
Meads
Dam & Overfall
Redcliff

0   1/2   One mile   1

Fig 22

225

Champion, a local shipbuilder who had just completed a small wet dock near Rownham Meads. He suggested building a dam across the Avon itself at Redcliff, south of Rownham Meads, with locks alongside.[3] This would transform the entire river upstream of the dam into a large 'floating harbour' and provide a greater depth of water at the entrance than in Smeaton's scheme. But various mills along the river would be affected, complications would arise with the existing dry docks and the city sewers, and the cost was estimated by Robert Mylne to be as high as £65,000.[4]

There the matter rested for twenty years. The Merchants rebuilt the quay walls at the Grove (completed in 1770 at a cost of about £10,000) and, having purchased the wet dock from Mr Champion, set about enlarging it for use by all ships off-loading combustible materials. This work was finished in 1778, the total expenditure amounting to rather more than £23,000.[5] Such modest improvements, however, were not considered to be sufficient by the more forward looking Bristolians and in 1786 the idea of a floating harbour was revived. In December the Merchants wrote to Smeaton asking him to recommend an engineer and if possible to come himself. He replied on 16 January 1787 naming Joseph Nickalls and Jessop.[6] Nickalls, who had worked as Smeaton's resident engineer on the Calder & Hebble Navigation and was President of the Society of Civil Engineers, examined the existing schemes and finally in November 1787 came up with a still more ambitious proposal of his own for damming the Avon at Black Rock, about 3 miles below the quays.[7] This had two great advantages; the river would be kept at high-tide level not only in the city but for some considerable distance down Clifton Gorge, and ships could enter or leave through the locks at the dam at any state of the tide. Bow hauling up to the quays for the whole 3 miles would be required, however, and it was far from clear how trade was to be maintained during the difficult operation of building a dam at this location.

Another opinion obviously being needed, the Merchants called on Jessop in February 1788. He came to Bristol in March[8] and reported on 19 May,[9] praising Nickalls' basic concept and suggesting a means of overcoming the problem of keeping a passage for ships while building the dam. But, after weighing the advantages and disadvantages, he came out in favour of Champion's scheme, modified by placing the entrance locks not alongside the dam at Redcliff but further downstream, leading through a cut in Rownham Meads to the floating harbour (Fig 23(a)). This part of Jessop's 1788 scheme foreshadows the Cumberland Basin and locks as finally built.

Smeaton, though in partial retirement, was now prevailed upon to consider the whole matter. He travelled to Bristol in October and in July 1789 produced one of his masterly reports together with detailed drawings and estimates.[10] Not without some regret he decided against the Black Rock proposal. He emphasised the practical advantages of Jessop's plan, which he investigated thoroughly, and gave careful consideration to the design of the dam at Redcliff. This of course had to be capable of discharging the flood flow of the Avon which, at this stage of the investigations, Smeaton took as 25,000 tons per minute (15,000 cusecs). At Rownham Meads he recommended a broad cut with two entrance locks 44ft and 30ft wide, the outer sills being 28ft below impounded level in the floating harbour. His estimate for the engineering works came to £74,000.

In September that year Smeaton, Jessop and Nickalls visited the site together[11] and, on the day before they left, Jessop wrote a memorandum to Jeremiah Osborne, Clerk to the Merchant Venturers, requesting that

during the winter he appoint some person, who may if necessary give evidence before Parliament, to observe the heights of the highest Avon flood, when the tide is out, at Bristol Bridge, and to observe by a Stop Watch the velocity of the water through the arches in three places thro each arch, and to enquire how many feet such flood may be lower than the highest which has been remembered. [Also] to cause two sections of the River . . . to be taken [at the site of the dam], the River on each side to be bored to a depth of 30 feet below the meadows, so as to know the strata, and borings to be made to the same depth in two or three places in the line of the intended cut.[12]

With the results of the borings and flood observations to hand,[13] Jessop submitted a second report on 25 February 1790 in which the dam was designed to discharge 37,000 tons of water per minute (22,000 cusecs) over the crest and through submerged sluices. He also reduced the depth of the outer sills of the entrance locks at Rownham to 24ft below impounded level and introduced a circular lock at the east end of the cut leading in to Merchants Dock and the floating harbour.[14]

Evidently the dam and the Avon floods gave rise to much discussion and, in particular, Jessop was asked how he had calculated the amount of water that could be discharged through the sluices and over the dam crest. By good fortune we have his reply, in a letter to Mr Osborne dated 19 November 1790:[15]

To make you compleatly acquainted with the Principles on which the calculations are founded, respecting the discharge of Water over

225

Cascades or through orifices, would take much time and some
Study; for having in the early part of my time endeavoured to make
myself acquainted with proven principles and having been once
satisfied with the Results, I have, as most practical men do,
discharged my memory in some measure from the Theory and
contented myself with referring to certain practical Rules which
have been deduced therefrom and corrected by experience and
observation.

After this preamble he goes on to say that the maximum possible
velocity of flow through an orifice is (in modern symbols) $v = \sqrt{2gh}$,
where g is the acceleration due to gravity and h the head of water above
the virtual centre of the orifice. But in some cases it might in practice be
only two-thirds of this, while in others it could be rather more by an
amount 'which only experience and nice observation can nearly
ascertain'. As for the flow over a dam or weir, he says the velocity of
flow (again using modern symbols) is slightly less than $\sqrt{2g} \cdot d/2$ where
d is the thickness of the sheet of water passing over the crest.

Writing the formula as $v = C\sqrt{gd}$ we find from a numerical example
in Jessop's letter that he takes $C = 0.95$, and working back from figures
in Smeaton's report very much the same result is obtained. So, as might
be expected, they were perfectly capable of making their hydraulic
calculations, even though the full theory of broad-crested weirs was not
published until 1849, by Bélanger.[16]

Whether a good estimate had been made of the flood flow in the
Avon is more difficult to establish, as modern observations are not
available so far downstream. From records of the Avon at Bath and of
its lower tributaries, however, we consider that the maximum flow
could be about 24,000 cusecs (40,000 tons per minute).[17] Nickalls,
called in to report on the mills, a subject on which he was an expert, and
on the flood problem[18] estimated a possible upper limit of 50,000 or
60,000 tons per minute; but these figures are certainly too high, and we
cannot help concluding that in tackling a problem of unprecedented
scale Smeaton and Jessop had produced a safe and economical design
based on sound principles of calculation and observation.

Arguments for and against the scheme and some alternative
proposals continued in Bristol.[19] But during October 1791 several
important meetings were held, both by the Merchants and the
corporation, at which it was decided firstly that:

the Plan and Design, improved by Mr Jessop, with the Approbation and under the sanction of Mr Smeaton, for the erection of a Dam at the Bottom of Rownham Mead, with Locks and other Constructions, are the most eligible,[20]

and secondly that a joint committee be set up thoroughly to investigate the practical and commercial aspects.

Jessop attended at Bristol for nearly three weeks during these deliberations, and it must have been at this time that he modified the sluices in the dam, making them larger and of simpler construction than those in his 1790 design.

No doubt he also laid down a programme for detailed surveys and further observations on river flow, and in December William White, the surveyor from Sand near Wells, began this work for the joint committee.[21] In July 1792 he was making drawings to be engraved by William Faden in London. Some more surveying was done in September, various alterations to the copper plate followed in December, and it was not until August 1793 that 500 copies of the printed map, with longitudinal profiles and sections of the rivers and details of the dam,[22] were available for distribution. A short 'Explanation' appeared at the same time. Finally, in October 1793, Jessop again visited Bristol and a 'Further Explanation' was published.[23] This set out the mode of operation of the scheme, the proposed dock dues and tolls for the bridge over the dam, and stated that the cost was unlikely to exceed £100,000.

At last an 'official' design had been adopted with the explicit intention of petitioning Parliament for a Bill. But this did not happen, principally as a consequence of the outbreak of war with France, which led to a decline in Bristol's shipping trade, but also from the fact that a serious objection had not been met. We refer to the removal of the tidal flow from a considerable length of the Avon. Just as at King's Lynn, with the proposed Eau Brink Cut, so at Bristol genuine fears were expressed that the exclusion of a large body of tidal water would have harmful effects on the river downstream. The engineers pointed out that the fresh water flow of the Avon passed through the floating harbour in their schemes, but they could not disprove pessimistic predictions concerning the downstream regime of the river. Indeed, as will be seen, Jessop ultimately accepted this criticism by adopting the concept of a 'tidal bypass', though other advantages were involved as well.

The first, and most imaginative, suggestion for a tidal bypass originated in December 1791 from a local vicar, the Reverend William Milton.[24] He proposed the diversion of the Avon in a new cut from

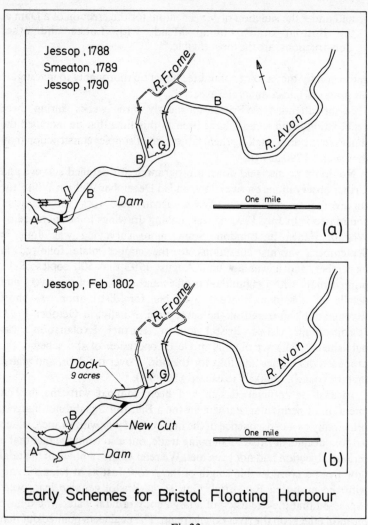

Fig 23

Temple Meads to Redcliff, with a weir at Netham and a feeder channel leading to a large floating harbour formed in the old course of the Avon by building locks at Temple Meads and upstream of Merchants Dock.

Mr Osborne immediately transmitted this suggestion to Jessop, who replied from London on 18 February 1792 as follows:[25]

I have taken the first hour of leisure since I came to Town, to peruse the sketch which you have sent me, with the description of a scheme for floating the Quays, in such a way as to avoid some of the objectionable points to the other schemes, particularly the check to the current of the tides, and inconvenience in some measure attending the floods. As the thought is a new one, I feel myself incompetent to give any decided opinion on the subject ... (but) I think the Idea ingenious, and that it does credit to the good sense and invention of the Author and it certainly deserves attention.

The strongest objection that appears on the face of it, is the want of that great desideratum of having the point of entrance and exit sufficiently low in the River, for ships to enter and leave the Port at Neap tides ... and I am afraid the expence of the scheme will stand too high in comparison with the remaining benefits, for I cannot with the Author lay that stress that he does on the advantages of the currents.

The cost indeed would have been higher, probably about twice as much as the 'official' scheme; and Jessop rightly adhered in his later designs to the entrance at Rownham. Nevertheless, he may be criticised for not having insisted in 1792, as he did in 1802, that by combining his Rownham entrance with Milton's tidal bypass an almost ideal solution could be achieved. Perhaps he was inhibited from changing a design which was less costly and had just been accepted both by the City and the Merchants. Smeaton, in correspondence with Osborne at this time, perfectly summed up such a view when he wrote:[26]

Excuse me when I say that I think you Gentlemen take too much *consideration*, if they mean to Act. It is impossible that every individual thing should be for the greatest possible advantage—it is enough that the leading circumstances are right, and in favour of the project.

However that may be, when trade began to recover around 1800 a whole crop of amateur schemes emerged predominantly based on the tidal bypass idea, though none of them in so thoroughgoing a manner as Mr Milton's. By 1801 official action could no longer be delayed and the joint committee, revived, called on Jessop for an opinion on two of the more promising of these proposals. In August he visited Bristol on his way from Somerset,[27] and wrote a letter to John Osborne (who had succeeded his father as clerk to the Merchant Venturers) on the results of his considerations towards the end of September. The contents of this letter are not recorded, but on 25 November 1801 he received a formal request to undertake a new investigation of the whole question of the port improvement.[28] This he did, again with William White as surveyor, and on 22 February 1802 submitted a long report accompanied by plans and estimates.[29]

Briefly, Jessop's scheme (Fig 23(b)) involved dams across the Avon at Redcliff and Canon's Marsh with a new cut between these places; an entrance lock and basin at Rownham led into the floating harbour (ie the old course of the Avon); a dam was also to be built across the mouth of the Frome and a dock, 9 acres in area, would be constructed in Canon's Marsh with a separate lock into the river for small vessels. By these means he retained the advantage of a ship lock in relatively deep water at Rownham, ample quay and dock space was provided and, through the new cut, the tidal flow in the Avon was wholly uninterrupted. The cost of the engineering works alone he estimated at £156,000.

The committee immediately accepted this plan as 'the most fit to be carried into execution'. Proposals were considered for raising the necessary capital. In March 1802 the corporation gave their assent. Jessop made some minor alterations in April. An 'Explanation' of the scheme and of the financial arrangements was drawn up, and on 24 April orders were given for printing copies of Jessop's plan, and of the 'Explanation'.[30] The subscription, opened on 31 May, reached its target of £150,000 three weeks later and the balance of £50,000 was to be obtained by a loan.[31]

Once again, everything seemed ready for an application to Parliament. But on 2 August 1802 the minutes record that a suggestion had been made in committee that the 'plan for improving the Harbour of Bristol may be carried with great advantage to the City by lengthening the intended Course of the Avon from Redcliff . . . into the Avon at Temple Meads'. In other words, Mr Milton's idea had suddenly been revived. Orders were immediately given for White to take levels and surveys as soon as possible, and Jessop was requested to come when 'Mr White can prepare for him'.

Only twelve days later, however, on 14 August 1802, Jessop attended the committee in Bristol and presented a report on a project embracing the new proposal and differing in no essential features from the work as carried out.[32]

The suggestion made in committee of returning to Milton's cut came from Thomas Hill, one of its members; but Jessop's response came so quickly, especially in view of his heavy commitments at the West India Docks, and with such insistence in favour of the revised scheme, that it is difficult to imagine he had not been considering the matter for some time and that the change in plan did not owe much to him.

Jessop opens his report with the following words:

> The Plan now submitted to your Consideration will probably be considered as embracing in the most extensive manner every Improvement of the Harbour of Bristol which has heretofore been suggested ... and compared with any former Plan the additional Advantages will bear the additional Expence; it may, when matured and finally adjusted, be considered as the most perfect.

He proceeds to give a description of the leading features and ends with a provisional estimate for the engineering works amounting to £212,000.

Here the joint committee had an unequivocal recommendation from their engineer of a project which satisfied all requirements and minimised, if it did not wholly remove, all reasonable objections. They approved the report, two days after receiving it, on 16 August.

All was now plain sailing. By November an 'Explanation' had been drafted, giving a full description of the mode of operation with proposals for raising a capital of £300,000, and a schedule of dock dues. By this time also a drawing had been prepared, almost certainly by White, to be engraved.[33] An interesting detail is that Jessop already envisaged two iron bridges over the New Cut. The engraved plan and the printed 'Explanation' were issued together in December.[34] Meanwhile, Jessop answered a question about the deposition of silt and rubbish in the harbour by pointing out that the use of a horse-operated dredger, as at Hull and Yarmouth, or such as the one being built for Mr Perry at Blackwall, provided a simple and economic solution.[35]

The drafting of the Bill began in January and the petition went to the Commons on 21 February 1803. Jessop had now revised his estimate for the engineering works to £253,000.[36] He gave evidence on 28 February. The engraving of the plan to be deposited in the House of Lords, slightly modified from the original version, was ordered from William Faden on 5 April[37] and at about the same time a brief technical explanation was printed.[38] The Bill had its first reading on 29 April; it was sent to the Lords in July, when Jessop again gave evidence; and finally, on 11 August 1803 the Act (43 Geo III, c.140) received the Royal Assent.

During the passage of the Bill, in addition to some minor amendments, it was decided that two entrance locks were necessary at Cumberland Basin, and that the locks at Bathurst Basin (originally planned for the Severn trows and other small craft) should be capable of handling ships. Some changes were also made in the feeder canal and its locks. According to a later statement by Jessop these alterations added about £36,000 to his engineering estimate,[39] so the figure by August 1803 came to approximately £290,000.

In the Act the Bristol Dock Company was incorporated with powers to carry out the works, purchase the necessary lands, raise a capital of £300,000 and charge specified dock dues. The entrance locks at Cumberland Basin were to have widths of 45ft and 33ft, with their downstream sills 3ft below low water,, and the level in the Floating Harbour was to be maintained at the 16ft gauge mark at the quays. As this was 22ft above low water at Rownham, there would normally be a 25ft depth of water above the sills, or 34ft at spring tides. Barge locks 17ft in width were to be provided at Temple Meads and Netham Weir. The feeder canal between these two places was to have a top width of at least 54ft and a minimum depth of 6ft, and the dimensions of the New Cut for the Avon between Temple Meads and Redcliff had to be not less than those of the old river course. The dam at Redcliff required a proper overfall but only the flow of the Frome and that part of the Avon diverted at Netham passed over this dam. Floods in the Avon would be discharged down the New Cut.

The main advantages of the final design, as compared with the scheme of February 1802, were (1) the Floating Harbour had an area of about 70 acres (excluding the entrance basins) instead of 37 acres; (2) all existing quays were included instead of only those along the Frome, and (3) the quays were linked by a navigable canal to the Avon and hence to Bath and the Kennet & Avon Canal, then nearing completion. Common to both schemes was an unrestricted, or virtually unrestricted, tidal flow.

In concluding this part of the Bristol story we note some interesting information on consulting fees and other professional charges. For his work in 1788–9 Smeaton's bill came to £220, based on fees of 5 guineas per day plus travelling expenses.[11] In 1791–2 Jessop charged 3 guineas per day plus travelling, and it was for his attendance at Bristol in October 1793 that his fees went up to 5 guineas; the standard rate for the rest of his career. William White the surveyor charged 2 guineas per day, and his total bill including payments to assistants and for travelling, from December 1791 to September 1793, amounted to £266. Faden's charge for engraving and printing 500 copies of the plan and *Explanation* in 1793 was £101.[21]

In the period from 1801 to August 1803 Jessop received a total payment of £406, White and his assistants £355, and the bill for printing and engraving came to £478, of which Faden received £165 for 800 copies of the deposited plan. The whole cost of surveying, designing and parliamentary proceedings, including £7,296 for legal charges, amounted to £11,129.[40]

To this should perhaps be added 100 guineas voted by the Dock Company in October 1803 for silver to be presented to the Reverend William Milton 'in Testimony of the high sense the Board entertain of his original suggestion communicated to the Merchants Hall in 1792 for the improvement of the port and Harbour of Bristol.'[41]

Construction

The Board of Directors of the Bristol Dock Company held their first meeting on 21 September 1803 and made the following appointments: George Webb Hall and John Osborne, Clerks; Joseph Edge, Treasurer; William Jessop, Engineer; and William White, Surveyor.[42]

Jessop attended the next meeting on 5 October and doubtless heard with pleasure of the gift to Mr Milton. He outlined the most urgent requirements as large scale surveys, particularly at Rownham, Trim Mills (the site of Bathurst Basin) and at Netham, marking out the lands which had to be purchased, and sinking shafts to ascertain the nature of the 'sand rock' known to exist in a half-mile length of the New Cut west of Bathurst Lock in the parish of Bedminster.

On 5 December 1803 Josias Jessop was appointed resident engineer, 'under the Direction of his father', at a salary of £500pa; this to be a full time job requiring 'his constant residence and attention to the works during their progress'. He came to Bristol on 14 February 1804.[43]

At a Board meeting ten days later Jessop reported that with White and Josias he had levelled and prepared an accurate section of the New Cut from Redcliff to Bathurst Lock, and he advised that the first contract should be for excavating that part which includes the sand rock, as this will be the heaviest work. He also produced drawings of the Cumberland and Bathurst Basins, and a recommendation for ordering six steam engines. Next month Josias made surveys and estimates for the towing path along what was to become the Floating Harbour. On 5 April 1804 Thomas Thatcher's tender for excavating soil above the sand rock was accepted.[44] He began work with about a hundred men on 1 May. On this occasion Mr Hall cut the first sod and the labourers each received 1s to drink to success of the undertaking.

Later in May Josias and White completed surveys of the New Cut from Bathurst Lock to Temple Meads, and Jessop again attended the

233

Board. He advised placing advertisements for contractors to undertake this part of the excavation, and also to provide the ironwork for two iron bridges over the New Cut. These are the bridges later named Hill's, on the Bath Road, and Harford, near Bedminster on the road to Bridgwater (see Fig 22).

At the same meeting Jessop was urged to expedite the delivery of four small ($5\frac{1}{2}$hp) engines from Butterley; they arrived later that year.[45] And on 21 May Josias received instructions to visit Mr Homfray at Cardiff to arrange for the purchase of a large steam engine which his father had reported might be procured there ready-made. This engine was duly obtained and erected in an engine house designed by Josias; its purpose being to drain the excavations in the eastern half of the New Cut. Meanwhile in June, Thatcher gained the contract for this work.

Specifications for the iron bridges were dispatched on 30 May.[46] On 18 June 1804, six tenders having been received 'for building two Iron Bridges according to the plan designed by Mr Jessop', a contract was awarded to the Coalbrookdale Company at a unit price of £9 18s per ton of iron plus £50 for superintending erection of each bridge, with a warrant for the ironwork to stand for a year and a day. The Directors must have been pleased to receive such a competitive tender from a firm of high repute.

In July Jessop visited Bristol to study a problem connected with the water at Trim Mills and to search for a quarry supplying high quality stone needed for lock quoins, springing courses in the bridges, and so on. Rock from the excavations could probably be used for general masonry, though it should be exposed to a winter's frost to test its durability. He also recommended that iron plates were desirable for the bridge decks, instead of oak planking as in his original design; that the bridge abutments should be started as soon as possible; and that iron rails be obtained for the contractors' railways. The Board immediately confirmed these recommendations and ordered them to be executed with dispatch. Consequently, we find Josias writing next day to Coalbrookdale about the iron plates,[47] and the clerks, a week later, sent out letters to six firms for costs of supplying 100 tons of iron rails;[48] these were to weight 38lb per yd and the section (a sketch was provided by Josias) was similar to that used on the Surrey Iron Railway. A contract went to Frere, Cooke & Powell of Clydach Iron Works near Abergavenny on 30 July; it was the first of several orders issued to this firm, who supplied at least 500 tons of rails during the next two years.

Still in Bristol, on 20 July 1804 Jessop wrote specifications for excavating the rock beneath Thatcher's first contract, and with White reported on means of maintaining the water supply to the parishes of St Mary Redcliff and Temple. This involved laying iron pipes and carrying them across the Cut on Harford Bridge. On the same day Josias was instructed to prepare plans for four inclined planes to be used in the excavations, and in August a second large engine, of 10hp, was ordered from Hazledine of Bridgnorth for draining the western part of the New Cut. It had to pump from a level 36ft below ground surface.

Next month, again on site, Jessop noted there were about 650 men now upon the work and, from the rapid progress being made, they would soon need further employment. He therefore thought it proper to contract for the excavations in Rownham Meads, for which he had marked out the ground and would at once prepare specifications, and to order another steam engine for use in this work. He added that although the Act directs the smaller (south) lock at the entrance shall be 33ft in width, he should have recommended 36ft. The following day an application was sent to Coalbrookdale for a 10hp engine to be used for pumping at Rownham.

At about the same time the rock excavation contract in the New Cut went to Hodge & Langman, orders for iron pipes were sent to Frere, Cooke & Powell, and in October Thatcher secured both the Rownham and Bathurst contracts. At the end of December 1804, completing a very busy year, Jessop reported that 480,000 cu yd had now been excavated but a slip of about 160yd in length had occurred in the Bathurst excavations. This, he said, was 'one of those accidents to which all great undertakings are more or less liable under the Denomination of unforeseen Contingencies'. However, as we shall see, it proved to be but the first of a whole series of slips on the job which caused serious delays and an expenditure of £35,000. In the same report Jessop recommended advertising for contractors for the masonry of the abutments of the iron bridges, and advised that a railway be laid down from the rock excavations past the two bridge sites and on to Temple Meads, for conveying sand-rock to the abutments. These he produced at a Board meeting on 7 January 1805, from Hanham; quarries at this place, about 4 miles from Bristol, having been found to provide excellent material.

Josias had already been instructed in November to prepare plans and specifications for mason's work of the Bathurst Locks and bridge abutments. These he produced at a Board meeting on 7 January 1805, and in February he set out the foundations of the bridges.[49]

By March 1805 Jessop had decided it would be necessary to construct retaining walls around Bathurst Basin rather than trying to stabilise the open-cut slopes. Agreements were made on 9 April with Hodge & Langman for building the walls and locks. On the same day Jessop reported the need for iron pipes 3ft in diameter to be laid under the canal for sewerage.

At the end of that month Josias sent in a long report detailing all the excavations carried out from 1 May 1804 to 27 April 1805, showing that 780,000 cu yd had been removed (including 135,000yd of rock) an amount which he said 'I believe is considerably more than has been done upon any single work in the same time'. Josias now had on his staff William Porteus, brought from the Lancaster Canal on Rennie's recommendation, as superintendent of masonry. In October the appointment of a superintendent of 'day work', that is of the work carried out by direct labour, was also sanctioned. The abutments of Harford Bridge had nearly been finished by September and those of Hill's Bridge were well forward. Work had also started, again with Thatcher as contractor, on the western end of the New Cut, and in November 1805 Thatcher & Richards secured the contract for building the Cumberland entrance locks; this involved driving a level from the pumping engine pit to the lock pit at a depth of not less than 44ft below ground surface. Iron castings for the locks were to be supplied from Butterley.

In his last report of 1805, made in December during his fifth visit that year, Jessop warned that it would probably be necessary to wall Cumberland Basin, on account of slips in the open slopes. An important addition to the scheme had also been proposed; namely, to build a road from the head of the feeder canal, crossing the dam at Temple Meads and continuing along the north side of the New Cut, over Redcliff dam and the entrance locks and on to Hotwells in the parish of Clifton.

The walling of Cumberland Basin, the increase in width of the south entrance lock to 36ft, and the new road, required more capital and additional parliamentary powers. A petition therefore went to the Commons in February 1806; the Bill passed without much difficulty, Josias Jessop gave evidence to the Lords, and on 23 May 1806 the company gained their Act. This sanctioned the works mentioned above and provided for an increase in the share subscription from £100 to £135. Just over a week later Jessop arranged a contract with Thatcher & Richards for walling the basin.

Thus, by the summer of 1806, the whole scheme was well under way. In a report dated 18 November Jessop expresses satisfaction with the progress achieved and says he has no reason to doubt the work can be completed within the time limited by Parliament, ie four years from the start of construction. Moreover, some saving in cost would arise from a decision not to build a lock between Cumberland Basin and Merchants Dock. An addition made in the 1803 Act, this was not in Jessop's original plan nor did he ever consider it to be justified.

A useful summary of the state of the works in September 1806 is given in a report by the Directors. By that time the total expenditure including land purchase, compensation and legal charges amounted to £262,000. Bathurst entrance lock, Harford Bridge, the barge locks at Temple Meads and excavation of the feeder canal, had all been completed; bridges over the canal, built with bricks made from the excavated clay, were nearly finished; piled foundations for the Cumberland locks had been constructed and the walls were in hand, while timber for the lock gates and swing bridges was now on site.

At this stage we must pause to give an account of the iron bridges. Virtually identical in design, these two structures together cost only £12,500 including the approaches,[50] but they are of much interest in the early history of iron-bridge construction. As already mentioned the abutments of Harford Bridge were completed by September 1805, those of Hill's Bridge were in forwardness, and the ironwork was ready to be fitted up. Thomas Thomas arrived from Coalbrookdale to superintend erection in October. On 8 February 1806 the local newspaper reported that Harford Bridge was practically finished and the arch ribs of Hill's Bridge were in position ready to be bolted together.[51] But in the morning of Thursday 20 February the ribs fell 'with a tremendous crash' injuring five men,[52] one of whom died a fortnight later. An investigation, made immediately by the architect James Foster and two masons, showed no faults in the abutments, and the Directors at an emergency meeting next day attributed the accident to neglect by the superintendent. The Shropshire firm accepted responsibility though they suggested some design modifications. Josias wrote to Coalbrookdale on 9 July saying he had delayed answering a letter on this point until he heard from his father, but meanwhile the Directors had decided no change should be made, so he hoped new castings (on the original plan) would be sent as soon as possible.[53] They arrived after about three months and the bridge was rebuilt by February 1807 or a little earlier. The ironwork of Harford Bridge, as we have seen, was safely in position in February 1806 and the bridge is noted as complete in September of that year.

A description of one bridge will serve for the other. The deck, 31ft in width overall, carrying the roadway and iron railings, was formed with flanged iron plates supported on bearer beams. Vertical spandrel pillars transferred the load to 6 cast iron ribs spaced at 6ft centres and cross-connected by 9 iron ties. Each rib, spanning 100ft with a 15ft rise, consisted of 2 castings bolted together through flanges at the crown and fixed at their lower ends to massive iron plates resting on the springing courses of the abutments (p 203). The ribs were 28in deep and 4in thick with perforations 12in square, to reduce the weight, leaving radial pieces 3in wide except at the cross ties where the metal had a breadth of 12in.[54]

The design could perhaps have been more robust, but certainly it was economical and a distinct advance on the rather primitive iron bridges built by Coalbrookdale in the 1790s at Buildwas (to Telford's plan) and at Bridgwater. Also the long but relatively light rib segments were preferable to the open-frame voussoirs adopted in Sunderland Bridge (1793-6) and subsequent bridges of the same style built by Walkers of Rotherham under Thomas Wilson's direction. Indeed, two of these had failed, at Staines (1804) and at Yarm (1806), and Rennie was having trouble with the bridge at Boston. The success of Jessop's Bristol bridges after they were brought into use in 1807 probably contributed to a renewed feeling of confidence in large span cast-iron structures, leading to the highly important bridges by Telford at Bonar (1811-12) and by James Walker at Vauxhall (1813-16).[55] We note that Harford Bridge survived until replaced in 1882; Hill's Bridge had a shorter life, being destroyed when struck by a 180 ton screw barge in 1855.[56]

On the main works 1807 was a year of steady progress clouded only by the loss of a Bill in Parliament. This had been submitted in February with the objects of gaining powers to charge increased rates (to offset rising costs) and to build a bridge over the Floating Harbour (later named Prince's Bridge) at the position shown in Fig 22. The Bill attracted much opposition, as might be expected, and was reintroduced in 1808. Fortunately, the company had meanwhile been able to raise a loan from the Bank of England so the objectionable clauses on rates were omitted, and the Act was obtained on 21 March 1808. Among its provisions the company was granted an extra year for completion of the works; a most welcome relief as the original date of May 1808 now was impossible to achieve.

In the House of Commons committee on the 1807 Bill, Jessop gave evidence on various technical matters and on the way in which the costs had increased.[39] Starting with his initial estimate of £253,000 he says that changes made in the plans during the parliamentary proceedings in 1803 added about £36,000 or, with the saving recently

238

proposed by eliminating the lock between Cumberland Basin and Merchants Dock, a net increase of £30,000. Remedial measures to stabilise the slopes of the New Cut had cost £18,000 and walling the entrance basins would add nearly as much again, bringing expenditure on these contingencies to £35,000. The new road sanctioned in 1806 might add a further £8,000 apart from land purchase, etc. Thus, by April 1807 when he presented these figures, Jessop's engineering estimate had risen to £326,000 and this did not include Prince's Bridge. Under cross examination he ventured the opinion that not all changes from the original plan were strictly essential, and he referred in particular to the enlarged Bathurst locks. The additional expenditure on these items could not be considered as having been thrown away, he said, but the extra convenience would not repay the cost.

In his technical evidence Jessop stated that Cumberland Basin was first intended to have open slopes, as in the basin at West India Docks, but there having been a great quantity of spring water in the stratum of sand beneath the clay, which he found could not be drained by a well, large slips took place which made it absolutely necessary to secure the sides by building a wall. At Bathurst Basin the nature of the soil, a soapy kind of clay which rose up from the weight of ground around it, made walling of this basin likewise unavoidable. As for the New Cut the nature of the soil was such as he had never met with in his life before, so exceedingly soft as to make it necessary to sink 17ft below the new river, replacing the cavity with stones.[57] Every pain had been taken to ascertain the nature of the soil in advance, without being able to discover it.

We may remark that not until another century had passed were the techniques of site investigation and soil testing advanced to the point where they could be of real use to the engineer in such conditions.

The design and construction of Prince's Bridge, under the Act of 1808, seems to have been entirely the responsibility of Josias. It was he who submitted the estimate (£15,000) to Parliament and gave evidence to the Lords.[58] On 2 May 1808 he delivered plans and specifications to Mr Richards the mason. The foundation stone was laid on 8 August and work began in November on the approach road from the south. The structure consisted of two stone piers carrying a swing bridge, and a floating caisson gate could be placed between the piers to divide the Floating Harbour into two parts so that either part could be drained separately of the other when required, for repairs and so on. The bridge was completed in time for the official opening in May 1809 at a cost of £14,300 including the caisson.[59]

Back in February 1808 Jessop and Hall reported the total expenditure as £395,000 with expected further net costs of £46,000. But on 11 June 1808 Josias had to report a disaster. In consequence of a high wind on Wednesday 8 June the tide had risen 4ft higher than expected and remained one hour longer than usual. This surge had broken over the bank acting as a cofferdam at Rownham and filled the entrance basin. Jessop rushed to Bristol, attending the Board on 15 June. The accident, he said, was very unexpected but had caused less mischief than he had any reason to look for. He approved a contract hastily made with Thatcher for remedial works. Five days later he reported that the tides had already been shut out and Thatcher was proceeding in a very able manner.

Nevertheless, this breach of the bank had to be regarded as a major setback. The costs involved amounted to nearly £15,000[50] and only by extraordinary exertions were the basin and its locks completed in time.

Jessop came to the site in August and again in September. At a Board meeting on 21 November Josias was told 'it is highly expedient and necessary that the most unremitting Exertions should be exercised on his part that all the various branches of the Works now in forwardness be completed with the utmost Dispatch'. Apart from Cumberland Basin, these included the dam at Temple Meads and Netham Weir. Slips were giving trouble at the latter place and on 2 January 1809 Josias, who really needed no further bullying, received orders from the desperately impatient Directors 'to give unceasing attention to the reparation and completion' of the structure.

This he undoubtedly did, for by the end of the month the Avon was diverted into its new channel. Moreover, on 13 January 1809, with what must have been a feeling of enormous relief, a contract was made for removing the bank at Rownham. On 2 April the first vessel entered Bathurst Basin and finally on the appointed day, 1 May 1809, the entire scheme was certified as complete.

To commemorate this event 1,000 labourers who had been employed on the works were entertained. The celebrations included two oxen roasted whole and a gallon of strong beer to each man, leading sadly but perhaps not surprisingly to a general scuffle between the English and Irish parties among the men who, it is said, had always been on bad terms.[59]

As usual there is no evidence that Jessop attended the opening ceremony of this, one of his greatest works. The Floating Harbour provided Bristol with the largest area of impounded water for shipping in the world and the Cumberland entrance locks formed the largest structure of the kind yet built (p 203). The leading dimensions are as follows: Floating Harbour: 70 acres, depth of water 15–25ft. Cumberland Basin: 4 acres. North entrance lock: 45ft wide, 200ft between gates, 34ft depth on outer sills at HWST. South entrance lock: 36ft by 185ft by 34ft. Bathurst Basin: 1¾ acres. New Cut: 2 miles long, 120ft top-water width. The costs are summarised in Table 4 from the official statement of expenditure up to March 1810.[50]

Josias stayed on until the end of 1810, finishing off various jobs such as the coping of the Cumberland wing walls, ordering a steam dredger from Butterley, making an inventory of the goods and equipment still on site, dealing with a slip in the river bank at Rownham, and fixing 'with most precise accuracy' a depth gauge on one of the quay walls. White was also engaged on surveys and various matters concerning dock property. Later, Josias was consulted by the Dock Company on the intended canal between Bath and Bristol, while his father made a last visit in August 1811 on some problem concerning Netham Weir.

Table 4

*Expenditure by the Bristol Dock Company
to 1 March 1810*

	£
Works under 1803 Act, including all contingencies	432,000
Works under 1806 and 1808 Acts	25,000
Salaries and wages	13,000
Purchase of lands, compensation etc.	104,000
Acts of 1806, 1808 and 1809	9,000
Interest charges and incidentals	17,000
	£600,000
Act of 1803	11,000
Total	£611,000

Clearly the Directors had a high regard for the Jessops, despite various troubles during construction and escalating costs which were, after all, practically unavoidable on very large engineering projects in those days or, indeed, at the present time. Jessop himself visited the works on twenty occasions, usually staying about a week; and of his son the Directors wrote in February 1813, in a report dealing with various queries which had been raised on expenditure:

Mr Josias Jessop with whose accuracy and attention to the Interests of the Company, they have every reason to be satisfied; and to whom it is no more than justice to state, that he acquitted himself in the important trust reposed in him with the most unsullied reputation and honor.

Unfortunately, there is no record of William Jessop's fees but we estimate his total charge cannot have been less than about £1,600 including the £406 for planning and parliamentary attendance in the period 1801–3.

12
ENGINEERING ROUND BRITAIN

We here briefly note other known work that Jessop did.

Waterways

Aire & Calder Navigation Late in 1792 Jessop reported upon how the navigation could be improved, but no copy has been found. It appears not to have been radical, and to have been overcome by events.[1]

Alford Canal Jessop and Hudson reported on and estimated a line in 1784. It was never built.[2]

Basingstoke Canal Jessop seems to have agreed the contract made in October 1788 with John Pinkerton,[3] and is therefore likely to have looked over the survey and advised on the layout of the works. The canal opened in 1794.

Breedon-Trent project In 1787 Jessop proposed a combined rail-canal link. It was not built.[4]

Bristol & Taunton (Western) Canal Jessop was asked in 1793 to chose between lines surveyed by Longbothom and White;[5] he chose White's as amended by himself.[6] In 1794 he looked over an alternative line proposed by a dissident Taunton-Uphill group,[7] and in early 1796 supported in Parliament a Bristol & Taunton Canal Bill, which was defeated. (See also Grand Western Canal.)

Caistor Canal In 1792 Jessop reported on this mania proposal for a canal from the Ancholme to Caistor. It was authorised in 1793, and part-built.[8]

Chelmer & Blackwater Navigation In 1796 Jessop and Mylne were arbitrators in a dispute with the owner of Hoe Mill.[9]

Don (Dun) Navigation Jessop reported on proposed improvements twice in 1801[10] and on a proposed railway from Tinsley to Sheffield in 1804. He also again surveyed for improvements in 1808.

Driffield Navigation Jessop was consulted in 1797 about the possible effect on the navigation of the Beverley & Barmston Drainage. His recommendations were broadly accepted and carried out.[11]

Flint Coal Canal and turnpike road Jessop planned the canal in 1785, and appeared on both Bills in 1788. They passed, but neither line was built.[12]

Foss Navigation Jessop reported in 1791,[13] proposing a scheme of combined navigation and drainage upwards from York. He appeared in Parliament on the Act of 1793, but was not thereafter concerned.

Glamorganshire Canal Jessop and Rennie arbitrated in a water rights dispute at Melingriffith. They jointly agreed upon the waterwheel-driven pumping engine that, when installed, worked from 1807 to 1942, and has now been preserved.[14] It may have given Rennie the idea for Claverton on the Kennet & Avon.

Gloucester & Berkeley Canal By 1796 this canal, authorised in 1793 and engineered by Mylne, was in trouble, both Jessop and Whitworth being then called in. Jessop reported on the canal, Whitworth on Gloucester Docks. The former's report[15] suggested two important deviations that were authorised by the Act of 1797, greater width and depth, swing instead of lift bridges, and a tidal basin between two locks at Berkeley instead of a double lock. In 1810 John Hodgkinson was asked to report on the canal and on a possible alternative termination at Hock Crib, and associated Jessop with himself in his report.[16]

Grand Surrey Canal In 1803 Jessop reported on the canal following the company's doubts about their engineer. He may have been consulted again in 1805.[17]

Grand Western Canal Between 1793 and 1796 Jessop was concerned with the Grand Western (Exe-Taunton), Bristol & Taunton, Kennet & Avon and Somersetshire Coal Canals, all then intended to be inter-linked. He reported on the Grand Western in 1793.[18]

Ipswich & Stowmarket Navigation In late 1789, Jessop surveyed the valley of the Gipping upwards from Ipswich for this navigation,[19] and appeared on it in Parliament. It was authorised in 1790. He provided drawings and specifications, but thereafter took no part in the works.

Kennet & Avon Canal Jessop was asked in 1794 to comment on Rennie's proposed line. He recommended that instead of the latter's 4,312yd summit tunnel, locks should be added to each end of a shortened summit length, and a short tunnel (the present Bruce tunnel) built instead. To supply this new summit with water a steam engine should be installed, (the present Crofton), thus saving the company £47,000 and two years of construction time. He also proposed that Rennie's line through Trowbridge should be shortened to save 2 miles, and that instead of the canal entering the Avon at Bathampton, it should be continued to Bathwick Ferry, whence Rennie later extended it further to Widcombe—the present magnificent canal line through Bath.[20] All these recommendations were adopted. He also firmly recommended that the canal should be built broad and not narrow: this also was agreed. (See also Grand Western Canal.)

In 1807 Jessop came back to support the Avon Towpath Bill in Parliament.

Lancaster Canal This canal was authorised in 1792 with the 31-year old Rennie as engineer. The company wanted Jessop to check his line,[21] but there is no record that he did.

By end-1800 canal lines being open on both sides of the wide Ribble Valley, the committee decided to ask Rennie and Jessop how best to cross it. They reported in May 1801 that an 'Embankment to the full height of the Lancaster Level [about 40ft] and a Stone Aqueduct will be most advisable', lockage to be provided up to the southern section of canal. Five years would be needed; meanwhile a railway with three inclined planes should be built.

Attached to the report was a design for the aqueduct. It was to be 640ft long and 57ft high from low water to the towpath, with three 116ft elliptical arches. The original drawing still exists:[22] Rennie's signature is painted on the watercolour; Jessop's counter-signature is added outside it, and the date 12 May 1801. Sadly, the aqueduct was never built, and the railway continued to serve. The design was probably Rennie's own, though the ideas behind it must have been discussed and agreed between the two men.

Leven Canal Jessop reported[23] upon this projected private broad canal in 1800. It was authorised in 1801 and opened soon afterwards.

Newcastle–Solway Firth canal project The canal mania period saw much interest in a canal link between the Tyne and the Solway Firth or Maryport that would also be a large-scale coal carrier. Local interests first employed Ralph Dodd, then William Chapman, the latter's reports of 1795 being referred to Jessop. The latter reported[24] in October 1795 from Maryport. With one exception, he concurred with Chapman's choice of line, and then recommended dimensions to take 'vessels such as are used on the Yorkshire navigations, about 14 feet in width, and 65 feet in length, which constantly navigate on the Humber, and on the sea coast of Lincolnshire . . .' On economic prospects he is very cautious. Estimates (they totalled £355,000) were signed jointly by Jessop and Chapman. The line was never built, though a small part of it later became the Carlisle Canal.

Regent's Canal About the end of 1812, Jessop joined two others on a committee to judge proposed designs for the canal's two tunnels.[25]

Rother (Western) and Arun Navigations Jessop reported on the Rother and an Arun extension in 1783, on the Rother again in 1790. Later he surveyed the river and produced drawings, eight of which survive in the Petworth House archives. They are signed and dated 1791. The navigation was opened in 1794.[26] We are grateful to Mr A. G. Allnutt for information on the drawings.

Somersetshire Coal Canal Jessop and Rennie did a joint report in 1794. It was rejected: this left Jessop calm, but Rennie furious.[27] They must have been appeased by the subsequent vicissitudes of the company.

Stratford-upon-Avon Canal In 1794 discussions began upon a short linking canal to the Warwick & Birmingham at Lapworth. In August the committee asked Jessop to superintend a survey of both the junction cut and the whole line to Stratford.[28] He must have looked over the surveys, for he was sworn in to appear before the Lords committee on the 1795 Bill that authorised the cut, though he seems not to have done so.

Thames Navigation In 1805 the Corporation of London, responsible for the river downstream of Staines, employed Rennie and Jessop to propose improvements to the navigation, then lockless. They reported[29] in December, proposing various locks and major deviation cuts. Heavily opposed by concerned landowners, Rennie in 1809 produced an alternative scheme without major cuts, which Jessop approved. With the number of locks reduced and their size increased, these proposals passed Parliament, and locks then began to be built under Rennie's supervision.

Thames & Severn Canal In September 1812 Jessop and Whitworth reported on the state of the Ewen springs.[30]

Trent/Tame/Anker scheme A plan of 1783–5 to join the upper Trent to the unfinished Coventry Canal at Atherstone upon which Jessop reported.[31] The Coventry Canal was completed instead.

Worcester & Birmingham Canal In 1810 an argument developed upon whether the company should build locks or vertical lifts down the Tardebigge slope. It hinged upon whether enough water could be found on the summit. Rennie said yes, but a group of shareholders disagreed, and employed Jessop to say no and to support lifts. His report[32] seems to be written from information given him: it is unconvincing, and it did not convince. There was enough water, and locks were built.

Wye River Jessop reported[33] in 1805 upon giving the river a horse towpath up to Hereford. After a further survey by Henry Price, it was authorised in 1809 and opened in 1811.

Water Supply

Sheffield water supply Jessop did a report[34] in 1785, but no action followed.

Land Drainage

Beverley and Barmston Drainage The first suggestion for draining the carrs north of Beverley is in Jessop's report of February 1788 on the River Hull,[35] where he enunciated the principle that the main drain should be quite separate from the streams, running under them in 'tunnels' where necessary, and should be taken to an outfall as far south as possible: preferably to the Humber. The River Hull and its tributary streams would, of course, have to be embanked. When the drainage of this area came under active consideration in 1796, Jessop submitted a report,[36] and so did Chapman. Chapman followed Jessop's ideas but additionally proposed diverting part of the upland waters through a new cut to the east coast at Barmston. Chapman's scheme was approved, Jessop took the Bill through Parliament in 1798 and the works (1799–1810) were carried out by Chapman.

Deeping Fen The proprietors of Deeping Fen, the landowners interested in draining about 17,000 acres of commons adjacent to the Fen near Spalding, and the River Welland Commissioners, were all concerned to improve the Welland outfall; indeed the Commissioners had been appointed under an Act of 1794 precisely to achieve that object, though by means of a somewhat peculiar scheme for diverting the Welland along a 7 mile cut to the mouth of the Witham. When, after several years, it became painfully obvious that nothing was likely to happen, the landowners initiated further investigations, with George Maxwell and Edward Hare as their consultants.[37] Sensibly, the Fen proprietors decided to join in, but with Rennie and Jessop as engineers. In May 1800 Rennie called for some extra surveying and, back in London, hoped that Jessop would join him on site in the third week of July. Jessop replied that he had to be in Yarmouth then but could get to Spalding at the beginning of August, adding 'I shall be in Town on Tuesday next; in the mean time if you do not fly away I may see you.'[38]

The four engineers wrote a joint report on 11 August. It recommends a straightforward improvement of the Welland's own outfall by opening a new channel to Fosdyke and makes proposals for draining the commons, and improving the Fen drainage, in a unified scheme.[39] Moreover, in a separate statement, Jessop and Rennie strongly advise the provision of a steam engine at Podehole as the only certain way of

247

securing a complete drainage of Deeping Fen.

By an Act of June 1801, based on this report, substantial works were carried out, including the Fosdyke Channel, and finally in 1825 under the direction of Benjamin Bevan two powerful engines (one supplied by Butterley) were installed at Podehole: a convincing if delayed confirmation of the prescient advice given in 1800.

King's Sedgemoor Drainage Between 1791 and 1795 about 11,000 acres of peat lands in King's Sedgemoor, in the Somerset Levels, were drained at a cost of £32,000 by a main drain $7\frac{1}{2}$ miles long leading through a $2\frac{1}{2}$ mile cut in the coastal clay belt to a new outfall sluice at Dunball on the Parrett Estuary.[40] William White made the surveys and John Billingsley, one of the drainage commissioners, says the decision to adopt this outfall was 'justified by the concurrent opinion of Mr White and of Mr Jessop, whose advice was taken'.[41] It is possible that Jessop later acted as engineer, but documents covering the period of construction are missing.

Lewes and Laughton Levels Smeaton submitted proposals in 1768 for draining the low grounds on both sides of the Ouse near Lewes. Part of his project was carried out, in the form of a cut at Piddinghoe and some river widening.[42] In 1787 Jessop re-examined the problems[43] and after a further survey he prepared a scheme, rather simpler than Smeaton's, on the basis of which an Act was obtained in 1791. It had the twofold purpose of improving drainage and the river navigation from Newhaven to Lewes.[44]

The works, with Cater Rand as resident engineer[45] and Francis Pinkerton as contractor, were well advanced by 1795 and largely finished, so far as the drainage was concerned, by 1800 at a cost around £16,000.[46] They consisted principally of two cuts and several miles of new river embankments.

Thorne and Hatfield Commons In 1801 Jessop advised on the drainage of Hatfield Common, Thorne Moors and Thorne Common, lying to the west and north west of Hatfield Chase. His report gives a straightforward plan for cutting new drains, enlarging some existing ones, and using as outfalls the drains alongside the Stainforth & Keadby Canal.[47] From later maps it seems that the scheme was executed in accordance with his proposals.

Nottinghamshire Commission of Sewers The minute books (in Nottinghamshire Record Office) show that Jessop did two little jobs in 1787 and 1790, and he appears as a Commissioner at intervals between 1795 and 1805. His brother Josias was also a Commissioner from 1794 to 1808.

Docks and Harbours

Cattewater Embankments In 1801 it was proposed to build embankments for reclaiming land in Lipson and Tothill Bays in the Laira Estuary at Plymouth, and by the sale of this land to construct the 'Embankment Road', thus providing a better route into the town. The Surveyor General asked Jessop's advice on the scheme and especially on its possible effects on Cattewater Harbour at the estuary mouth. Jessop reported favourably and the works were carried out. In 1806 he gave evidence to a Select Committee on further proposals for embanking Chelson Bay on the opposite (east) side of the estuary.[48]

Folkestone Harbour Jessop produced plans and estimates in 1806 for a harbour of 19 acres at Folkestone,[49] and gave evidence in Parliament in the following year. The Folkestone Harbour Company obtained their Act in July 1807. Ten years later about £35,000 had been spent. The works were subsequently completed, though on a somewhat reduced scale from the original intentions, with a £10,000 Exchequer loan.[50]

Hull Docks In 1793 the Commissioners of Customs called for reports by Jessop,[51] Thomas Morris and Capt Huddart on the siting of a second dock at Hull. They all recommended a position similar to that finally adopted in 1802 for the Humber Dock, engineered by Rennie and Chapman.

Littlehampton Harbour Jessop presented a report in 1806, but owing to lack of funds nothing much was done until 1825, with a new Act and Jesse Hartley as consulting engineer.[52]

Liverpool Docks In April 1800 Jessop submitted a lengthy report on the modernisation and extension of Liverpool's docks.[53] It formed the basis of later improvements.

Lyme Regis Harbour Jessop's report of 1805 on repairs and improvements of the pier (called the Cobb) is addressed to Lieut-Gen Morse,[54] as maintenance of Lyme Regis Harbour at this period was carried out by the Board of Ordnance.

Newhaven Harbour Jessop included a note on the harbour in his 1787 report on Lewes and Laughton Levels.[43] The accompanying sketch plan[55] was not issued with the printed report.

Portsmouth Harbour Jessop and Capt Huddart reported jointly with Robert Mylne, at the latter's request, on the state of Portsmouth Harbour and the probable effects of embanking certain marshes within its area.[56] We have not traced their report, but it was completed in July 1796.[57]

Plymouth Breakwater At the request of the Admiralty, Jessop considered the scheme proposed by Rennie and Joseph Whidbey for

249

constructing a massive breakwater in Plymouth Sound.[58] He thoroughly approved.

Rye Harbour Jessop reported in 1786 on the enlargement of a channel $\frac{3}{4}$ mile in length along the east and south sides of Rye town, to a top width of 118ft and a depth of 13ft.[59] The work, which included underwater blasting of rock, was completed by John Pinkerton in August 1787 at a cost of £4,000. A dam was also built across the River Rother, at the head of the channel, to divert the whole flow of the river through the channel to the so-called New Harbour, running from the south-west corner of the town down to an entrance at Winchelsea Beach.

But this impeded drainage of low grounds further upstream, so the New Harbour was abandoned and a cut made from the channel into the old course of the river[60] which, after improvements, became the lower part of Rye Harbour as we know it today.[61] Jessop's channel remains as the upper part of the harbour.

Shoreham Harbour Jessop's report of July 1800 on this harbour carries to an extreme the restriction of proposals to suit the current financial resources of his clients.[62] A few years later Rennie went to the other extreme with a grandiose scheme, and it was left to Chapman, in 1815, to pursue a practical middle course.

Sunderland Harbour In 1807 construction of the piers at Sunderland Harbour reached a critical stage, and before proceeding further the Harbour Commissioners called on Jessop for a detailed report. He arrived in Sunderland at the beginning of December, spent two weeks on site staying with Matthew Shout the harbour engineer, and wrote up his conclusions immediately after returning home.

The report, with a postscript dated 12 January 1808, and an engraved plan, was printed at Sunderland.[63] Jessop warmly approved what Shout had done since taking office in 1804; he gives precise recommendations for the lines along which the North and South Piers should be extended; makes accurate estimates of the cost; comments wisely on several other questions raised by the Commissioners; and adds an idea, of immense value as events were to prove, for reclaiming land south of the harbour entrance.

An Act for increased powers was obtained in 1809. The Butterley Company supplied a steam dredger in 1811. Work proceeded on the piers until Matthew Shout died, still a young man, in 1817. They were built exactly as laid down in Jessop's report and by 1817 had reached almost to the limits proposed by him (see p 204). The harbour was now one of the finest in Britain. Jessop received 100 guineas for his report and expenses.[64]

250

Watchet Harbour Among the drawings listed in Telford's collection[65] we find: 'Plan of the Harbour of Watchet with a Design for an Eastern Pier' and 'Section of a Pier for Watchet Harbour', both signed W. Jessop 1797. They no longer survive in this collection.

Workington Harbour One of Jessop's earliest printed reports, with a fine engraved plan, was written in 1777 on Workington Harbour.[66] Later that year the Bill failed to pass the Commons.

Yarmouth Harbour The South Pier at Yarmouth, as Jessop saw it on his first visit in 1798, had been rebuilt in the 1750s. Extending from the shore into quite deep water, it was a massive structure formed by timber piles and planking infilled with chalk and flint stones, but now, after forty years' exposure to the sea, was falling into disrepair.[67] Jessop makes very practical suggestions for its reinstatement and for improving the harbour itself.[68]

The Commissioners accepted his proposals and obtained an Act in March 1800 for increased duties, to finance the work. Meanwhile, Jessop visited the harbour again in July and October 1799, and on the latter occasion was appointed engineer.[69]

Reconstruction of the pier took place between 1800 and 1806 at a cost around £18,000, with John Drury as resident engineer. Jessop came to Yarmouth six times during this period. He returned in 1808 with designs for a new jetty and again in 1809 with drawings for rebuilding Yarmouth Bridge.

The bucket ladder horse dredger at Yarmouth, built in 1786, was naturally of great interest to Jessop, and we have from his pen the only known contemporary description of this machine.[70] Knowledge of its working details, and those of the similar machine at Hull, must have been a help to him in designing the bucket-ladder steam dredgers for the Caledonian Canal in 1804 and for Aberdeen Harbour in 1806.

Bridges

Menai Straits The first proposals for taking a road across the Straits came in 1783 from John Golborne and Joseph Nickalls, in the form of an embankment with a navigation lock or openings spanned by drawbridges. Both schemes were reviewed by Jessop who, in January 1784, came up with a less objectionable design for a timber bridge on piles with three drawbridge spans.[71] Applications to Parliament in 1785 and 1786 for powers to built such a bridge proved unsuccessful. Much later, in 1802, his opinion was sought by Rennie on plans for a cast-iron arch bridge at the same location.[72]

Selby Bridge In response to the clear need for a road bridge over the Ouse at Selby, to replace the ferry, a petition went to the Commons in March 1789, but met heavy opposition from York, from the navigation interests and from landowners fearing increased risk of flooding. Jessop was called in. To a meeting of subscribers in December he stated that a bridge could be built 'without material impediment to the navigation and without any injury whatsoever to the land owners',[73] and followed this with a long, well reasoned report. Three points of particular interest emerge: a traffic census had been taken during a twenty-day period in December 1789; Jessop had measured the maximum river velocity (it was considerably less than in the Don at Goole), and the bridge would be on single rows of timber piles with a swing or lifting section for the passage of masted boats.[74]

However, a second petition foundered, so the case went to arbitration. This had a successful result and led to an Act being passed in April 1791. A model of the bridge (p 204), now in the Science Museum, is said to have been exhibited in Parliament.[75] It may date from 1791.

According to the minute book of the Company of Proprietors, Jessop was asked to produce plans and specifications, and to consult John Carr on the swing section.[76] This would be to fulfil a clause in the Act requiring approval of the method of opening by engineers named by the navigation Trustees.

The bridge was opened to traffic in September 1793. It had a width of 21ft with a deck carried on oak beams and massive crosshead beams on oak pile trestles, leaving a 35ft main navigation span.[77] The swing section, resting on roller bearings, could be opened or closed by the operation of gearing in one minute. It survived until 1970.

13
JESSOP THE MAN

It seems likely that during the summer of 1783 Job Brough, clerk to the Trent Navigation and himself living in Newark, suggested to Jessop that the couple move from Fairburn to a house there that could be rented from Lord Middleton.[1] Certainly by March 1784 they were occupying a 'house, homestead and close' in Appleton Gate, the street which passes the east end of Newark church.[2] The three-storey brick house, built probably not long before the Jessops moved in, scarcely stands out from the good eighteenth-century line of the street. The ground floor is now occupied by Wigfall's shop; the close has been built over.[3]

As well as being the place where Trent Navigation meetings were held, Newark was on the Great North Road, fully turnpiked well before Jessop's day, and the Foss Way, and therefore a good centre for a busy man wishing to get quickly south to London and Parliament, north to Yorkshire and beyond, east to Lincoln or west to Leicester.

On 3 November 1786, surprisingly soon after his arrival and a tribute to his social standing, he was elected an alderman, an office held until his move to Butterley in 1805. Busy as he was all over the country, he could seldom get to meetings, though he did so at least once in most years. The new town hall, classical with pillared entrance, still stands in calm dignity in the central square, crowded with the weekend market, and the natural centre of the town. Here Jessop held the office of mayor twice, in 1790–1 and 1803–4.[4] Here too stood the Saracen's Head Inn, rebuilt in 1721, which had from 1752 to 1772 been kept by John Ridghill (also Newark's postmaster and later an alderman), father of Sarah, the wife of Jessop's brother Josias. William was made a justice of the peace on 28 January 1805, but only held office till he left Newark in the autumn. At a Council meeting on 28 November 1805:

'. . . the Resignation of William Jessop Esquire as an Alderman (who has left the Town) was read and it was thereupon resolved and ordered that the Town Clerk do write a letter to Mr Jessop to express their great regret on his being obliged to tender his resignation and to

253

offer him their best wishes for his Health and Happiness.'[5]

Josias had become a skilled clock and watchmaker and also silver-smith, living in London from 1781 at 38 Southampton Street, where Jessop often stayed when in town. He married Sarah Ridghill (the name is also spelled Redgill and Ridgill) in January 1786, and from 1787 to 1790 seems to have lived both at Newark and Southampton Street. About 1790 he gave up his London business and moved to what may have been his wife's house in Northgate. Sadly, Sarah died in October 1790. Josias did not marry again, but remained at Newark until his death in 1808. His memorial in Newark church was probably put there by William: 'an affectionate Brother, a pleasant & chearful companion, a sincere & steady Friend'.

Their sister Mary married Samuel Brooke, born in 1746, son of the Rev Samuel Brooke, then a rector and later headmaster of Leeds Grammar School. Samuel Brooke had been apprenticed to the printer Thomas Harrison of Paternoster Row in London, the first of the famous Harrison printing family, with whom he went into partnership about 1772 as Harrison & Brooke. They printed *The London Gazette*, and worked for the government as well as private clients. Brooke died in 1798, but his son Samuel continued the business in partnership with his mother. Given Jessop's position in the Smeatonian Society, it is not surprising that his brother-in-law was invited to join the Society in the 'Artist' class of honorary members in 1793, or that he printed Vol I of Smeaton's *Reports* in 1797. His nephew was appointed printer to the Society in 1799 and printed Vol II of the *Reports* in 1812 and *Miscellaneous Papers* in 1814.

After Josias had left London, Jessop often used to stay with his sister when in town, while her husband was alive at 7 Chatham Place (at the north end of Blackfriars Bridge) and after his death at 35 Paternoster Row until the end of 1802, when his address becomes the London Coffee-house. We find Jessop putting in a word for the firm when he could: M & S Brooke printed for the Grand Junction Canal Company for some years from 1802 onwards, and the Surrey Iron Railway committee minutes.

Of the Jessops' children the eldest, John, born in 1779, entered the Army at 19, and saw almost continuous military service until 1815. Then, severely wounded at Quatre Bras and having earned a CB, he married in 1820 and retired to Butterley where he lived until his death in 1869, aged 90. Josias, the next son, died comparatively young and a bachelor in 1826, after a career which included harbour and railway

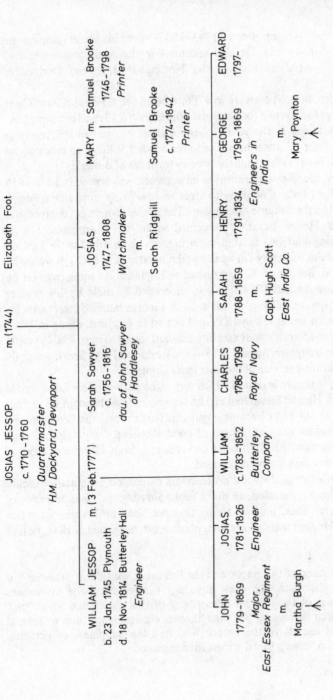

Fig 24 Jessop's family. His young brother Samuel (b. 1749), about whom nothing is known, has been omitted

engineering. William junior (1783–1852) spent his life developing the Butterley Ironworks. He also became a leader of the ironworks and colliery owners' interests in the Nottinghamshire and Derbyshire areas.[6]

Charles, born at Newark in 1786, entered the Navy as a First Class Volunteer (an avenue for potential officers) aged 13, and the same year was lost at sea in the wreck of the *Lutine*, whose bell still hangs at Lloyds. Poor Charles: he wrote to his brother William to recommend life in the Navy rather than the 'smoky furnaces of Butterley'.[7]

Henry, the fifth son, trained as an engineer, was sent to India in 1815 by the East India Company to erect an iron bridge and steam engine supplied by the Butterley Company. The bridge project got delayed, but in 1818 Henry became concerned with two businesses, one in engineering and one in ship repairing, which in 1820 he bought on behalf of the Butterley Company and named Jessop & Co. It was to be long-lived. Becoming ill, he returned to England, did some engineering work[8] and died in 1834. He was succeeded in India by his brother George, who had also gone out in 1818. George married there; after his wife's death he retired in 1839 and settled in England, dying in 1869. William and Sarah's youngest boy Edward seems to have died in youth. Their one daughter, Sarah (1788–1852), married Hugh Scott, a captain in the maritime service of the East India Company.

Jessop's family is one of which any eighteenth-century father could be proud. He and Sarah had lost no babies, and had brought up all their children. Four boys became engineers, two entered the Services, and their daughter married a man of good standing. Only John, George and Sarah married. Both boys had children, from whom a number of present-day Jessops are descended.

Jessop's straightforward professional career, his satisfactory family life, his high reputation, all make more puzzling the disappearance of his papers. This, indeed, seems to have been deliberate, for when Samuel Hughes was writing Jessop's memoir, published in 1844, he had to say:[9]

> The author of this paper and the Publisher consider it necessary to state, that although they have not derived from the immediate relatives of the late Mr Jessop any of that assistance which they ventured to expect, yet their thanks are eminently due to several valued friends of the author who had the happiness of personal intercourse with that distinguished engineer.

Why a family (responsibility, we take it, lay between John as the eldest and William as active at Butterley) with every reason to be proud of their father, took this line we do not know and guesswork is fruitless. Their refusal led, however, to Jessop's work being less well known, and his reputation less regarded, than history requires.

What sort of a man was he? How did he do his work? And what is our estimate of his achievement?

Alone among his major contemporaries, he was taught engineering by a great engineer, and early introduced, through the Smeatonian Society, to the community of engineers. Somewhat of a late developer for those times, Jessop remained Smeaton's assistant until he was 27. A biographer says:

> ... there is reason to believe, that his early and constant connection with that eminent engineer, created a degree of timidity in the exercise of his own talents; for we have good authority for stating, that, for some years after the expiration of his articled service, he was almost unwilling to undertake business on his own account ... This conduct may, no doubt, be partly attributed to his having become necessary to Mr Smeaton, and to the uninterrupted mutual confidence and esteem which always subsisted between them."[10]

Jessop became, not primarily an architect like Robert Mylne, nor a great bridge builder like Telford or Rennie, but a man whose especial skill lay in handling water and earth. A glance at Smeaton's *Reports* for the years between 1759 and 1772, when Jessop was with him, shows his background: waterworks and fen drainage, harbour works and lighthouses, bridges and water mills, iron works and industrial equipment, river navigations and canals. Most were clearly relevant to Jessop's later work: Smeaton's building of the Calder & Hebble and involvement with the Aire & Calder to his river work; his early activity on the Forth & Clyde[11] and the Grand Canal of Ireland to canal engineering; on the Holderness Levels and the Witham to later drainage works; and at the Carron Ironworks to his partnership in Butterley. Moreover, Smeaton had been abroad to the Low Countries, and brought back with him both practical knowledge of how others did things, eg built locks, and acquaintance with such engineering classics as Belidor's *Architecture Hydraulique* (1737–53).

So Jessop, with the sea in his blood from old Josias and with Smeaton's harbour works as training, became the greatest harbour engineer of his day, building three of the then biggest dock systems,

Ringsend (Dublin), Bristol and the West India, and many smaller works. Sea and inland water met in major drainage schemes, such as Holderness or Axholme. They met also in river engineering. Here Jessop was unrivalled: Trent, Thames, Shannon, Don, and a dozen smaller streams were made better navigations thanks to him; only on the Severn did his proposals fail to overcome opposition, and leave that river unimproved throughout the canal age and its bankside industries to suffer accordingly.

His earlier views on rivers are succinctly set out in the preamble to his report of 1782 on the Trent, those of his maturity in a letter he wrote in 1795 to the Board of Agriculture:

> While canal navigations are avowedly safe, easy and certain, except in times of frost, I cannot agree with those who maintain, that they are in all cases preferable to river navigations: ... there are numberless instances where river navigations are preferable to canals; first, because they are generally effected at the least expence; and secondly, because when obstructions are removed or avoided, they are susceptible of more expedition; except in the few weeks in a year where they are annoyed by floods; for being less incumbered with bridges, and having generally a greater width, vessels are enabled to make use of sails; and at such times the labour of horses is saved. On the river Trent, which, compared with some others, is very imperfect, goods are conveyed seventy miles for 8 shillings per ton, including freight, tonnage, risk, and profit of the boat owners; there are but few canal navigations on which the expence of conveyance is not half as much more; and I consider the expence of conveyance as the chief criterion. In point of expedition, vessels frequently make a voyage of seventy miles, and back again in a week, including the time of lading and unlading; this had been done by the same vessels for ten weeks successively ... [12]

River channels should be kept of navigable depth by dredging and restriction of their width; lock tails should be as short as possible so that bars formed after floods could be scoured away.

His views on mills that competed with navigations for water were brisk. Nearly all were inefficiently designed. If they were to be reconstructed to work economically, they would need less water; therefore it would pay navigation companies to subsidise mill-owners to do the work, eg on the Don or the Bain to Horncastle. If there were still competition, let the company buy out the mill, and then let it conditionally upon its use not interfering with navigation.

Jessop came to canals with ideas gained from Smeaton's and his own river experience. Locks should be broad to take craft of an economic size; so, out of all his works, he was only seriously involved with one narrow canal system, the Ellesmere. Traffic should be able to move freely; and so on his canals we rarely find a staircase pair (we recollect only one, on the Grand Canal) except only on the Caledonian, where economy allied to ample water forced staircases upon him and Telford. Water supply should be plentiful and assured; even a river navigation might have a reservoir, as on the Foss, and canals either reservoirs or steam engines or both to supplement natural streams. Once provided, water should be used economically; therefore locks should be well built, and their falls as nearly as possible equalised, a policy he carried out especially to his satisfaction on the Rochdale. Boats should pass quickly; therefore lock sluices should be large. For the same reason he at first disliked side-ponds,[13] but later installed them on the Grand Junction because saving water was more important than the extra time taken.

The *Edinburgh Encyclopaedia* said of him:

> In the important articles of Locks, Wharfs and Retaining Walls, he introduced an entirely new form, composed of nearly one half the quantity of materials employed by the French and early English engineers . . .[10]

This is further explained by Telford[14] who attributes to Jessop the retaining wall of uniform thickness with a small backward inclination or batter 'so as by retiring the centre of gravity, to enable the wall to resist better the lateral pressure'. We have seen Jessop recommending this idea, coupled with counterforts increasing in projection towards the top, on the Thames in 1789. Telford also implies that Jessop introduced the curved-profile wall, and relates that 'the use of inverted arches for the bottom of locks was not, he (Jessop) said, much known at that time'.

Certainly it would be difficult to find earlier examples than Jessop's 1791 designs for curved-profile dock walls, and inverted arch foundations for the entrance locks, at Ringsend; walls of uniform thickness with a batter and counterforts (exactly as described in Jessop's 1789 Thames Report) and inverted arches were used in the Ellesmere locks (1794); while curved walls and lock inverts appear on a massive scale at the West India Docks in 1800—to be adopted by Rennie and other engineers in subsequent large dock works.

Floodwater reservoirs to supply canals go back, in British practice, to Smeaton's Townhead Dam and Reservoir, completed in 1773, for the Forth & Clyde Canal, but Jessop laid out the first canal to be supplied entirely in this way: the Grantham in 1793. A year before he had written a paper 'Observations on the Use of Reservoirs for Flood Waters'.[15]

All admit that inland navigation promotes prosperity, he says, but the greatest obstacle is want of water in dry seasons, industry or agriculture having already 'taken possession of the ground, and occupied the streams of water'. Therefore, collect winter floodwater, and use it in the summer. Though this is not always possible: 'Where the soil is porous, and the substrata so open as to absorb the rains as they fall, there are no floods', but this is not so with clay soils, where 'so little is absorbed, and so much suddenly glides off from the surface, that the extremes of scarcity and exuberance are the necessary consequences'. In theory, indeed, and 'leaving expence out of the question, it is possible to conceive ... that the waters of all rivers might by art be equalized throughout the year'.

Jessop did not excel with his waterway structures, other than those that sprang directly out of his skill with water and earth. Though with Outram he had successfully built Butterley Tunnel, he had enough troubles with Braunston and Blisworth to convince him that tunnels should be avoided if possible, and otherwise shortened to the utmost. And so the young Rennie's ebullient proposals for long summit tunnels on the Rochdale and the Kennet & Avon were, for the first, eliminated, and for the second, much shortened. Jessop preferred building a few more locks and providing a reservoir or a steam engine, to the unknown geological perils of tunnels. And who, knowing how long it took to cut the first Harecastle, Standedge, Sapperton or Morwellham, would blame him? Again, unlike Rennie, he was somewhat unhappy with masonry aqueducts. Only one of his, that on the Barnsley Canal, now demolished, compares with the best of other engineers.

Water and earth were his elements, but to them he added iron and steam. Perhaps because of what Smeaton had done at Carron Ironworks, Jessop understood iron. So we find him laying iron rails on the Leicester Navigation's railways, sponsoring iron trough aqueducts at Pontcysyllte and Chirk, designing iron bridges at Bristol, and in December 1799 recommending an iron railway to promoters who had asked him to survey for a canal from Wandsworth to Croydon. Therefore partnership in an ironworks came naturally to him: the range of his technical knowledge would be widened on the one hand, and on the other his engineering work would naturally result in orders to Butterley.

Steam engines, too, he used naturally, as when he ordered one in 1791 for draining the foundation excavations at Ringsend, one of the earliest examples in the field, and when on many later occasions he employed them for pumping or grinding mortar. He often recommended their use also for pumping to canal reservoirs or for back-supply up lock flights; and he was the first engineer to produce fully practical plans for steam drainage of fenland.

By about 1785, with Smeaton in partial retirement, Jessop came to the head of his profession and during the next twenty years he took part in parliamentary business on engineering Bills more frequently than anyone else. This is true to a quite remarkable extent for canals.

One can distinguish four periods in the Canal Age that lasted from about 1760 to 1840. The first, which older men like Thomas Steers and Thomas Yeoman had helped to bring about, was dominated on one side by John Smeaton, on the other by the Duke of Bridgewater, his agent John Gilbert and James Brindley. Brindley in turn gathered round himself a group containing one outstanding engineer, Robert Whitworth, and several very competent ones, including Hugh Henshall, Samuel Simcock and Thomas Dadford senior. Brindley himself died in 1772, but his assistants maintained his tradition for the next ten years and more.

Then came Jessop—alone—to tower over the period from 1785 to 1805. On his shoulders fell the weight of the canal mania. The following table, listing witnesses sworn before appearing at House of Lords committees on canal and navigation Bills, illustrates this. If we take the mania as lasting, in its widest extent, from 1789 to 1796, then four engineers took the brunt: Robert Mylne and Robert Whitworth, both older than Jessop; Jessop himself; and the younger John Rennie. We see Whitworth, heavily committed to the Forth & Clyde, but taking his part; Robert Mylne, only once a promoters' engineer,* usually an outside expert on water problems; and Rennie, first appearing in 1792, landing two plums,† but also many of the duds of 1796.†† These three appeared 29 times between them; Jessop appeared 27 times, the only engineer to appear in each of the 8 years. Moreover, except for some projected branches of the Grand Junction, and parts of the Ellesmere, Leicestershire & Northamptonshire Union and Foss, every waterway

* The Gloucester & Berkeley Canal.
† The Kennet & Avon and the Lancaster.
†† The Grand Western, Tamar, Leominster and Polbrock.

for which he appeared in those years was built and opened. Of the other competent engineers of the time, Samuel Bull appears 6 times, Benjamin Outram, Charles Handley and John Varley 4, Josiah Clowes, John Dadford and Thomas Dadford junior* 3 each. John Smeaton, at the end of his career, and Thomas Telford, at the beginning of his, each appear once.

	1789	1790	1791	1792	1793	1794	1795	1796	Total
Bull, Samuel			1		2	2		1	6
Jessop, William	1	2	2	3	9	4	4	2	27
Mylne, Robert	1		1	1	2		1		6
Rennie, John			2	6	3			5	16
Whitworth, Robert		2			2	3			7
Other Engineers of note									
Bennet, William			1		1	1		1	4
Clowes, Josiah			1		2				3
Dadford, John					2	1			3
Dadford, Thomas jun		1		1	1				3
Handley, Charles					1	1		2	4
Outram, Benjamin	1			1	1	1			4
Smeaton, John			1						1
Snape, John			1		2	1	1		5
Telford, Thomas								1	1
Varley, John	1			1	1	1			4
	4	5	8	9	32	18	6	12	94

After 1800 Jessop turned his attention increasingly from canals to dock and harbour works, and by 1805, aged 60, he began to seem a little old-fashioned beside the rising men: Rennie and Telford, who dominate the third canal period, shading in the 1820s to the fourth and last, when George Leather is the leading name.

A number of things strike one about Jessop as one reads his surviving reports and letters.

First, his strong commonsense and appreciation of the possible with engineering following both economics and balance of the interests concerned. Unlike the early Rennie, for instance, he never submits a report that proposes the best possible; it is always to achieve what is necessary at minimum cost, and with the least likelihood of anything

* One of these appearances may be of his father.

going wrong, either in construction or subsequent maintenance. As a man involved in the public business life of Newark, he knew the value of money and the difficulty of raising it; knew also enough about likely traffic on any waterway to size up what was needed to carry that volume; learned enough also about the interests and ambitions of local leading men to feel what they would agree to and what would be too much for them. Therefore shareholders seldom complained about Jessop's involvement.

Our point is made by his *Edinburgh Encyclopaedia* biographer;[10] what is said should be related to, eg his aqueduct failures on the Cromford Canal:

> He constantly devoted his whole mind to the subject before him, and from which all personal considerations seemed excluded ... his uniform aim was to accomplish his purposes by the simplest and most economical means: these he sometimes carried to a length to which the average talents of mankind could not always do justice in the execution; but he invariably declined to screen personal responsibility by unnecessary expenditure, upon the grounds, that it was the business of an engineer, and what ought chiefly to distinguish him from the common workman, to effect his purposes rather by ingenuity of construction, than quantity of materials; that it was an imperative duty rather to risk occasional partial failures from imperfect workmanship, than uniformly to persevere in an unpardonable waste of capital; and that no clamour of ignorance, or prejudice, or consideration of personal interest, should for a moment deter him from this conduct.

In those days engineers were expected to offer sensible advice upon the economic prospects of the enterprises they were engaged upon. Jessop did so: witness, for instance, his Trent report of 1 March 1791, with its careful analysis of existing traffic, and conclusion that it was unlikely that thorough canalisation of the river would earn the tolls to pay for it. Having leanings towards mathematical economics, he developed a theory relating the traffic-attracting power of a canal to its length. One example occurs in his and Barnes' report of 8 April 1799 on the proposed Blisworth Railway:

> ... in the extension of a Canal from any given point which supplies a Country with necessaries (and particularly when Coal is the principal Article) the extension encreases the quantity of Conveyance, in a duplicate ratio of the length to which it is extended, making allowances for local exceptions ...

263

If such an extension be 6 miles long, a person will go 3 miles to it rather than use land carriage from the beginning; at 12 miles he will go 6, and at 18 miles 9 miles. 'On this principle you will conceive that a Canal will accommodate a triangular district of Country'. Braunston Wharf to Blisworth is $13\frac{1}{2}$ miles, and to Stony Stratford Bridge 21 miles, a proportion of 9 to 14. Therefore the 'Area of Country comprehended within the triangle, the perpendicular depth of which is from Braunston to Blisworth, will be to the Area of that from Braunston to Stratford as the square of nine to the square of fourteen'.

Second, Jessop's approach was imaginative. His writings are full of the touches that show feeling, an entering into the lives of his workmen and of ordinary people, an appreciation of how life is lived, of how things really are and how much details matter, however humdrum the water and earth in which he deals.

For instance, we may remember that at Chirk he wanted to replace an embankment 'which would shut up a view of the valley' by an iron aqueduct which 'instead of an obstruction ... would be a romantic feature in the view'; at Pontcysyllte his anxiety for the safety of men working on the piers; or the remark in his Trent report of 4 July 1811[16] that a fortnight's stoppage for lock reconstruction 'should be in the time of Harvest, when the Boatmen may find some employment'.

He sees with a discerning imagination the future amenity value of the canals he is building. When high blank walls were suggested to face approach embankments to a bridge on the Paddington Branch,[17] he proposes that houses should be built along them: 'the ground rent ... would be worth more because the views from them up and down the Canal would never be interrupted ...'[18]

Again, reporting on a section of the Grand Canal to be used by passenger boats, he suggests that it might be 'a popular measure, becoming the public spirit of a Great Company' to appropriate a certain annual sum to plant waste canal-owned ground 'with such Trees as may be suitable to the soil'. The cost would be small, and 'the Beauty & shelter it wou'd give to the Canal will at least be worth part of the cost of it, and any thing tending to make a Journey pleasurable, will operate as an inducement to many to chuse the pleasant way; but at all events it would, in time, become a source of emolument that wou'd amply repay the expence'.

Third, his original mind, and keen interest in life and people, which ranged over all kinds of engineering matters, and also wider into public affairs.

As early as May 1777 he had written to the Royal Society of Arts on behalf of Joseph Pèart, a Leeds barber who had invented a repeating clock.[19] In 1784 we find him writing to James Watt to ask how successful a new pattern of oil lamp was that Matthew Boulton had showed him at Soho, and how much it cost.[20] His fertile mind shows again in his 1795 answer to Sir John Sinclair, President of the Board of Agriculture (a chartered society, not a government department), who had written seeking his view on improvements.[12]

An early advocate of transport structure planning, Jessop suggests 'a general survey of the kingdom', with the object 'of giving facility to the conveyance of the various products of the island, from parts where they are useless, to others where they are valuable'.

> With such a map before you, you might in your study generally ascertain the practicability of making water communications from one part of the country to another; whether they might be conducted on one level, or what rise and fall must be encountered: from hence, assisted by a mineral survey, and by the various information which will be obtained under the institution to which you have devoted so much attention, you might draw the outlines of a general system, which would stand upon record, to be referred to when any local project may be brought forward.

Following from this he suggests the preparation of contoured maps:

> Imperfect as our present maps are, they give tolerable information of the relative situations of roads and rivers, and of the distance of places from each other; but they convey no adequate ideas of the respective heights or depressions of the surface. Taking the mean between high and low water of a neap-tide as the level of the sea, if level lines were traced ... at equal heights above each other (for instance twenty feet), and those lines were surveyed and laid down on a map ... one might ... ascertain within a few feet the height of any given point above the level of the sea.

And he goes on to recommend that bench-mark stones could be set up, at selected positions, to be used as a basis for local surveys.

The Trigonometrical Survey had been started in 1791, and was to produce its first Ordnance Survey map in 1801, but contours were not to be added till half a century later.[21]

Jessop goes on to refer to his earlier paper on reservoirs, but now expands his ideas to include their use for the combined purposes of agricultural irrigation and fisheries. Finally he puts forward ideas on road maintenance. So far as we know, he did no road engineering, but his travels must have brought much to his mind about the state of the roads. Writing, of course, just before the time of such great road engineers as Telford and MacAdam, he said:

> I do not know any thing in this country ... that has been more neglected than the proper construction of wheel-carriages, and the formation of roads.

He first makes the point that current policy is that broad wheels help to roll the road; therefore turnpike trusts charge special low tolls when they are used. But, he explains, as usually made and fitted, they do not naturally lie parallel to each other or present a flat surface to the road. Thus they do more damage than narrow wheels because of the heavier loads they are allowed to carry. In his opinion, cylindrical wheels are needed, a view he later advanced in more detail based upon experiments made by himself and his son William at Butterley.[22]

On road construction he had two points: 'one where roads are repaired with stone is the neglect of breaking the stones, which ought to be left not larger than walnuts', and the other that whereas on the turnpikes the men, in scraping off the mud, remove much good road material with it, the sensible thing is to wash the mud off leaving the gravelly particles in the ruts. Then, on the return of dry weather 'the road will dry more in one day, than with the mud on it will dry in a week'. A few trusts already did this, and some years later he persuaded the surveyor of the Derby to Alfreton turnpike to adopt the method.[23]

Jessop here partially anticipates the two principal points that J L MacAdam was to put to the 1810 committee[24] and which were the basis of his road policy: cleaned materials laid in small pieces. We may note that Dr Albert,[25] whose chapter on Trust road repair should be consulted, says that MacAdam's idea 'of using cleaned material was not new but his insistence on small, uniform size was'. We know now that Jessop said it in 1795; indeed it was implied in his Breedon report of 1787.

Fourth, his personal way of doing business. He does not seem to have had an office at Newark, but worked from his home probably without an assistant, though one guesses he must have had a draughtsman. Most of his reports were written in his own hand, sometimes hurriedly, in coffee houses or hotels or spare bedrooms, but usually at home after returning from a job. Something like forty of them were printed, but far more are recorded as manuscript copies in minute

266

books or in separate folios. It is clear, also, that where he was himself involved in construction, as on the Grand Canal or the West India Docks, to take but two examples, his reports were only the tip of the iceberg. Much more was done by talking—to chairmen and committee-men, to the local engineers, and to the workmen actually doing the job.

From his reports and letters, too, we see a man kind to his colleagues and juniors, firm in giving instructions, ready to change his mind when necessary and to admit mistakes.

> Totally free of all envy and jealousy of professional rivalship, his proceedings . . . were free from all pomp and mysticism, and persons of merit never failed in obtaining his friendship and encouragement.

So writes his first biographer,[10] and adds:

> . . . his manners were simple: when disengaged from business, and in the company of intimate friends, he not unfrequently displayed a playfulness of disposition, and a fund of entertaining anecdotes.

In the profession of civil engineering, Jessop's importance can scarcely be exaggerated. He formed the link between Smeaton and the generation of Rennie and Telford; he never failed to act with the highest professional integrity; directly or by example he trained many engineers, among them Benjamin Outram, Ralph Walker and his own son Josias. With Mylne, Whitworth and Rennie he reorganised the Society of Civil Engineers in 1793, and he was on the Society's Special Committee for publishing Smeaton's collected reports, the first volume of which appeared in 1797.[26]

Turning now to his method of working: after preliminary surveys for a scheme by a land surveyor or assistant engineer, working under his direction, Jessop prepared a report and estimates and gave evidence in Parliament. Up to this stage he was acting solely as a consultant, as he explained in 1793 in a letter to Sir Joseph Banks:[27]

> I have . . . for some years past never further engaged in any undertaking at the outset of it than to investigate the practicability, and to attend the Bill through Parliament . . . If when an Act is obtained the parties choose to consult me further I shall be at their service so far as I can consistent with prior engagements.

Quite often, and of course on all of what became his major projects, he was then appointed engineer to design and direct construction, with a resident engineer permanently employed to supervise the works. The frequency and timing of Jessop's site visits would depend to some extent on the problems arising, and partly on the urgency of other commitments, but where we have detailed information (eg Holderness, Trent, Yarmouth, Bristol, etc) he generally went to the site between one and five times a year during construction, for several days, and in special cases (eg the West India Docks) far more often and for longer periods.

On other occasions his responsibility ended when the Act had been obtained or when his report was submitted. With a highly competent resident engineer, as at Sunderland Harbour, for instance, this proved to be perfectly satisfactory. But sometimes, and particularly during the mania, a compromise procedure was adopted; Jessop made 'designs for the principal works sufficient for the information of any man qualified to superintend the execution' and endeavoured to find such a man,[27] without himself being able to accept appointment as engineer. In the unusual circumstances of the time this arrangement is understandable, but it was terribly difficult to find properly trained and able canal engineers not already engaged on the bigger schemes; and Jessop had the misfortune to be caught out in this way on the Horncastle Navigation, with the formidable Sir Joseph Banks as principal client, soon after a similar fiasco on the Sussex Ouse. Banks knew about the latter, from Lord Sheffield, and we consider it probable that these two incidents may have kept Jessop out of the Royal Society, over which Sir Joseph reigned as president from 1778 to 1820. At any rate some reason must exist, in view of Jessop's generally eminent and distinguished career, for his non-election to the Royal and we can think of no more likely explanation.

Coming now to the later part of that career: in the autumn of 1805, after Benjamin Outram's tragically early death, the Jessops moved to Butterley Hall and William junior took over the day to day running of the ironworks, in which he must often have needed his father's advice. For this reason and because of his age, rising 61 at the time of the move, we may regard Jessop's great days as over. His work on the Grand Junction and Ellesmere Canals was done by 1804, the West India Docks by 1805, the Port of London and Yarmouth Harbour by 1806, the year also of his last visit to Ireland. But three jobs he kept, Bristol until 1808, the Caledonian Canal until 1812, and the Trent Navigation to his death; and one new one he took on, Kilmarnock Railway with Troon Harbour. Otherwise, the years 1806 to 1812 were mostly concerned with consulting and arbitration work.

In May 1808 Jessop made his will, and late that year his brother Josias died. In his last years, it is said, William 'suffered much from paralysis'—perhaps arthritis, perhaps a stroke, though he made his way with Telford to Corpach in October and to Aberdeen in November 1812, and later that month to Chesterfield on the drainage of Gringley Carrs. However, by 27 April 1813, his son was writing to the Trent Company to excuse his father's attendance: 'You will perceive that my father's state of health & faculties are so much impaired that his attendance at your meetings is to him a great inconvenience & I fear of little service to the Trent.'[28] Nicely, the Trent committee continued him as their engineer till he died, and his salary until the year of death was completed.

William died at Butterley on 18 November 1814, two months before his seventieth birthday. On the 22nd he was buried in Pentrich churchyard, to which on 21 December 1816 Sarah followed him. There are memorials in the church to him, to her, and their son Josias.

As we have told his life from its beginning at Devonport to its end at Pentrich, we have come to love the man. We hope that, with all its imperfections, William Jessop, Engineer, will look down from the corner of the Elysian fields where such as he are happy together, and approve our work.

PORTRAITS

There are four portraits of Jessop. The first, in the National Portrait Gallery (p 34), was drawn in 1796 by his friend George Dance.[1] Another of much the same date, in the style of Robert Hancock, is reproduced in Samuel Hughes' memoir[2] and copied in Smiles' *Lives of the Engineers*.[3] It seems also to have been used by Walker in his well known engraving *Distinguished Men of Science in Great Britain, living in 1807–8* (published 1862). The third portrait, in oils, belongs to one of Jessop's descendants[4] and is shown on p 33. Painted probably around 1805, no great structure or dock or waterway is sketched in behind him; instead, a row of leather-bound books. On the table beside him is another, with a marker in its pages, and in his hand he holds a spectacle case. The fourth was presented to the Institution of Civil Engineers by his son William in 1848. It is a copy, painted by Edwin Williams about 1845, seemingly taken from the family portrait. A reproduction can be found in Sir Alexander Gibb's book on Telford.[5]

ACKNOWLEDGEMENTS

We are indebted to far more people, and to the staffs of far more libraries and organisations, than we can possibly name here. We thank them all for the trouble they have taken over our enquiries, the patience they have shown, the material they have provided, and the local research they have done for us.

Miss Anthea Beamish (Mrs Webb) collected much of our basic material, and constructed for us a working chronology and subject index. Mrs Ruth Heard, formerly Mrs Delany, transcribed all Jessop's Irish reports for us, and has been our adviser throughout the writing of Chapter 5. Colonel P J K Warren, who with his late wife, herself a Jessop, wrote the privately-printed *The Jessop Family*, has greatly helped and encouraged us; Mr W M Hunt found for us the Banks correspondence, and Mr Guy Hemingway has made available to us the results of his researches at Newark and in the Trent area. Dr Michael Lewis and Messrs Cameron, Faulkner, Goodchild, Hemingway, James, Rattenbury, Stephens, Tew and Tyson are among those who have kindly read draft chapters or parts of chapters.

We would like to thank Mrs Dawn Bijl, Charles Hadfield's patient secretary; Miss Diana Lombard for her work in the City and Port of London Archives, and Miss Ursula Schüler for tracing many of the plans and maps. Lastly, our gratitude goes to our wives, Alice Mary and Nancy, who have accompanied us on practically all the field work and encouraged us at our desks.

In the end, of course, we alone are responsible for the final text, and any mistakes are ours. We shall be grateful to be told of any corrections, and also of any Jessop documents or references unknown to us.

We should like to thank the following for illustrations: Plates: 1, Mr Robert T. Jessop, Edinburgh; 3, National Portrait Gallery; 4 and 5, Berkshire Record Office; 6, 7, 8 and 9, Leicestershire Record Office; 10, National Library of Ireland; 11, photograph by Harry Arnold; 12, Science Museum Library; 13, Philip Weaver; 14, Institution of Civil

Engineers; 15, Young & Co's Brewery, Wandsworth; 16, Croydon Public Library; 17 and 18, Port of London Authority; 22, The Director, Science Museum. Text illustrations: 6, Humberside Record Office; 12, Public Record Office.

NOTES

Those who want more information about river navigations and canals
of the British Isles will find it in the volumes of the 'Canals of the British
Isles' series. References to this series have not therefore been given in
the notes that follow. All waterway records are in the Public Record
Office (BTHR) unless otherwise stated.

Notes to Chapter 1

1 John Smeaton, *Narrative of the Building . . . of the Edystone Lighthouse*, 1813, 30.
2 *Edinburgh Encyclopaedia*, art 'Jessop, William', *11*, August 1817.
3 We are grateful to the late Mrs M Beckford for finding William Jessop's baptismal date, and to Messrs A P Miller and G H Anthony for Elizabeth Foot's, though the latter identification is a probability only.
4 Smeaton, op cit, 45, 57.
5 *Edinburgh Encyclopaedia*, art 'Jessop, William'.
6 For Weston, see R H Weston, *Letters and Important Documents relative to the Edystone Lighthouse*, 1811.
7 J Smeaton to R Weston, 18 January 1764. Smeaton's *Letterbook* (Institution of Civil Engineers).
8 R Weston to J Smeaton, 3 July 1764, loc cit.
9 Wakefield Metropolitan District Archives, Goodchild Loan MSS.
10 *Reports of the late John Smeaton, FRS*, 1812, II, 173.
11 Leeds & Liverpool Canal, Yorkshire Committee Minute Book, 18 April 1771; General Assembly Minute Book, 19 April, 27 September 1771.
12 Smeaton, *Reports*, op cit, 1812, II, 131.
13 Aire & Calder Navigation Committee Minute Book, 29 October 1777.
14 The printed *Plan of the River Air from Haddlesey Bridge to Armin, with the Track of a proposed Canal from Haddlesey to Brier-Lane* (Newland), dated 1772, by W Jessop, Engineer, shows river locks at each end, and a single intermediate lock (BTHR/PRO RAIL 800/95/2). The printed report of 25 November 1772 is in the University of London Library.
15 Smeaton, *Reports*, op cit, II, 151, 5 December 1772.
16 *Plan of the proposed Canal from the River Air at Haddlesey to the River Ouse at Selby, by W Jessop, Engineer. ND.* (Leeds City Library). The later alteration at Selby is marked on this copy.
17 *Journal of the House of Commons*, 22 February 1774.
18 For the Grand Canal, see Ruth Delany, *The Grand Canal of Ireland*, 1973.
19 *Letters between Redmond Morres Esq and John Smeaton in 1771 and 1772 . . .*, Dublin, 1773.
20 Smeaton, *Reports*, op cit, II, 252ff.
21 Grand Canal Company Minute Book, 7 October 1773.
22 Smeaton, *Reports*, op cit, II, 278.
23 William Chapman, *Observations on the various systems of Canal Navigation*, 1797, 6.
24 For the Fusina plane, see M J T Lewis, *Early Wooden Railways*, 1970, 43–5, and A W Skempton, 'Canals and River Navigations before 1750', *A History of Technology*, 1957, III, 441n.

25 Vittorio Zonca, *Nuovo Teatro di Machine et Edifici*, 1607, 58–60. See also Plate 22 of Lewis, *Railways*, op cit.

26 An unlikelier alternative to Zonca would be Grollier de Servière, whose *Receuil d'Ouvrages Curieux* was published in 1719. Accompanying a short text, this illustrates an incline up which a wheeled carriage can transport a boat, motive power being two capstans geared to a vertical wheel taking the cable. Rails do not seem to be used, and there is no counterbalancing. The whole thing is probably imaginary.

27 Lewis, *Railways*, op cit, 289.

28 For Ketley plane, see Charles Hadfield, *British Canals*, 5th ed, 1974.

29 A W Skempton and Esther Clark Wright, 'Early Members of the Smeatonian Society of Civil Engineers', *Trans Newcomen Soc*, XLIV, 1971–2, 23–4.

30 Aire & Calder Navigation Committee Minute Book, 4 July 1774.

31 He seems to have moved to Cawthorne in the early 1760s—the parish register describes him in 1764 and 1772 as 'gardener'. He left the village after 1772, probably to become a full-time contractor, for in that year he was for the first time given the title 'Mr', the mark of a substantial man. His new home for some years was at North Cave in the East Riding. There is some information on the Pinkertons in John Pinkerton, *Abstract of the Cause just arbitrated between the Birmingham . . . Canal . . . Company . . . and John Pinkerton*, 1801, (Salt Library, Stafford).

32 A plan of the Castleford, Methley, Woodlesford, Knostrop and Leeds cuts, signed by W Jessop, is in the County Archives, Registry of Deeds, Wakefield.

33 Aire & Calder Navigation Committee Minute Book, 29 October 1777.

34 *York Courant*, 12 May 1778.

35 Aire & Calder Navigation Committee Minute Book, 18 October 1779.

36 Calder & Hebble Navigation Committee Minute Book, 20 February 1776.

37 Ibid, 15 December 1779.

38 The Aire & Calder Minute Book for 9 April 1779 refers to land at Haddlesey bought from Mr Sawyer.

39 For much information about William Jessop's family, we are indebted to *The Jessop Family*, by Joan T and P J K Warren, 1971, privately produced.

Notes to Chapter 2

1 Almost certainly not John Smith jun of Yorkshire and the Nene, but the John Smith, born c1746, who was based at Burton-on-Trent between 1771 and 1775, and at Packington, Leics, from 1780 to 1803. He died in 1820.

2 Loughborough Navigation Minute Book, 24 September 1777.

3 It is copied verbatim into the Loughborough Company's Minute Book for 15 December 1777.

4 Chester Canal Minute Book, 22 January 1779 and subsequent entries.

5 For the story, see Dudley Canal Minute Books between 26 September 1785 and 20 July 1787.

6 Lords committee, 9 May 1793.

7 *Nottingham Journal*, 5 February 1791.

8 There are references in the *Newark Herald*, 2 January 1793, Eden's *State of the Poor*, 1797, Dickinson's *History of Newark*, 1820, Shilton's *History of Newark*, 1820, and Pigot's *Directory of Notts*, 1822. The last three seem to derive from Eden. In 1795 the firm was known as Sketchley, Handley, Jessop & Marshall: Samuel Sketchley was mayor of Newark in 1778, 1791 and 1804; William Handley a Newark banker and brewer, both being Trent committee-men and Cromford Canal shareholders. Richard Marshall was probably a connection of William Handley's wife, and another Newark resident.

9 Wakefield Metropolitan District Archives, Goodchild Loan MSS.

10 *Leicester Journal*, 27 May 1780.

11 Ibid, 17 June 1780.

12 *Observations on the Present State of the River Trent*, ND (BTHR/PRO).

13 *Report of William Jessop, Engineer, on a Survey of the River Trent, in the Months of August and September, 1782, relative to a Scheme for Improving its Navigation* (BTHR/PRO).

14 Trent Navigation Minute Book, 24 June 1783.

15 Ibid, 7 October 1783.

16 Ibid, 7 September 1784.

17 Staffordshire & Worcestershire Canal Minute Book, 20 April 1784.

18 Newark, 10 August 1784 (ICE Library, Telford Collection).

19 Bewdley, 30 October 1784 (loc cit).

20 J Plymley, *A General View of the Agriculture of Shropshire*, 1813, art on 'Canals', 1797, 287.

21 Newark, 30 January 1786 (Staffordshire RO, D.260/M/E/430/29).

22 *Plan of the River Severn from the Meadow Wharf near Coalbrookdale to the City of Gloucester*, 1786. (Waterways Museum, Stoke Bruerne).

23 JHC, 6 February 1788.

24 A North of England waggonway, usually with wooden rails.

25 *Leicester Journal*, 5 November 1785.

26 There are three reports in the Loveden papers, Berkshire RO (D/ELV/153); Whitworth's of 7 January 1786, Jessop's from Newark of 12 January, and a joint one of 20 January. That Jessop signed the last one above Whitworth suggests that he was the principal employed.

27 *A Plan of the intended Canal & River Navigation from Thrinkston Bridge to Leicester, shewing its communications with the River Wreak to Melton . . .* Surveyed in 1785. Unsigned. (Leicester RO).

28 The Bridge Act is 27 Geo III c 15.

29 *Edinburgh Encyclopaedia*, art 'Jessop, William', 11, August 1817.

30 The Thames Commissioners' Minute Book, 20 May 1786, contains Jessop's own MS report and drawing (Berkshire RO).

31 Oxfordshire RO W1 VII/4.

32 Ibid.

33 It is transcribed in the Thames Commissioners' Minute Book in the Port of London Authority archives.

34 *The Report of William Jessop Engineer on the State of the Navigation . . . between Oxford and Lechlade; and on the Means of obtaining a depth of Water of three Feet Six Inches . . . from a Survey taken in July and August*

1789. Mr. Jessop's Second Report (ICE Library).

35 *Estimate of the Expence of making Navigable the River Ouse, from Lewes into Barcomb Mill-Pond*... (East Sussex RO).

36 Letter, WJ to Lord Sheffield, ND (East Sussex RO).

37 Letter, WJ to Lord Sheffield, 23 October 1790 (loc cit).

38 Letter, WJ to Lord Sheffield, 6 December 1791 (loc cit).

39 Letter, WJ to Lord Sheffield, 3 September 1792 (loc cit).

Notes to Chapter 3

1 *Report of Mr Jessop, Engineer, on a Design for a Canal, from Langley Bridge to Cromford*..., Newark, December 13, 1788, *Derby Mercury*, 18 December 1788. A printed original is in the Sutro-Banks papers, University of San Francisco (xeroxes in the Natural History Museum Library).

2 Cromford Canal Minute Book, 4 November 1789.

3 Ibid, 10 December 1793.

4 For a detailed and comprehensive early history of the firm, see Philip Riden, *The Butterley Company 1790–1830*, (Wingerworth, 1973).

5 A W Skempton, 'A history of the steam dredger, 1797–1830', *Trans Newcomen Soc*, 47 (1975).

8 Evidence by William Jessop in *Report of the Trial ... at the Instance of James Neilson against William Baird for the Infringement of the Hot Blast Patent*, Edinburgh, 1843.

7 Trent Navigation Minute Book, 21 July 1789.

8 Letter, WJ to Job Brough, London 13 March 1790, Trent papers, Nottingham University Archives.

9 Trent Navigation Minute Book, 4 May 1790.

10 Ibid, 7 September 1790.

11 A copy is in the Waterways Museum, Stoke Bruerne. It mainly considers whether a 4ft deep navigation, perhaps with up to seventeen locks as well as the two existing at Newark, at a cost of some £70,000, would pay for itself. Jessop is dubious whether it would.

12 *Observations respecting the State of the River Trent Navigation and the proposed Canal from Shardlow to Nottingham*. Survey by John Smith on 17–19 July 1792 (BTHR/PRO).

13 Trent Navigation Minute Book, 8 February 1793.

14 *To the Company of Proprietors of the Trent Navigation*, Nottingham, 8 July 1793, printed (BTHR/PRO RAIL 879/2).

15 Trent Navigation Minute Book, 5 August 1793.

16 Trent papers, Nottingham University Archives.

17 *Leicester & Nottingham Journal*, 16 July 1790.

18 *A Plan of the intended Navigation from Loughborough to Leicester ... Survey'd in 1790 by Chrisr Staveley Junr, Willm Jessop Engr.* (BM c.10.c.24(30)).

19 JHC, 11 February 1791.

20 Leicester Navigation Minute Book, 29 August 1792.

21 Giving evidence before the Lords committee on 11 April 1797, Staveley

said it was 'nearly completed'.

22 The plan listed in note 18 above also includes 'the intended Navigation from the Leicester Navigation to Melton Mowbray'.

23 *Lincoln & Stamford Mercury*, 7 September 1792. *A Plan of the intended Navigation from Melton Mowbray . . . to Oakham, Wm Jessop Engineer. Survey'd in 1792 by C. Staveley Junr*, (BM c.10.c.24(31)).

24 *Mr Jessop's Observations as to ye manner of making the canal*, MS, Dunn papers, MD 1739.37/1747.10 (Sheffield PL).

25 Nottingham Canal Minute Book, 19 November 1790.

26 Rees, *Cyclopaedia*, art 'Canal'.

27 For the Nutbrook Canal, see Peter Stevenson, *The Nutbrook Canal*, 1970.

28 Nutbrook Canal Papers, Derbyshire RO.

29 *Mr Jessop's Report on the several Lines of the intended Derby Canals*, Newark, 3 November 1792, printed (Nottingham University Library).

30 Drury-Lowe papers, DE 63–68, Nottingham University Library.

31 See V I Tomlinson, 'Early Warehouses on Manchester Waterways', *Trans Lancs & Cheshire Antiq. Soc.*, Vol 71, 1961.

32 Michael Handford, *The Stroudwater Canal, 1729–1763*, 1976.

33 J Farey, *A General View of the Agriculture and Minerals of Derbyshire*, III, 295–6.

34 Ashby Canal Minute Book, 8 November 1792.

35 Ibid, 10 June 1793.

36 Dated from Ashby, 14 June 1793, it is in BTHR/PRO.

37 Warwickshire RO. Later engraved as *A Plan of the Ashby de la Zouch Canal with the Cuts or Branches therefrom. R. Whitworth, W. Jessop Engineers. J. Smith Surveyor 1794* (BM. c.10.c.24 (1)).

38 Commons committee, 25 February, Lords committee 28 March 1793.

39 It was published in W Pitt, *A General View of the Agriculture of Stafford*, 1794, rpt 1796.

40 Samuel Hughes, 'Memoir of William Jessop', *Weale's Quarterly Papers on Engineering*, I, 1844.

41 *Report of W. Jessop, Engineer, on the means of making a compleat Navigable Communication between the Witham and the Fosdike in Lincoln*, ND (1791), printed (BM).

42 *The Report of William Jessop, Engineer, on the Practicability of Widening and Deepening the Communication between the River Witham and the Fosdike Canal . . .*, London 29 February 1792, printed (Bodleian Library, MS D D Dashwood E 2/10). We are grateful to Sir Francis Dashwood for permission to use this item).

43 *To the Commissioners of the Witham Navigation*, Newark, 20 June 1793, printed (Scottish RO, GD 51/15/19).

44 *To the worshipful the Mayor and Corporation of the City of Lincoln*, Lincoln, April 26 1808, printed, Sutro-Banks papers, University of San Francisco (xeroxes in Natural History Museum Library). Extracts were published in the *Lincoln & Stamford Mercury* for 6 May 1808.

45 Witham Drainage Commissioners Minute Book, 5 July 1774 (Lincolnshire RO).

46 *Report on the means and expence, of making navigable the Kyme Eau and River Slea from the Witham to Castle Causeway, above the Town of*

Sleaford, 25 November 1791, printed (B.S.14/1/2, Spalding Gentlemen's Society).

47 *The Report of W. Jessop, Engineer, on the Practicability and Expence of making a Navigable Communication between the River Witham, and the Town of Horncastle*, 1791, printed (Sheffield PL).

48 Letter, WJ to Sir Joseph Banks, Bristol, 1 November 1793 (loc cit).

49 Spalding Gentlemen's Society, loc cit.

Notes to Chapter 4

1 Plan taken from the map of Norfolk published in 1797 by William Faden.

2 Norfolk Court of Sewers, 5 January 1785.

3 Ibid, 22 November 1785.

4 Letters from Robert Whincop to Watt, 5 August and 24 August 1790 (B & W. Box 4 W) and 19 October 1790 (B & W. Box 5 VI).

5 Letters on Marshland Drainage from Watt to Whincop, 8 August and 28 August 1790; and to Jessop, 3 November and 21 December 1790 (B & W. Office Letter Book 14).

6 Jessop's reports on the drainage of the Country of Marshland, Norfolk, (a) to HM Commissioners of Sewers. Lynn, 12 October 1790; (b) to the committee. Newark, 27 December 1790. (MS copies, Northants RO (Smith Collection).

7 Letters from Jessop to Watt, 15 October and 6 December 1790 (B & W. Box 4 J).

8 Correspondence between Robert Wild and James Watt on Middle Fen Drainage 1788–9 (B & W. Box 4 W, and Office Letter Book 14).

9 Jessop was assisted by William Walton of King's Lynn. (Court of Sewers, 9 February 1791).

10 These figures apply where the lift is 7 or 8ft and are therefore comparable to Jessop's scheme for Marshland Fen drainage. The data are given by Joseph Glynn, 'Draining land by steam power' *Trans. Soc. Arts. 51* (1836) 3–24, and R L Hills, *A Short History of the Drainage of the Fens* (Norwich, 1967).

11 G. McLeod, 'Recent land drainage pumping stations' *Journ Inst Water Eng 4* (1950) 469–80.

12 Rennie's report to the Proprietors of Estates in Marshland, 29 January 1793 (BM 1474. d.4 and Northants CRO Smith Collection).

13 Jessop's evidence on the Eau Brink Bill, 26 February 1795, in *Second Report from the Committee* (Parliamentary Reports, Vol 15).

14 R B Grantham, 'On arterial drainage' *Min Proc Inst CE 19* (1859) 53–85. He gives the total cost of the Eau Brink Cut as £600,000.

15 The main source of information on Holderness Drainage is provided by the Minute Books of the Trustees 1764–1832 (Humberside RO).

16 *The Report of John Grundy ... concerning the Drainage of the Low Grounds and Carrs ... in Holderness*, 30 December 1763 (Hull, 1764).

17 The Award is dated 13 May 1775. A printed copy (H.R.O. DCHO 6/1) was published by Anthony Bower in 1781.

18 *Observations on the Drainage of certain Low Grounds on the east side of*

the *River Hull*. By 'A Friend of the Undertaking'. Printed May 1786 (H.R.O. DDIV 29/6).

19 Holderness Minutes, 13 May 1786.

20 *Report of William Jessop, Engineer, on the State of Drainage of the Low Grounds and Carrs ... in Holderness ... and the Means of compleating the same*, Newark, 17 July 1786 (Hull, 1786).

21 An inverted syphon taking a drain under a stream or another drain is known as a 'fox' or 'tunnel', though sometimes the term 'culvert' was also applied.

22 Holderness Minutes, 13 June 1787.

23 Holderness Minutes, 13 April 1791.

24 Reports by Smeaton on Lewes Laughton Level (1768), Thomas Tofield on Deeping Fen (1768), George Kelk on Everton Drainage (1773) and James Creassy on the Fens (1777).

25 East Riding Court of Sewers, 9 May 1787.

26 *Report of W. Jessop, Engineer, on a Survey of the River Hull ... to near Stone Ferry*. Newark, 11 November 1787 (Hull, 1787); MS Report on River Hull. Newark, 11 February 1788; *Report of William Jessop, Engineer, on a survey of the River Hull ... to Ayke Bridge* Newark, 3 July 1788 (Hull, 1788). (Hull University Library DDSY 103/11, 12 and 13).

27 East Riding Court of Sewers, 1 November 1788.

28 Bower's report and estimate for this work are given in Holderness Minutes 9 February 1793. The Trustees record their satisfaction in the completion of the scheme in July 1795.

29 H E Strickland, *A General View of the Agriculture of the East Riding* (York, 1812). Further information on costs is given in the Holderness Drainage Account Book 1781–1832.

30 Holderness Minutes, 13 May 1797; and Jessop's report *To the Committee of the Driffield Navigation Commissioners ...* Driffield, 23 April 1797 (Hull, 1797).

31 See Chapter 12.

32 *Report to the Commissioners of the Beverley and Barmston Drainage*. By Jessop, Rennie and Chapman. Beverley, 30 November 1804 (Hull, 1804).

33 Jessop's report on Dalton's scheme is transcribed in Holderness Minutes, 21 December 1805.

34 *The Report of Mr Edward Page upon the better drainage of the Lands within ... Holderness Drainage*, 3 May 1831 (Beverley, 1831).

35 MS. 'Report to the Commissioners ... for Inclosing, Draining and Improving the Commons and Waste Ground within the several parishes of Epworth, Haxey, Belton and Owston in the Isle of Axholme.' By W Jessop and Joseph Hodskinson. Epworth, 12 October 1795 (Nottingham University Library. HCC 6169).

36 An outline of the complex history of draining Hatfield Chase and Misson Level can be found in George Dunston *The Rivers of Axholme* (London, 1909).

37 Plans of Drains and Banks of the Level of Hatfield Chase, 1801 (Nottingham University Library HCC 9047).

38 Isle Commons Drainage Commissioners' Award (1803). This and the Haxey Minutes are in the Epworth office of the Axholme and Butterwick

Drainage Boards. Mr G R Haywood, Clerk of the Boards, kindly allowed us to examine these records and various maps.

39 Copy of a map of the Isle of Axholme annexed to the Commissioners' Award (Nottingham University Library, HCC 9049).

40 W Peck, *A Topographical Account of the Isle of Axholme* (Doncaster, 1815).

41 George Dunston op cit.

42 MS. 'Report of John Smeaton Engineer upon the Case of Misterton Soss and Snow Sewer Drain belonging to the Honble the Participants of Hatfield Chase from a view taken thereof August 14th 1764' (Nottingham University Library, HCC 6164).

43 MS. 'A Scheme for Embanking, Draining and Preserving the Low Grounds in Scaftworth, Everton, Gringley, Misterton and Stockwith in the County of Nottingham, by George Kelk 1773'. (Notts CRO, DD 2P 25/7).

44 A brief description of the drainage is given by Richard Dixon, engineer to the Chesterfield Canal, in a MS report dated 11 September 1790 (Notts RO, DD 2P 25/9). The same archives (2P 25/10–12) contain 'Instructions for Mr Dyson to make an Estimate of a Drain from the River Bycar Dike below the Soss westward into Gringley Car and a Sluice opposite to the Soss' and a copy of the estimate itself.

45 The Drainage Act is 36 Geo III, c.99.

46 Everton Drainage Commissioners' Minute Books (June 1796 to the present day). The following account of the drainage works, and of various meetings, etc, is based on these books. We are indebted to Mr J A Walker of Bawtry, Clerk to the Everton Internal Drainage Board, for permission to examine them and other documents in his keeping.

47 Magnus Charity papers 11/1–49, calendared by Notts RO.

48 Drainage Commissioners' Award (Notts RO. QDU 1/1).

49 John Rennie's notebook No 59, entry for 27 November 1804 (National Library of Scotland).

50 Letter from Jessop, Newark 8 June 1801, to E S Godfrey (Magnus Charity papers 11/37).

51 Joseph Glynn, loc cit.

52 Michael Williams *The Draining of the Somerset Levels* (Cambridge, 1970).

53 John Billingsley *General View of the Agriculture of the County of Somerset* (Bath, 1797). This includes a plan for improved drainage in the Axe and Brue valleys drawn by White in 1794. Billingsley had earlier been associated with White, and Jessop, on the King's Sedgemoor scheme: see Chapter 12.

54 Except for the South Drain of the Brue system.

55 JHC, 3 June 1801 and 15 April 1802.

56 Details of the Brue Drainage are taken from the Commissioners' Proceedings 1801–7 (Somerset Record Office). See also the map (Fig 20) in Williams op cit.

57 Eventually, in 1940, the 5 mile Huntspill Cut provided the South Drain with an independent outfall. The cost of this would have been prohibitive in the original scheme.

58 Brue Drainage Award, with a large-scale map by White (SRO).

59 Accounts of the Brue Drainage Commissioners (SRO).

60 Progress of the Axe Drainage works can be traced from letters and the Clerk's expense accounts (A.D.2 and A.D.4 in SRO).

61 At Hobb's Boat near Bleadon, as suggested by Billingsley op cit. Other locations had been proposed in reports by Josiah Easton (1800) and John Sutcliffe (1801), see Williams op cit.

62 Letter-report by Robert Anstice, Bridgwater 18 May 1805 (A.D.2, SRO).

63 Summary of Accounts of the Axe Drainage Commissioners (A.D.4, SRO).

Notes to Chapter 5

1 For the Grand Canal, see V T H & D R Delany, *The Canals of the South of Ireland*, 1966, and Ruth Delany, *The Grand Canal of Ireland*, 1973. Except where noted, all reports and letters referred to in this chapter are transcribed into the Minute Books of the Grand Canal Company; these are in the custody of the Coras Iompair Eireann at Heuston Station, Dublin.

2 *Reports of the late John Smeaton, FRS*, Vol 2 (1812) 247–77.

3 For the Barrow Navigation, see Delany, *South of Ireland*, op cit.

4 The *Leicester Journal*, 16 July 1785, says that a survey is to be made for the proposed Leicester Navigation, but this will be delayed because its engineer, Jessop, has gone to Ireland.

5 Grand Canal Minute Book, Vol 7, 23 December, 1789.

6 Smeaton, *Reports*, op cit, 266–7.

7 For the Royal Canal, see Delany, *South of Ireland*, op cit.

8 Jessop's report, Newark, 26 July 1790.

9 Bernard Mullins and M B Mullins, 'On the origin and reclamation of peat bog'. *Trans Inst Civ Eng Ireland*, Vol 2 (1846) 1–48.

10 Jessop's report, Tullamore, 15 November 1801.

11 Grand Canal Minute Book, Vol 22, 23 March 1802.

12 Jessop's report, Dublin, 19 September 1794.

13 Letters from Jessop to Boulton & Watt, Dublin, 23 July, 6 and 10 August, 1791 (Boulton & Watt Collection, Box 6 'D', Birmingham Library).

14 The sketch (PRO RAIL 844/19/8) came into possession of William Cartwright of the Lancaster Canal, probably via Archibald Millar. It is reproduced by permission of the Public Record Office.

15 Jessop's report, Dublin, 25 June 1792.

16 Jessop's report, Dublin, 14 July 1792.

17 Letter from Archibald Millar, 6 October 1792, to Boulton & Watt (Box 6 'D', Birmingham Library).

18 In fact, it was to run south of the Brosna to its eventual termination at Shannon Harbour, near Banagher. No northern branch was built.

19 Not until after 1827 was this done, or the aqueduct built.

20 Letter from William Chapman, Dublin, 17 August 1793 to Matthew Boulton (Boulton correspondence, Birmingham Library).

21 Irish Parliamentary Papers. 13 March 1794. Jessop's report is dated Dublin, 17 August 1793.

22 Hull University Library, Sykes Papers.

23 Three reports by Jessop, all dated Dublin, 19 September 1794.

24 The engine, purchased in May 1794, had a 16in cylinder.
25 For the Shannon Navigation, see Delany, *South of Ireland* op cit and V T H Delany, 'The development of the River Shannon Navigation', *Journ. Transport History*, November 1958.
26 Information from Mr Patrick Flanagan.
27 Grand Canal Minute Book, Vol 11, 19 September 1794.
28 Letter from Jessop, Newark, 16 January 1796.
29 Grand Canal Minute Book, Vol 13, 20 September 1796.
30 Jessop's report, Dublin, 16 September 1796.
31 Grand Canal Minute Book, Vol 13, 4 May 1796.
32 Letter from Jessop, Newark, 24 November 1796.
33 Letter from Richard Griffith, 11 November 1797, to William Jessop.
34 Reply from Jessop, Newark, 30 November 1797, to Griffith.
35 Jessop's report, Dublin, 27 December 1797, preceded by a letter written from Philipstown, 11 December.
36 Mullins, loc cit.
37 The Report of William Jessop, Civil Engineer, respecting the Practicability and Expence of making a Harbour for large vessels at Dunleary, to communicate with the new Docks by means of a Canal, Dublin 29 April 1800. Printed in *Facts and Arguments respecting the Great Utility of an Extensive Plan of Inland Navigation in Ireland* (Dublin, 1800).
38 Letter from Jessop, Newark, 15 August 1800.
39 Mullins, loc cit.
40 Jessop's report, Dublin, 26 December 1797, and two sets of queries and answers also written in Dublin, 4 and 8 January 1798.
41 Letter from Jessop, Tullamore, 15 November 1801, with a postscript dated 17 November.
42 Jessop's report, Dublin, 1 December 1801.
43 Rhodes' report, 24 April 1802.
44 Jessop's report, London, 4 June 1802.
45 Jessop's report, Dublin, 4 February 1806.
46 *The Jessop Family*, op cit.

Notes to Chapter 6

1 For background, see Alan H Faulkner, *The Grand Junction Canal*, 1972.
2 Grand Junction Canal Minute Book, 15 November 1797.
3 *To the Committee of the Subscribers to the Grand Junction Canal*, Northampton, 24 October 1792, printed (BM).
4 Presumably Jonathan Woodhouse, who in 1802 supplied an engine for Tring summit, and Matthew Boulton of Boulton & Watt.
5 Grand Junction Canal Minute Book, 3 June 1793.
6 Ibid, 16 December 1793.
7 Ibid, and Lower District Committee Minute Book, 24 June, 21 November, 16 December 1793.
8 Jessop had realised by May 1794 how leaky the Wendover branch through the chalk was likely to be when he wrote in his report of the 24th: '. . . what is done will be gradually tried with Water, for much of the ground in this

line is very leaky, and must be lined with Earth, and be saturated with muddy Water'.

9 Report of 18 May 1794, Lower District Committee Minute Book, 20 May. This formed the basis of his report of 24 May to the General Committee, which was printed and circulated to shareholders (Northants RO).

10 Lower District Committee Minute Book, 20 May 1794.

11 Ibid.

12 Ibid, 11 August 1795.

13 Grand Junction Canal Minute Book, 1 June 1795.

14 Ibid, 24 June 1795. Letter transcribed in full.

15 Letter from James Barnes to John Clark, *quo* bookseller David Bickersteth's catalogue No 32.

16 Grand Junction Canal Minute Book, general assembly, 7 June 1797.

17 See Rennie and Whitworth's report of 7 May 1796, Rennie's *Notebooks* I 363ff, and Barnes's report, ibid, I 346 (ICE Library).

18 Rennie's *Notebooks*, I 340 (loc cit).

19 WJ to Boulton & Watt, 25 January 1796 (Boulton & Watt Collection, Birmingham PL Archives Dept).

20 Rennie's *Notebooks*, I 342 (loc cit).

21 Report, 3 February 1796, ibid, I 346 (loc cit).

22 Report, 6 February 1796, ibid, I 353 (loc cit).

23 Rennie's *Notebooks*, I 363 (loc cit).

24 Grand Junction Canal Minute Book, 5 July 1797.

25 Lower District Committee Minute Book, 15 November 1796.

26 Grand Junction Canal Minute Book, 15 March 1797.

27 Ibid, 13 September 1797.

28 Ibid, 10 January 1798.

29 Ibid, 12 September 1798.

30 Ibid, 9 January 1799.

31 Ibid, 22 February 1799.

32 Ibid, 13 March 1799.

33 Report dated London, 14 April 1800, transcribed in full in BTHR/PRO RAIL 830/40, 174–7.

34 The water supply project was eventually implemented by the Grand Junction Water Works Company, with Rennie as engineer, from 1811 onwards. See H W Dickinson, *Water Supply of Greater London*, 1954, 98–101.

35 Grand Junction Canal Minute Book, 3 November 1801.

36 Ibid, 28 November 1801.

37 The specification is dated 1 May 1802. It was presented to the committee on 6 May and is transcribed, with Jessop's covering letter to Praed, in the Minute Book.

38 Report of 6 December 1802, transcribed in Minute Book for 13 December 1802.

39 Grand Junction Canal Minute Book, 31 October 1801.

40 Ibid, 11 February 1802.

41 A Rees, *Cyclopaedia*, 1819, art 'Canal', and Faulkner, *Grand Junction Canal*, op cit.

42 Report of 2 June 1802, transcribed in full in the minute book for 8 June 1802.

43 Samuel Smiles, *Lives of the Engineers*, 1862, II, 147.

44 Rochdale Canal Minute Book, 7 April 1791 (Rochdale Canal Co, Manchester).

45 Ibid, 9 December 1793.

46 Ibid, 30 December 1793.

47 The account is taken from Rennie's *Notebooks*, volume on the Rochdale Canal (ICE Library).

48 Rochdale Canal Co's records.

49 Royal Commission on Canals and Waterways, IV, 1908.

50 It was in fact 38ft at greatest depth.

51 A mile south of Chadderton towards Failsworth.

52 Dean head was where the summit tunnel had been intended.

53 L T C Rolt, *Navigable Waterways*, 1969, 59. See also Ruth Delany, *The Grand Canal of Ireland*, 1973, 60–1, and A Rees, *Cyclopaedia*, 1820, under 'Oblique Bridges'.

54 Being lower than Grand Canal bridges and without towpaths, the bridges of the County of Kildare Canal were replaced when the Grand Canal took it over in 1808.

55 Quoted in the company's report for the shareholders' meeting of 5 May 1796 (Rochdale PL).

56 *Third Report, to the Chairman of the Committee of the Rochdale Canal*, Manchester, 19 April 1797 (Manchester PL, Archives Dept, M84/2/2/3).

57 Rochdale PL.

58 Aire & Calder Navigation Minute Book, 20 September 1792.

59 *A Plan of the Intended Navigable Canal from the River Calder near Heath Hill . . . to Barnby Bridge*, 1792 (Jessop, Gott and Wright) (BM: c.25 d.2 (92)).

60 Barnsley Canal Minute Book, 12 June 1794.

61 Ibid, 28 July 1798.

62 Pinkerton v Barnsley Canal Co at the Rolls. In Chancery 4 March 1805 (Wakefield Metropolitan District Archives, Goodchild Loan MSS).

Notes to Chapter 7

1 Joseph Turner, *A Description of the Intended Canal from Shrewsbury to Chester and Liverpool* (1791) (Wirral Central Library, Birkenhead).

2 Ellesmere Canal Proprietors' Minute Book, 7 November 1791.

3 Ibid, 9 January 1792.

4 Ibid, 23 August 1792.

5 As transcribed in the minute book, the report reads '970 yards'. This seems to us likely to be a mistranscription for '970 feet'. Unfortunately, no other copy of this report is known.

6 For Telford, see Sir Alexander Gibb, *The Story of Telford*, 1935, and L T C Rolt, *Thomas Telford*, 1958.

7 Ellesmere Canal Committee Minute Book, 23 September 1793.

8 Six different drawings for both broad and narrow locks on the Ellesmere

Canal survive; five in the Waterways Museum at Stoke Bruerne, one in private hands. All are in similar style. Three, clearly originals, are signed W Jessop 1794 (one of these is reproduced on p 102); the others, presumably copies, are unsigned.

9 *Aris's Birmingham Gazette*, 7 April 1794.

10 William Reynolds's Sketch Book (Science Museum Library). A collection of engineering drawings by various hands, dating mostly from 1793 to 1796, mounted in a modern folio. Duncombe's drawing is No 1, and Telford's No 110.

11 *Eddowes' Salopian Journal*, 29 July 1795.

12 Letter from Telford to Davidson, 9 October 1796 (Gibbs Collection, Box 60 (6), ICE Library).

13 MS report dated Shrewsbury, 14 July 1795 (Shrewsbury County Library, Deed No 15025).

14 Shrewsbury Canal Minute Book, 14 March 1795. For details of the Longdon aqueduct and other iron structures of this period see R A Paxton, *The Influence of Thomas Telford on the Use of Improved Constructional Materials*, MSc thesis, Heriot-Watt University (ICE Library).

15 *Shrewsbury Chronicle*, 17 April 1795.

16 Peak Forest Canal Minute Book, 22 April 1795.

17 Ibid, 23 April 1795.

18 R Fulton, *A Treatise on the Improvement of Canal Navigation*, 1796, vii and 10.

19 List of drawings in the Telford collection (ICE Library).

20 This letter has survived by a fortunate chance among the correspondence from Telford to Matthew Davidson. A transcript is in the Gibbs collection, Box 80 (6), ICE Library, and we are indebted to Sir Angus Paton for a photocopy of the original. Rolt in his *Telford* erroneously dates it 26 June.

21 A rough copy of this report is in the County Library, Shrewsbury, Deed No 15031.

22 Report of 21 October 1795, (loc cit).

23 Gibb Collection, Box 80(6), ICE Library.

24 Ibid, Box 73 (3). Estimates for Chirk aqueduct.

25 County Library, Shrewsbury, Deed No 15036.

26 Report of 24 January 1800, printed, loc cit, Deed No 15037.

27 The estate was leased to William Hazledine until 1820 (*Salopian Journal*, 6 January 1813). If the lease were for twenty-one years, this suggests its beginning in 1799. If so, it ties in with the resumption of work on the aqueduct in late 1799, for now a local source for the ironwork and skilled men to erect it were available.

28 Gibb Collection, Box 73(3), ICE Library.

29 Jessop had railways much in mind at this time—he was just starting to build the Surrey Iron Railway.

30 County Library, Shrewsbury.

31 *Report to the General Assembly of the Ellesmere Canal Proprietors . . . to which is annexed, The Oration, delivered at Pontcysylte Aqueduct, on its first opening, November 26, 1805.*

32 Ed J Rickman, *Life of Thomas Telford, Civil Engineer, written by himself . . . 1838*, 33ff.

33 A report by the committee, printed with the oration, gives interesting figures of costs and fees: total expenditure to December 1805, £459,000; cost of Pontcysyllte, £47,000; payments to Jessop, £1,104; Telford, £3,640; Duncombe, £4,402; Denson, £1,782; William Turner, £763.

34 For the Caledonian Canal, see A D Cameron, *The Caledonian Canal*, 1972.

35 Appendix to *Third Report from the Committee on the Survey of the Coasts, etc. of Scotland*, JHC, Vol 58, Pt II, 1007.

36 *A Survey and Report of the Coasts and Central Highlands of Scotland, Made . . . in the Autumn of 1802, by Thomas Telford, Civil Engineer, Edin. F.R.S.*, 15 March 1803.

37 Jessop's is Appendix 4 to the *Third Report*, op cit, 1014.

38 *First Report of the Commissioners for the Caledonian Canal*, 28 March 1804.

39 Letter, WJ to the Rt Hon the Speaker of the House of Commons, Newark, 9 August 1803 (Scottish RO, M.T.I/1/3).

40 Letter, TT to John Rickman, 27 September 1803 (loc cit, M.T.I/1/22).

41 Letter, WJ to the Commissioners, Newark, 29 September 1803 (loc cit, M.T.I./1/26).

42 Loc cit, M.T.I/1/174.

43 Loc cit, M.T.I/1/46.

44 Loc cit, M.T.I/1/55.

45 *Report on the intended Inland Navigation from the Eastern to the Western sea, by Inverness and Fort William; including Estimate of the Expence of completing the same. By William Jessop, Engineer*. Appendix C of the *First Report*, op cit.

46 Scottish RO, M.T.I/1/174.

47 Loc cit, M.T.I/1/72.

48 Letter of 9 June 1804 to Telford. Appendix D of *Second Report*.

49 Scottish RO, M.T.I/1/203.

50 In draft form, loc cit, M.T.I/1/174. In final form, Appendix B of the *Second Report*.

51 Caledonian Canal MSS 626.9 (412.1), ICE Library.

52 'Instructions from Mr Wm Jessop Civil Engineer to Mr John Telford, for marking out the Caledonian Canal 1804', loc cit.

53 Institution of Civil Engineers, Easton Gibb Collection. The river Loy passes under the canal near Banavie.

54 Scottish RO, M.T.I/1/99.

55 1,000yd of railway from Bersham, 2 miles from Butterley, ½ mile from Aberdeen.

56 Scottish RO, M.T.I/1/113.

57 Loc cit, M.T.I/1/160.

58 Loc cit, M.T.I/1/162.

59 The list of drawings once owned by Telford, in the ICE Library, includes: 'Plan and Elevation of a Swing Bridge for the Caledonian Canal. By W. Jessop'. It cannot now be found.

60 The above from the *Third Report of the Commissioners*, 23 May 1806.

61 October 1806, Appendix C to the *Fourth Report*.

62 Clachnaharry, 14 November 1808. Appendix C of the *Sixth Report*.

63 Scottish RO, M.T.I/1/174.

64 Inverness, 18 October 1809, Appendices B and C of *Seventh Report*.

65 Estimate dated 18 October 1809 from Inverness, signed by both engineers. Scottish RO, M.T.I/1/203.

66 Appendix B to the *Eighth Report*.

67 Scottish RO, M.T.I/1/203.

68 Appendix C to *Ninth Report*.

69 Scottish RO, M.T.I/4/151.

70 Loc cit, M.T.I/5/96.

71 Loc cit, M.T.I/5/102.

72 In their October 1811 report, Jessop and Telford referred to Banavie locks as '*Neptune's Staircase*, if we may be permitted to use the appellation applied by the Workmen to the Chain of Locks on Corpach Moss'.

73 Samuel Hughes, 'Memoir of William Jessop'. Weale's *Quarterly Papers on Engineering, 1*, 1844.

74 'Report of William Jessop, Esq., Civil Engineer, on the Extension of the Pier at Ardorssan', 18 July 1808. Printed in *Second Report of the Commissioners on Tidal Harbours*, Parl. Papers 1847 *32*, 523.

75 Report on Aberdeen Harbour, by W Jessop and Thomas Telford. Edinburgh 14 October 1805 (Aberdeen Town House Library. Transcripts of papers on the harbour in this archive are in the Gibb Collection 80/3, ICE Library).

76 Three drawings by W Jessop, dated 1806 (formerly in the Telford Collection, ICE Library).

77 'Estimate by Messrs Telford and Jessop of the Expense of executing their Plan of Improvements for the Harbour of Aberdeen'. London 7 April 1810. Printed in *Reports upon the Harbour of Aberdeen* (Aberdeen, 1834).

78 Letter from Jessop and Telford, Aberdeen 10 October 1810 (Town House library). Their drawing of the North Pier section, signed and dated 1810, is in the Rennie collection (National Library of Scotland, Box 8, F 1).

79 Report by Jessop and Telford, Aberdeen 14 October 1811. Printed in *Minutes of Evidence taken before the Committee of the House of Commons on the Aberdeen Harbour Bill* (Aberdeen, 1828) pp 4–5.

80 Report by Jessop and Telford, Aberdeen 10 November 1812 (Town House Library).

Notes to Chapter 8

1 Leicester Navigation Minute Books; entries from 11 April 1793 to 16 May 1794, and 7 October 1796.

2 Robert Abbot, 'The railways of the Leicester Navigation Company', *Trans Leics Arch & Hist Soc 31* (1955), 51–61.

3 C F Dendy Marshall, *A History of British Railways down to the year 1830* (Oxford, 1938).

4 Charles E Lee, *The Evolution of Railways* (London, 1943).

5 M J T Lewis, *Early Wooden Railways* (London, 1970).

6 Lewis (p298) estimates that at least 200 miles of wooden railways were in use by 1775, virtually all with edge-rails.

7 Lewis (pp260–6). The iron strips on wooden rails at Coalbrookdale were

roughly 4in wide by $1\frac{1}{2}$in thick.

8 The iron rails had a top width of $2\frac{1}{2}$in, bottom width 3in and were nearly 2in thick. Letter from William Tait 17 March 1791. Madeleine Elsas *Iron in the Making: Dowlais Iron Company Letters* (Cardiff, 1960), 171.

9 Monmouthshire Canal Committee Minutes, 7 August 1792. Payments for rails are entered on 30 April and 28 May 1793.

10 John Farey *General View of the Agriculture and Minerals of Derbyshire* Vol 3 (London, 1817), 376–80.

11 Letter from William Jessop junior, Butterley, 9 June 1821, to Jeremiah Cairns relating to rails for the Stockton & Darlington line: quoted by Madeleine Elsas (op cit), 172.

12 Robert Stevenson, editorial notes on railways in *Prize Essays and Transactions of the Highland Society of Scotland* Vol 6 (Edinburgh 1824), 131–2.

13 Leicester Navigation Minutes. 12 November 1819, the rails have been taken up. 4 July 1825, about 25 tons have been sold at 10 guineas per ton and about 200 tons remain unsold. 2 July 1832, the Company still has about 15,000 rails, 3ft long ... they have 'a larger portion in contact with the wheel' than rails of the Liverpool & Manchester Railway (bearing surface $2\frac{1}{4}$in wide). 7 July 1834, 'the old Rails were of cast iron laid upon short Rails or pads of Wood resting upon Wood Sleepers'. 4 January 1836, by now about 150 tons remain and are sold as scrap for £4 5s per ton.

14 A W Skempton & A Andrews 'Cast iron edge-rails at Walker Colliery 1798'. *Trans Newcomen Soc 48* (1978). T-section fish-belly rails 3ft long weighing 32lb excluding chair, top width 3in, depth at mid-span 5in.

15 Science Museum, Inv No 1892–113. Cast iron T-section fish-belly rail 3ft long weighing 35lb including end flanges, top width $2\frac{1}{4}$in, mid-span depth $4\frac{1}{2}$in.

16 Science Museum, Inv Nos 1892–108, 1900–218. Cast iron I-section fish-belly rails 3ft long weighing 40lb, top width 1in, mid-span depth $4\frac{3}{4}$in, bottom flange 2in wide. The Butterley invoices, in Furnace Ledger B, for rails and blocks run from December 1813 to December 1815 (Derbyshire RO).

17 Science Museum, Inv No 1892–107.

18 J A Birks & P Coxon, 'The Mansfield & Pinxton Railway' *Railway Mag 95* (1949), 222–33.

19 Lewis (op cit), 283–5.

20 Shropshire Canal Minute Book, 10 December 1790.

21 R A Mott, 'Tramroads of the eighteenth century and their originator: John Curr', and the discussion on this paper particularly by M J T Lewis & W N Slatcher. *Trans Newcomen Soc 42* (1969) 1–23.

22 John Farey (op cit), 288–9, 295.

23 P J Riden, 'The Butterley Company and railway construction, 1790–1830', *Transport History 6* (1973), 30–52.

24 In a letter of 3 December 1799 to the Ashby Canal Company, Outram recommends a gauge of 4ft 2in as preferable to the 3ft 6in adopted at Crich and Little Eaton. C R Clinker & Charles Hadfield, see note 29.

25 Derby Canal Committee Minutes, 23 December 1793. Subsequent orders were made with other foundries.

26 *Derby Mercury*, 14 May 1795 reporting the opening of the Little Eaton Railway; the same journal 12 December 1793 carried an advertisement for the supply of iron rails 3ft long weighing 28lb.

27 Peak Forest Canal Minute Book, 10 December 1794.

28 Joseph Wilkes, 'On the utility of iron rail-ways', *Repertory of Arts & Manufactures 13* (1800), 167–71.

29 C R Clinker & Charles Hadfield, 'The Ashby-de-la-Zouch Canal and its railways', *Trans Leics Arch & Hist Soc 34* (1958), 53–76.

30 S Mercer, 'Trevithick and the Merthyr tramroad', *Trans Newcomen Soc 26* (1948), 89–101.

31 Grand Junction Canal Minutes, 4 October 1799.

32 Victor A Hatley, *Rails over Blisworth Hill*, Northants Historical Series No 2 (1970).

33 Charles Hadfield, *The Canals of South and South East England* (Newton Abbot, 1969).

34 [Minutes of] *A General Meeting of the Subscribers to the Plan for Constructing an Iron Railway from Wandsworth to Croydon* (London, 1800). This contains the following five papers:

35 Report ... on the Proposition for Making a Navigable Canal from the River Thames at Wandsworth, to Croydon. W. Jessop, Pater Noster Row, 9 December 1799.

36 Minutes of meeting held 12 December 1799.

37 Report on visit, 22 July 1800.

38 Minutes of meeting held 24 July 1800.

39 Report to the Chairman of the Committee for the Surrey Iron Railway, W Jessop, 10 December 1800.

40 'Estimate of the Expence of Making an Iron Railway from Wandsworth to Croydon and Hack Bridge near Carshalton. With a Lock, Cut and Bason to Communicate with the River Thames'. W. Jessop 31 January 1801 (MS in House of Lords RO).

41 *A Plan of the Intended Iron Railway from ... Croydon to the River Thames at Wandsworth* [1801].

42 Anon, 'The early railways of Surrey', *The Engineer 89* (1900), 7–8, 57–8.

43 John Farey's article on canals and railways in Rees' *Cyclopaedia*, Vol 6 (London, 1806).

44 James Malcolm, *A Compendium of Modern Husbandry principally written during a survey of Surrey* (London, 1805).

45 Letter from W B Luttly, Wandsworth 7 May 1810, to Mr Tritton. (Guildford Muniment Room 85/2/4/1, item 111).

46 The painting has been dated by Mr Sorenson of the London Museum to the period 1820–30.

47 *House of Commons Committee on the Liverpool & Manchester Railway, 1825*. George Leather's evidence, 421, 430–1.

48 Information kindly supplied by the Chief Librarian, Wakefield District Council.

49 Draft tender for constructing the Surrey Iron Railway, signed by Joseph Outram junior, 1 July 1801 (Derbyshire RO). We are grateful to J G James for a transcript of this document.

50 Butterley Furnace Ledger B, 94.

51 *Minutes of the Proceedings for the Extension of the Surrey Iron Railway* (London, 1802). This contains the following four papers:

52 Minutes of meeting held 3 June 1802.

53 Minutes of meeting held 29 September 1802.

54 Report to the Chairman of the Committee for the Extension of the Surrey Iron Railway, W Jessop, London Coffee-House, 7 October 1802.

55 Minutes of meeting held 7 October 1802.

56 'Estimate of the Expence of making an Iron Railway from Croydon to Reigate with a Branch to Godstone'. W. Jessop [1803]. The engraved plan was deposited 18 April 1803 (House of Lords RO).

57 Butterley Furnace Ledger B, 169.

58 Accounts entered in Butterley Furnace Ledger B between pp155 and 259.

59 *House of Lords Sessional Papers 10* (1826), 57–64. Josias Jessop's evidence on the Liverpool & Manchester Railway, 14 April 1826.

60 James Malcolm op cit. For details of the route of the SIR and the Croydon Railway see Charles E Lee *Trans Newcomen Soc 21* (1940), 49–79, and C E C Townsend Ibid *27* (1950) 51–68. We are greatly indebted to Mr Lee for access to his notes and records.

61 Butterley Ledger B, 11 August 1804.

62 [W. G. Tharby] 'The gauge of the Surrey Iron Railway' *Railway Mag 113* (1967), 465–6.

63 Butterley Furnace Ledger B, 198.

64 E F Carter, *An Historical Geography of the Railways of the British Isles* (London, 1959).

65 Butterley Furnace Ledger B, 204.

66 Reports Nos 2 to 8 of the Commissioners for the Caledonian Canal (London, 1805–11).

67 Shown in Plate 20 of the *Atlas to the Life of Thomas Telford* (London, 1838).

68 *Report by Mr. Telford, relative to the proposed Railway from Glasgow to Berwick-upon-Tweed; with Mr. Jessop's Opinion thereon* (Edinburgh, 1810).

69 Robert Stevenson *Report relative to various Lines of Railway, from the Coal-Fields of Mid-Lothian to the City of Edinburgh and Port of Leith*, 28 December 1818 (Edinburgh, 1819).

70 Letter from Scott Titchfield (later the 4th Duke of Portland) to the Earl of Eglinton, 22 April 1806 (Nat Library of Scotland MS 9814, f24).

71 Kilmarnock Railway Deposited Plan (House of Lords RO). This also shows Troon Harbour.

72 The following account is largely taken, by kind permission of Dr Baron F Duckham, from an unpublished dissertation of the University of Strathclyde by D Taylor on the *Kilmarnock–Troon Railway*, November 1970. This is based principally on the Minute Books of the Company (Scottish RO).

73 These details are given in a description of the railway by William Aiton, *General View of the Agriculture of the County of Ayr* (Glasgow, 1811).

74 William Strickland, *Reports on Canals, Railways, Roads and other Subjects* (Philadelphia, 1826). Strickland gives detailed drawings of the rails, but these must have been replacements as they are much heavier than

the original 40lb.

75 Clement E Stretton, *The History of the Liverpool and Manchester Railway*, Leeds, 25 July 1901, 16pp (Manchester PL).

Notes to Chapter 9

1 *Report from the Committee appointed to enquire into the best Mode of providing sufficient Accommodation for the increased Trade and Shipping of the Port of London*, 13 May 1796.

2 Ibid, Appendices G and H.

3 Philip Banbury, *Shipbuilders of the Thames and Medway* (Newton Abbot, 1971).

4 *Memoir of William Vaughan, Esq., F.R.S.* (London, 1839).

5 *The London Docks*, plan by Daniel Alexander, engraved by J Cary, 1794.

6 JHC *51*, 297, 8 February 1796.

7 Journal of the Court of Common Council (hereafter CCJ) *74*, 46, 29 January 1794 (Corporation of London RO).

8 MS 'Report to the Committee of Common Council, appointed to consider whether any and what improvements are necessary and proper to be made in the Port of London by an extension of the Legal Quays', W Jessop, John Rennie and John Foulds, London, 10 April 1794 (Nat Library of Scotland, Rennie Collection, Box 13, F2).

9 George Dance's Journal (MS in CLRO).

10 Society of Civil Engineers Minute Book, 23 November 1798 (Inst Civ Eng Library).

11 Dorothy Stroud, *George Dance, Architect 1741–1825* (London, 1971), 150–6.

12 CCJ *76*, 114, 18 February 1796.

13 'Account of Ralph Walker, Esq.' *European Mag 44* (1801), 331–2.

14 JHC *52*, 143, 30 November 1796.

15 JHC *52*, 269, 14 February 1797; CCJ *77*, 182, 17 May 1797.

16 CCJ *77*, 218, 5 July 1797 reporting a summary of the West India merchants' proposals made in June, and that the Port Committee would start investigations of the scheme.

17 MS 'Report to the Deputation of the Committee of Common Council for Improving the Port of London and the Committee of West India Planters', W Jessop, George Dance and Ralph Walker. Guildhall, 29 August 1797 (transcribed in CCJ *77*, 330–3, 16 January 1798).

18 *A Plan of the proposed Docks in the Isle of Dogs for the West India Trade* [By Dance, Jessop and Walker] engraved by Metcalf [September 1797]. The date is given in Dance's Journal.

19 CCJ *77*, 329–343, 16 January 1798.

20 CCJ *78*, 27–48, 24 May 1798.

21 'Estimate of the Expence of the Alteration intended to be made in the Plan of the Docks', W Jessop and Ralph Walker, November 1798. Printed as Appendix A in *Minutes of the Evidence taken at the Committee on the Bill . . . for the Port of London (City Plan)*, 7 May 1799.

22 *A Plan of the Proposed Canal and Wet Docks for the West India Trade in*

the Isle of Dogs, Dance, Jessop and Walker. Engraved by Metcalf [December 1798] Ibid, Appendix D.

23 *Minutes of Evidence (City Plan)*, 1799.

24 Ralph Dodd, *Letters to a Merchant on the Improvement of the Port of London*, November 1798 (London, 1798).

25 *Report from the Select Committee . . . on the Port of London*, 1 June 1799.

26 Jessop was marginally involved. His 'Report on the Effect of Deepening and Embanking the River Thames' is printed as Appendix G in the *Third Report of the Select Committee*, 28 July 1800; and his answers to queries on Telford's proposed 600ft span iron bridge are in the *Report from the Select Committee*, 3 June 1801.

27 Jessop's first bill is given in CCJ *76*, 234, 17 June 1796, and there is a memo on his daily fees in Dance's journal, March 1796. His total payment up to July 1799 is recorded in Misc MS 234.7 (CLRO); it was divided equally between the Canal and the West India Docks.

28 The cost of the 1799 Act is given in CCJ *82*, 260, 20 May 1805. From Misc MS 234.7 we learn that £5,900 was chargeable to the City for the Canal. The balance of £11,700 was charged to the West India Dock Company.

29 The revision of plans in July and August 1799 can be traced from entries in Dance's journal and early papers in the West India Docks Minute Book (Port of London Authority Library).

30 'Accounts of Money received and paid by the Chamberlain of the City of London in pursuance of an Act of parliament of the 39th year of George the third for . . . the Port of London' (CLRO).

31 Except for a Rough Minute Book covering the period April 1803 to June 1804 (PLA).

32 Locks are shown on the City Canal in a plan which dates from November 1799 (PLA, West India Docks portfolio, Sheet 14).

33 Dimensions of the canal and locks are taken from the following sources, which are in agreement within very close limits: John Dyson's contract 24 July 1800 (CLRO), Rennie's notebook No 70,1813 (Nat Lib Scotland, Rennie Coll, Box 27) and Sir John Rennie *Theory, Formation and Construction of Harbours*, Vol 3 (1854).

34 *Minutes of Evidence (City Plan)*, 1799. Records of borings summarised by Ralph Walker.

35 Boulton & Watt Engine Book (Birmingham Ref Lib) lists the engine for the Isle of Dogs Canal, in 1800, as 15hp single-acting with a 30in diameter cylinder and 6ft stroke; and notes that it was made double-acting in 1803.

36 Port Committee Contracts Book, 1799–1811 (CLRO). This contains the original contract documents for work at the City Canal, for removing Blackwall Rock and for deepening the East India moorings.

37 Jessop's evidence on the City's application for a further instalment from the Consolidated Fund: JHC *57*, 251, 22 March 1802.

38 *European Mag 48* (1805), 157.

39 CCJ *83*, 343, 26 February 1807.

40 Nathaniel Gould, *Historical Notice of the Commercial Docks* (London, 1844).

41 William Smith's Memorandum on Blackwall Rock, November 1804. Quoted by Joan Eyles, 'William Smith, Richard Trevithick and Samuel

Homfray', *Trans Newcomen Soc 43* (1971), 137–61.

42 Information on the Blackwall Rock job is taken mainly from Trinity House Minutes 1802–6 (Trinity House), the Port Committee's Account Book of the £100,000 Fund, 1803–9 (CLRO) and the Rough Minute Book 1803–4 (PLA).

43 Port Committee Rough Minute Book, 6 June 1804.

44 Trinity House Minutes, 15 November 1804, refer to the 'Method of Mining by a Cylinder' proposed in a report to the Port Committee by 'William Jessop Esq. their Engineer'; which report had been transmitted to Trinity House on 12 November.

45 Goods invoiced 1 March 1805 for Blackwall at £266 in Butterley Furnace Ledger B (Derbyshire RO). This sum appears in the Port Committee's Accounts as paid in July for the cylinder, etc. Joseph Glynn, quoted in *Weale's Quarterly Papers on Engineering 1* (1843), gives a brief description of the cylinder and rock breaking equipment evidently derived from drawings or notebooks still extant at Butterley in his day.

46 Spedding's contract, 16 January 1806, is in the Port Committee's Contract Book (CLRO).

47 Port Committee's Account Book of the £100,000 Fund for the Improvement of the Port of London (CLRO).

Notes to Chapter 10

1 Information in this chapter is taken principally from the West India Dock Company Minute Books (Port of London Authority library). These run from August 1799 and the first sixteen volumes cover the period of construction up to 1806.

2 *Minutes of Evidence taken at the Committee on the Bill . . . for the Port of London (City Plan)*, 7 May 1799.

3 The Blackwall Basin later had walls but it is certain that the sides originally were earth slopes, like the City Canal.

4 These are the design depths based on Trinity High Water datum and a 'standard' 18ft spring tide, established in 1800. This datum is close to mean high-water springs, but the tidal range is actually rather more than 18ft.

5 We are grateful to Mr Edward Sargent for a photograph of the original drawing (PLA Engineer's Office No 6760108) from which our tracing has been made.

6 A short description of the Blackwall swing bridge is given in *European Mag 42* (1802), 214–15, where it is said to be 'on a new and improved plan'.

7 Report by Jessop, 24 August 1802, transcribed in Minute Book 4.

8 'Account of the West India Docks' *Gentlemans Mag 74* (1802), 867–9.

9 Dimensions of the locks have been compiled from the Minute Books, Rennie's notebook No 70 of 1813 (Nat Lib Scotland, Rennie Coll) and Sir John Rennie, *Theory, Formation and Construction of Harbours*, Vol 3 (1854).

10 'West India Docks' *European Mag 42* (1802), 213–17.

11 *Gentlemans Mag 76* (1806), 671.

12 Walker's report and estimates occupy twenty-four pages in Minute Book No 1. The plan is in the West India Docks Portfolio, sheet 14 (PLA). A later plan by Walker probably dating from May 1800 is sheet 10 in the same portfolio.

13 The reports by Rennie, Morris and Jessop are transcribed in Minute Book No 1.

14 *An Accurate Plan of the Docks for the West India Trade, and the Canal, in the Isle of Dogs.* Published 7 May 1800 by John Fairburn. A third edition, published 24 August 1801, shows additional details including the steam engines.These and several other engraved plans are in the West India Docks portfolio at the PLA.

15 Letter from Jessop, Newark, 9 December 1802, to the Chairman of Directors. Transcribed in Minute Book No 4.

16 The engraving, endorsed 'With Ralph Walker's Compliments to John Rennie Esq.', is in the Rennie Collection at the Institution of Civil Engineers.

17 Details of the cofferdam are taken from Jessop's specifications dated 25 September 1801 (Minute Book No 3) and a report by Jessop and Walker on the failure, 10 August 1802 (Minute Book No 4).

18 *Gentlemans Mag 72* (1802), 777.

19 *European Mag 42* (1802), 213–17.

20 Rennie's report, 28 October 1802, is transcribed in Minute Book No 4.

21 Report by John Hughes written in 1820 and quoted in *The Architect, Engineer and Surveyor 4* (1843), 5–6. He refers to the steam engine 'so much noticed' at the West India Docks excavations, which suggests it was a novelty in 1804–5.

22 *Annual Accounts of the West India Dock Company from July 1799 to February 1822* (PLA Library).

Notes to Chapter 11

1 For an excellent general account see A F Williams 'Bristol Port plans and improvement schemes of the 18th century.' *Trans Bristol & Glos Archaeological Soc 81* (1962), 138–88.

2 *Proposal for laying the Ships at the Key at Bristol constantly afloat*, John Smeaton, 26 January 1765 (Bristol, 1765).

3 *Plan . . . of the intended Scheme for a new Cut, Dam and Chamber to keep the Shipping always afloat*, William Champion, January 1767.

4 *Mr Mylne's Report and Opinion*, 12 January 1767 (Bristol, 1767).

5 Patrick McGrath, *The Merchant Venturers of Bristol* (Bristol, 1975), 154–6.

6 Ibid, p158.

7 Report on the Black Rock Scheme, Joseph Nickalls, 22 November 1787 (MS in Bristol RO).

8 Letters from Jessop to Jeremiah Osborne 1788–91 (Merchants Hall, Bristol). We are indebted to Dr M. Handford for drawing our attention to these, and to Mrs P H Brewer for transcripts.

9 'Mr Jessop's Report to the Society of Merchants of the City of Bristol',

Newark, 19 May 1788 (MS copy in BRO).

10 'The Report of Mr John Smeaton, Engineer, to the Committee of the Merchants Company', 1 July 1789 (MS copy in BRO). The drawings are in 'Smeaton's Designs', Vol 5, f187–8 (Royal Society library).

11 Smeaton's 'Machine Letter Books', Vol 1 p100 (ICE Library).

12 Letter from Jessop, Bristol 24 September 1789, to Jeremiah Osborne (Merchants Hall).

13 Reports on the borings and flood observations, by Solomon Roach (MSS in BRO).

14 'Mr Jessop's Report, Explanation, and Estimates of Locks & Dam across the Avon at Rownham Meads, To the Society of Merchants of the City of Bristol', London, 25 February 1790 (MS copy in BRO). The drawings referred to in this report cannot be found.

15 Letter from Jessop, Newark, 19 November 1790, to Jeremiah Osborne (Merchants Hall).

16 Hunter Rouse & Simon Ince, *History of Hydraulics* (Univ of Iowa, 1959), 150.

17 *Flood Studies Report*, Vol 4, pp353–6 (Natural Env Res Council, London, 1975). We are indebted to the Wessex Water Authority for an estimate that Jessop's figure of 22,000 cusecs represents approximately the 'hundred year' flood flow at Bristol.

18 Reports by Joseph Nickalls, 31 August 1790 and 14 October 1790 (MSS copies in BRO).

19 Jessop was in correspondence with Liverpool in October 1791 on dimensions of the docks there, and on 13 November 1791 he wrote to Richard Bright on the silting and sewers problems (BRO).

20 Minutes of Common Council, 29 October 1791. These and the Minutes of subsequent meetings of the Joint Committee are copied into the Bristol Dock Company Minute Books, Vol 1, hereafter referred to as *Bristol Minutes* (BRO).

21 Accounts of fees submitted by White, Faden and Jessop for the period December 1791 to October 1793 (BRO).

22 *A Plan of Part of the Rivers Avon and Frome . . . and the Proposed Dam, Locks and Canal*, Jessop and White, 1792. Engraved by W Faden, 1793.

23 *A Further Explanation of the Dam and Works proposed to be erected across the River Avon, at Rownham Meads, for the Improvement of the Harbour of Bristol, as laid down in an engraved Plan and Section designed by Mr Jessop, Engineer* (Bristol, 1793).

24 Address to the Committee of the Society of Merchants by William Milton, 3 December 1791 (MS copy in BRO).

25 Letter from Jessop, London, 18 February 1792, to Jeremiah Osborne (BRO).

26 Letter from Smeaton, 23 January 1792 to Jeremiah Osborne (MS copy in BRO).

27 Bristol Minutes, 20 August 1801.

28 Bristol Minutes, 25 November 1801.

29 'Report to the Corporation of the City of Bristol and to the Society of Merchants', W Jessop, Bristol, 22 February 1802 (Bristol minutes, Vol 1, 60–6).

30 *Design for Improving the Harbour of Bristol. By William Jessop, 1802.* Engraved by Cook & Johnson. Issued with *Explanation of the Plan proposed for the Improvement of the Harbour of Bristol* (Bristol, 1802).

31 Bristol Minutes, 19 June 1802.

32 'Report to the Corporation of the City of Bristol and the Society of Merchants', W Jessop, Bristol, 14 August 1802 (Bristol Minutes, Vol 1, pp91–5).

33 Drawing endorsed 'Plan for improving the Port of Bristol proposed in Joint Committee by Mr Thos. Hill and reported by W. Jessop, 14 August 1802' (BRO).

34 *Explanation of the Plan for Improving the Harbour of Bristol, submitted . . . in the month of December 1802* (Bristol, 1802) with an engraved *Design for Improving the Harbour of Bristol. Wm. White del. 1802.*

35 Letter from Jessop, London Coffee House, 2 November 1802, to the Joint Committee (Bristol Minutes, 6 November 1802).

36 The request to Jessop and White to complete their estimates for submission to Parliament is dated 13 January 1803 (Bristol Minutes). Jessop's engineering estimate of £252,824 plus £47,000 for purchase of lands (by White) is with the deposited plan in the House of Lords RO. This estimate pre-dates amendments to the Bill.

37 *Design for Improving the Harbour of Bristol by Wm. Jessop Civil Engineer, W. White Surveyor.* Engraved by W Faden, 1803. Deposited in the House of Lords 8 July 1803. The letter from John Osborne, 5 April 1803, to Faden is copied in Bristol Dock Company Letter Book 1803–17; hereafter referred to as Bristol Letters (BRO).

38 *Explanation of the Design for Improving the Harbour of Bristol* (London, 1803).

39 'Abstract of Evidence by Mr William Jessop, Civil Engineer, given before the Committee of the House of Commons, 25 April 1807' (BRO).

40 Costs of obtaining the 1803 Act are detailed in Bristol Minutes, 25 February 1813.

41 Bristol Minutes, 5 October 1803.

42 Unless noted otherwise, details of the progress of construction and reports by William and Josias Jessop are taken from Minutes of the Bristol Dock Company: Vol 1 up to December 1804; Vol 2 January 1805 to February 1811, and Vol 3 February 1811 to June 1816 (BRO). See also the paper by R A Buchanan, 'The construction of the Floating Harbour in Bristol, 1804–1809'. *Trans Bristol & Glos Archaeol Soc 88* (1969), 184–204.

43 John Osborne to William Jessop, 28 January 1804 and to William White, 6 February 1804 (Bristol Letters).

44 The contract was with Thomas Thatcher and James Sharp, but Sharp's interest lay only in the financial side and he proved to be a nuisance. He left the partnership in June 1805. (Letters 26 February 1805, Minutes 10 June 1805).

45 Butterley Furnace Ledger B, 214.

46 G W Hall, 30 May 1804, to the Coalbrookdale Company, enclosing specifications (Bristol Letters). They were also sent to Richard Parsons, Thompson & Hazledine, Homfray Tappenden & Birch, Aydon & Elwell, and John Wilkinson.

47 Josias Jessop, 51 Park Street, Bristol, 17 July 1804, to the Coalbrookdale Company with a sketch of the iron plates. On 9 November 1804 he wrote again, clarifying some points in the specifications (Bristol Letters).
48 Hall and Osborne, 23 July 1804, to the six iron founders mentioned above and to Frere, Cooke & Powell (Bristol Letters).
49 In a letter of 21 February 1805 Josias Jessop asks Coalbrookdale for dimensions of the span 'exactly as the Ribs are cast' as he is ready to set out the bridge foundations (Bristol Letters).
50 *Receipts and Expenditure of the Bristol Dock Company to 1 March 1810* (BRO).
51 *Felix Farley's Bristol Journal*, 8 February 1806.
52 Ibid, 22 February 1806. The accident is attributed to 'the cross-ties not having been fastened in'.
53 Josias Jessop, 9 July 1806, to Edmund Darby (Bristol Letters).
54 Details of the Bristol bridges are given by Telford and Alexander Nimmo *Edinburgh Encyclopaedia 4* (1812), 541–2 and by Charles Hutton *Tracts of Mathematical and Philosophical Subjects*, Vol 1 (London, 1812), 153–5.
55 For a general discussion of early cast-iron arch bridges see R A Paxton *The Influence of Thomas Telford on the Use of Improved Constructional Materials*. MSc Thesis, Heriot-Watt University, 1975 (ICE Library).
56 J F Nicholls & John Taylor, *Bristol Past and Present* (Bristol, 1882), 225 and 347.
57 This appears to be a reference to counterfort trenches of the type later used extensively for stabilising slips in railway cuttings.
58 'Estimate of the probable expence of erecting a Bridge over the River Avon at Princes Street', Josias Jessop, Bristol, 28 January 1808 (House of Lords RO).
59 John Latimer *Annals of Bristol in the Nineteenth Century* (Bristol, 1887), 16.

Notes to Chapter 12

1 Aire & Calder Navigation Committee Minute Book, 9 February 1792, 31 January 1793.
2 Joseph Crow, *A Report concerning the . . . draining of certain marshes in the neighbourhood of Alford . . .* (Lincoln City Library). Jessop's report has not been found.
3 *Hampshire Chronicle*, 6 October 1788.
4 *Report of William Jessop Engineer on . . . an easy Communication between the Earl of Stamford's Lime Works and the River Trent*, MS, BTHR/PRO RAIL 803/12.
5 *Felix Farley's Bristol Journal*, 28 September, 7 December 1793.
6 Ibid, 21 December 1793.
7 Letter, Rennie to W.J., 5 May 1794 (Nat Lib of Scotland, Rennie Coll); *Felix Farley's Bristol Journal*, 14 June 1794.
8 Ancholme Commissioners Minute Book, 3 October 1792; *Lincoln & Stamford Mercury*, 13 July, 23 November 1792; *Newark Herald*, 9 January 1793.

9 A E Richardson, *Robert Mylne*, 1955: diary entries, 3, 8, 29 June, 29 July 1796, 170–1.

10 London Coffee House, 11 February 1801, printed, Sheffield PL; *To the Chairman of the Proprietors of the River Dun Navigation*, Sheffield, 2 August 1801, printed, Sheffield PL.

11 *To the Committee of the Driffield Navigation*, Driffield, 23 April 1797, printed, Hull Univ Lib, Sykes papers. Also Driffield Old Navigation Minute Book, 3 July 1798.

12 George Lloyd, 'The Flint Canal Company', *Journal of the Flintshire Historical Society*, 1962, and parliamentary proceedings on 28 Geo III c. 72 and c. 101.

13 His report was dated 19 November 1791 from York, and printed in the *York Chronicle* of that date. See also Foss Navigation Minute Books.

14 Glamorganshire Canal Committee Minute Book, 7 May 1805.

15 His report, dated London 13 June 1796, is transcribed into the Gloucester & Berkeley Canal Proprietors' Minute Book, 15 August 1796.

16 Gloucester & Berkeley Canal Committee Minute Book, 15 November 1810. Hodgkinson and Jessop attended personally with their estimate.

17 Grand Surrey Canal Minute Books (PLA Archives).

18 *Mr. Jessop's Report on his survey of the Grand Western Canal*, November 1793, printed, Exeter City RO.

19 *A Plan of the Intended Navigation from Stowmarket to Ipswich, by Isr Lenny, Surveyor, and W. Jessop, Engineer*, 1790 (Suffolk RO).

20 *To the Chairman of the Committee of Management of the Kennet and Avon Canal*, Bath, 17 July 1794 (BTHR/PRO, Kennet & Avon Canal Records).

21 Lancaster Canal Committee Minute Book, 12 August 1792.

22 Report in Minute Book. Aqueduct drawings, BTHR/PRO LC3 20 and 21. See also Rennie's letters to Jessop (Nat Lib of Scotland, Rennie Coll).

23 *Report on a plan for a navigable Canal from the River Hull to . . . Leven . . .*, undated, MS (Univ of Hull Lib, Sykes papers). Plan in Natural History Museum, Banks-Sutro Coll.

24 *Report on the Proposed Line of Navigation between Newcastle and Maryport . . .*, Newcastle, 1795, printed.

25 Herbert Spencer, *London's Canal*, 1961, 39.

26 See P A L Vine, *London's Lost Route to the Sea*, 3rd ed, 1973.

27 Rennie to W J, 13 October 1794 (Nat Lib of Scotland, Rennie Coll).

28 Stratford-upon-Avon Canal Committee Minute Book, 18 August 1794.

29 City of London, Thames Navigation Committee Minute Book, 1 August 1805 (PLA Archives).

30 Thames & Severn Canal Committee Minute Book, 8 September 1812.

31 Printed in *Aris's Birmingham Gazette*, 20 January 1783. See also ibid, 9 June 1783.

32 Printed in *Aris's Birmingham Gazette*, 11 February 1811.

33 *Report of Mr. Jessop on the Improvement of the Navigation of the River Wye*, Bristol, 21 August 1805, printed (Hereford City Lib).

34 *The Report of William Jessop, Engineer, On an Enquiry into the Practicability of forming Reservoirs for Water . . .* (Sheffield PL).

35 MS *Report on the River Hull*, W Jessop, Newark, 11 February 1788 (Hull

Univ Lib DDSY 103/12).

36 *The Report of Mr. Jessop, respecting the Drainage of the Low Grounds lying on the Wolds or West-Side of the River Hull, Frodingham Carrs, Lisset, &c.* Newark, 14 July 1796 (Hull, 1796).

37 Papers on the drainage of Deeping commons (Brownlow Coll, Lincolnshire RO).

38 Letter from Rennie, 27 June 1800 to Jessop, and Jessop's reply from Paternoster Row, 28 June 1800 (Rennie Coll, Box 7, Nat Lib Scotland).

39 *The Report of Messrs Jessop, Rennie, Maxwell and Hare, on the Drainage of Deeping Inclosed Fen and the Commons adjoining thereto*, Spalding, 11 August 1800 (Spalding, 1800).

40 Sedgemoor Drainage. Summary of Commissioners' Accounts, and *A Plan of Kings-sedgemoor Drains* by Wm White 1795 (Somerset RO).

41 John Billingsley, *General View of the Agriculture of the County of Somerset* (Bath, 1797).

42 J H Farrant, 'The evolution of Newhaven harbour and the Lower Ouse before 1800', *Sussex Archaeol Coll*, 10 (1972) 44–60.

43 *Correspondence between the Right Hon Thomas Pelham and Mr Jessop relative to the Improvements of the Navigation of the River Ouse, and the Drainage of Lewes Levels* (Lewes, 1787).

44 Letter from Jessop, Lewes 31 January 1791, to Thomas Pelham with 'Estimate of the Expences of improving the Navigation of the River Ouse between Newhaven and Lewes and of Draining Lewes Levels', (MS in East Sussex RO).

45 T W Horsfield, *The History and Antiquities of Lewes and its Vicinity* (Lewes, 1824), 216.

46 D F Gibbs and J H Farrant, 'The upper Ouse navigation 1790–1868', *Sussex Indust Hist*, No 1 (1970), 23–40.

47 *Report to the Owners of Land interested in the intended Inclosure of the Commons and Wastes in Thorne and Hatfield*, W Jessop, Newark 19 March 1801 (Doncaster, 1801).

48 *Report from the Select Committee on the Embankments in Catwater*, Parl Papers, 1806, Vol 3. In evidence, Jessop also summarises the 1801 enquiries.

49 'Plan for a Harbour at Folkestone', W Jessop 1806. One of four drawings in the same hand (Folkestone PL).

50 JHC, 11 February 1818.

51 *The Report of William Jessop, Esquire, relative to the making of a New Dock at Kingston upon Hull*, Newark, 1 July 1793 (Hull, 1793).

52 'Report to the Commissioners of Arundel Port', William Jessop, Arundel 12 May 1806. Printed in W B Prichard, *A Treatise on Harbours* (London, 1844).

53 'Report to the Chairman of the Dock Committee at Liverpool', W. Jessop, Newark 4 April 1800. Transcribed in the Dock Committee Minutes for 1 May 1800 (Liverpool RO).

54 'Report on the Harbour at Lyme Regis', W Jessop, London, 1 December 1805 (Lyme Regis Borough Archives). We are indebted to Mr Henry Chessell for a transcript of the report.

55 'Sketch of the Piers at Newhaven with the proposed Extension', W. Jessop

1787' (East Sussex RO).

56 *Report from the Select Committee on the Embankments in Catwater.* Evidence by Robert Mylne (Parl Papers, 1806, Vol 3).

57 Mylne's diary, 8 July 1796 and earlier entries. A E Richardson, *Robert Mylne*, 1955.

58 'Report of Mr William Jessop, to the Right honourable the Lords Commissioners of the Admiralty', Plymouth 23 August 1806. Printed in *Papers relating to Plymouth Sound*, Parl Papers 1812, Vol 10.

59 'Report of Mr Wm Jessop Engineer, on the State of Levels from Scots float Sluice and the New Harbour, and on the Practicability and Effect of the proposed Improvements of the Harbour', Rye 24 May 1786. Transcribed in Rye Harbour Commissioners Minute Book Vol 2 for 9 June 1786. See also minutes for 22 February 1787 (East Sussex RO).

60 Rye Harbour Minutes, 6 and 16 November 1787.

61 Jessop and Rennie, with their report of 26 February 1801 (Rennie's MS reports, Vol 2, ICE Lib), were among the engineers involved in this work.

62 'Mr Jessop's Report, concerning the Practicability and best means of improving Shoreham Harbour', Newark, 17 July 1800 (Petworth House Archives).

63 *A Report on the Present State of the Piers of Sunderland Harbour, and the Means recommended for their Improvement by W. Jessop.* Butterley, 19 December 1807 (Sunderland, 1808).

64 A W Skempton, 'The engineers of Sunderland harbour, 1718–1817', *Indust Archaeol Review*, I (1977), 103–24.

65 ICE Library.

66 *Report of William Jessop, Engineer, on the State and Means of improving and enlarging the Harbour of Workington*, Pontefract 24 January 1777.

67 Yarmouth Port & Haven Commissioners Minute Book, 1750–1823 (Norfolk and Norwich RO).

68 'Report to the Commissioners for repairing, improving and maintaining the Harbour of Yarmouth', W Jessop, London, 23 May 1798 (NNRO).

69 Copies of eight letters from Jessop to the harbour commissioners and Town Clerk dating from 1799 to 1809 are in NNRO.

70 Letter from Jessop, London, 28 July 1800, to Lord Egremont (Petworth House Archives).

71 'The Report of Mr Jessop Engineer on a view and enquiry relative to the making a Road over the River Menai', (MS T/HO.2 in the Telford Collecton, ICE Library). See also JHC, 1 March 1786.

72 Letter from Jessop, London Coffee-house, 8 February 1802 to Rennie. Printed in *Second Report from the Committee on Holyhead Roads and Harbour*, 1810.

73 *York Courant*, 8 December 1789.

74 Report in the form of a letter from Jessop, Newark, 23 January 1790, to Lord Downe and others (Sheffield City Library).

75 Science Museum, Inv No 1964–20.

76 We are indebted to Mr T M Percy, clerk to the Company of Proprietors of Selby Bridge, for this information.

77 M V Woolley, 'Design and reconstruction of Selby Swing Bridge', *Highway Eng*, *20* (1973), 14–23.

Notes to Chapter 13

1 Letter from Jessop, Fairburn, 15 August 1783, to Job Brough (Trent Navigation Coll, Nottingham Univ Library).

2 Jessop's home address was Newark in a letter of 11 March 1784 to Wedgwoods (Univ of Keele).

3 Mr Guy Hemingway has kindly given us much local information about Newark.

4 List of mayors in the Gilstrap Library, Newark, on the back of a printed copy of Charles I's charter.

5 Newark Corporation Minute Book.

6 We are indebted to Colonel and Mrs P J K Warren for information in the privately-printed *The Jessop Family* which they compiled in 1971. Mrs Warren, lately deceased, was a descendant of William Jessop.

7 Letter in possession of Lloyds of London.

8 Henry Jessop estimated for the Ferrysides branch of the proposed Stockport Junction Rly, the main line of which was estimated by Joseph Locke (House of Lords RO). It is dated January 1830. We are grateful to W S Skillern for this reference.

9 Samuel Hughes, 'Memoir of William Jessop', *Weale's Quarterly Papers on Engineering*, Vol 1, Pt II (1844), 32pp.

10 *Edinburgh Encyclopaedia*, Vol 11 (1817), 735–7, article on 'Jessop, William'. The author of this article says he had known Jessop for more than twenty years.

11 In a letter of 8 November 1796 to James Watt jun, Jessop says '. . . when I was in Scotland with Mr Smeaton on the commencement of the Forth and Clyde Canal' (Boulton & Watt Coll).

12 'Letter from William Jessop Esq to the President of the Board of Agriculture, on the Subject of Inland Navigations, and Public Roads', W Jessop, No 7 Chatham Place, London, 19 March 1795. *Communications to the Board of Agriculture*, Vol 1, Pt III, 176–82 (London, 1797).

13 William Pitt, engineer of the Wyrley & Essington Canal, having heard that someone was trying to patent side-ponds, wrote: 'In a conversation I had a few days ago with Mr Jessop at Lichfield, on this subject, he informed me that the idea is at least a hundred years old, and has been repeatedly rejected; and that the reason why it has been abandoned was principally the delay occasioned by passing locks of that kind . . .'

14 Thomas Telford, 'Navigation, Inland', *Edinburgh Encyclopaedia*, Vol 15 (1821), 209–315.

15 'Observations on the Use of Reservoirs for Flood Waters', by W Jessop, May 1792; in W Pitt, *General View of the Agriculture of the County of Stafford*, (London, 1794), 39–44.

16 Waterways Museum, Stoke Bruerne.

17 Probably Harrow Road bridge outside Paddington Basin.

18 Jessop's report of 14 April 1800 to the Grand Junction Canal Committee (transcribed in PRO, RAIL 830/40, 174–7).

19 Letter from Jessop, Pontefract, 4 May 1771, to the Secretary of the Society of Arts (RSA Library A8/16).

20 This was the Argand lamp. See H W Dickinson, *Matthew Boulton* (1937), 129–31.

21 Philip Buache published a chart showing submarine contours in 1752. Theoretical studies of contouring applied to topography were made in France in 1771, and in 1777 Charles Hutton used the method in making a gravity survey of a Scottish mountain. The first large land area map using contours appeared in France in 1799 by J U Dupain Triet. Jessop's ideas, in 1795, were therefore very advanced. (We are grateful to Dr Brian Harley for information).

22 Select Committee on Roads and Highways. First Report 1808, Appendices 3 and 4; Second Report 1808, Appendix 4.

23 Ibid, First Report, appendix 17.

24 *British Parl Papers*, 1810–11 (240) iii, 855.

25 William Albert, *The Turnpike Road System in England 1663–1840* (1972), 143.

26 A W Skempton & Esther Wright, 'Early members of the Smeatonian Society of Civil Engineers', *Trans Newcomen Soc 44* (1971), 23–42.

27 Letter from Jessop, Newark, 28 January 1793, to Sir Joseph Banks (Banks-Stanhope Coll, Spalding Gentlemen's Society). We are indebted to Mr W M Hunt for this reference.

28 Letter from William Jessop jun, 27 April 1813, to E S Godfrey (Nottingham Univ Library, Trent Navigation Coll).

Notes to Portraits

1 National Portrait Gallery, No 1147. Reproduced by permission of the Director and Trustees.

2 Samuel Hughes, 'Memoir of William Jessop', *Weale's Quarterly Papers on Engineering*, Vol 1, Pt II (1844), 32pp.

3 Samuel Smiles, *Lives of the Engineers*, Vol 2 (1861), 197.

4 Reproduced by permission of Mr Robert T Jessop of Edinburgh. Col P J K Warren kindly supplied a photograph.

5 Sir Alexander Gibb, *The Story of Telford* (1935), opposite p32.

INDEX

Cumberland basin, locks, 203, 224, 231-3, 236-7, 239-41
Curr, John, engineer, 173
Customs & Excise, Comms of, 187, 190-1, 249

Dadfords, the, engineers, 13; John, 262; Thomas, sen, 25, 42, 261-2; Thomas, jun, 25, 141, 171, 262
Dalton, John, engineer, 74
Dance, George, surveyor, painter, 34, 187-92, 199, 270
Daventry, branch, reservoir, 110, 113, 115
Davidson, Matthew, engineer, 144, 149, 152, 160, 164
Davies & Jebb, surveyors, 147
Davies, William, contractor, 149, 151-2
Dearne & Dove Canal, 134
Dee River, Nav, 139, 141-2. 144-5, 151
Deeping Fen, drainage, 247-8
Delany, Ruth, author, 86
Denson, Thomas, engineer, 141, 148, 152
Denton reservoir, 56
Deptford, 184-5, 189
Derby, 26, 47, 53-4, 266
Derby Canal, 47, 50-1, 53-4, 61, 145, 173
Derrythorpe (Axholme), 75
Derwent River, 25, 40, 43, 47, 53
Derwent aqueduct, 43-4
Devonport, dockyard, 11-12, 269
Dickinson, Samuel, surveyor, 59
Diglis, 27-8
Dodd, Ralph, engineer, 190-1, 245
Dodder River, 89
Don River, Nav, 24, 30, 54, 57, 77, 110, 243, 247, 252, 258
Doonane, 109
Dowland, James, surveyor, 80
Drayton, reservoir, 115
Dredgers, 46, 162, 167, 196-9, 208, 219, 231, 241, 250-1
Driffield Nav, 20, 74, 243
Drury, John, engineer, 251
Dublin, 15-16, 86, 88-9, 92-5, 100, 105-6, 108-9
Dublin-Kingstown Ship Canal project, 104
Ducart, Davis, engineer, 17-18
Dudley Canal, tunnel, 24
Duncombe, John, engineer, 139-43, 147, 152
Dunn, William, engineer, 51
Dunstable, branch, 114
Dyson, John, sen, contractor, 20, 59-60, 75, 77, 80, 83, 194
Dyson, John, jun, contractor, 194-5, 210, 219

Dyson, Thomas, contractor, 80-2

East India Company, 191, 256
East India docks, 191, 197, 199, 219
Easton, Alexander, engineer, 164-5
Eau Brink Cut, 66, 227
Edenderry bog, embankment, 90, 95, 98-100, 103-5
Edge, Joseph, treasurer, 233
Ellesmere, branch, 139, 148
Ellesmere Canal, 102, 139-53, 160, 259, 261, 268
Ellison, Richard, lessee, 57
Epworth, 75
Erewash Canal, 24-5, 40, 42, 47, 52-3, 60
Erewash River, valley, 24, 29, 52
Evans, Richard, engineer, 86, 94-5, 98
Everton, 77-8, 80, 82
Everton, Gringley & Misterton drainage, 77-84, 194

Fairburn, 22, 253
Farey, John, author, 171-2, 178
Fenny Stratford, 110, 112, 114, 120, 122, 125
Fentiman, John, contractor, 195, 219
Ferry drain (Axholme), 75, 77
Ffrwd branch, 148
Fletcher, E.G., surveyor, 41-2
Fletcher, James, Joseph, Samuel, engineers, 112
Flint Coal Canal, turnpike road, 244
Foakes, John, surveyor, 175-6
Folkestone, harbour, 249
Fore Dike (Holderness), 69, 72-4
Forest Line, see Leicester Nav
Fort Augustus, 158, 165
Fort William ,153, 156, 181
Forth & Clyde Canal, 13, 16, 54, 257, 260-1
Fosdyke (Welland), 247-8
Foss River, Nav, 244, 259, 261
Fossdyke, The, 56-7
Foster, James, architect, 237
Foster, Samuel, engineer, 73, 76-7
Foulds, John, engineer, 186-7, 189, 191, 193
Frankton, 141, 148
Frome River, 222, 230, 232
Fulton, Robert, engineer, 146, 149

Gainsborough, bridge, 25-7, 30, 47, 84
Ganstead carr, stream, 69, 72
Gauntley, William, sen, 82
Gauntley, William, jun, 83

Stone bridge (Bristol), 222
Stony Stratford, branch, 110, 113-14, 120-1, 264
Stratford-upon-Avon Canal, 246
Stretton, Clement E, author, 172, 183
Strickland, H. E., author, 74
Sunderland, bridge, 146, 238; harbour, 204, 250, 268
Surrey Iron Railway, 161, 168-9, 174-81, 234, 254, 260
Sussex Ouse, *see* Ouse
Sutton Courtenay, lock, 36
Sutton Drain (Holderness), 69, 73
Swannington, 29, 49-50
Swine Carr (Holderness), 69, 72

Tame River, 246
Tarrant, Capt, Gen, engineer, 86, 108
Tattershall, 59
Taunton-Uphill Canal project, 243
Teale, Jonathan, surveyor, 75
Telford, John, engineer, 160-1, 165
Telford, Thomas, engineer, 46, 85, 135, 141-67, 181, 238, 251, 257, 259, 262, 266-7, 269-70
Temple Meads (Bristol), 228, 230, 232-3, 235-7, 240
Thackray, Joseph, engineer, 84
Thames River, Nav, 30-2, 35-6, 46, 60, 67, 110, 112-14, 175-6, 178, 184ff, 246, 258-9
Thames & Severn Canal, 31-2, 36, 246
Thatcher & Richards, contractors, 236
Thatcher, Thomas, contractor, 194-5, 233-6, 240
Thorne Common, Moors, 248
Thringstone, bridge, 29, 50, 168
Ticknevin, 88, 95
Tinsley-Sheffield Rly project, 243
Todmorden, aqueduct, 132-3
Torksey, 26, 56, 60
Torne River, 77
Townshend, Thomas, engineer, 132
Trail, John, engineer, 16-17, 86, 88
Treacher, John, engineer, 36
Trent bridge, *see* Nottingham
Trent Canal project, 47
Trent River, Nav, 13, 23-7, 30, 42, 46-9, 52-3, 56, 60-1, 75-8, 80, 83, 113, 121, 243, 246, 253, 258, 263-4, 268-9
Trent/Tame/Anker Nav project, 246
Trent & Mersey Canal, 25, 27, 47, 53, 60, 112, 173
Trim mills (Bristol), 233-4
Tring, 110, 112-14, 117, 122, 124-5
Trinity House, 185, 187, 192, 197-8
Triple Sluice, *see* Misterton Soss
Tritton, George, chairman, 179

Troon, harbour, 181-2, 268
Tullamore, 91, 95, 99, 103, 105
Turner, Joseph, promoter, 139
Turner, William, engineer, 139, 141-2, 144, 147
Tyley, William, contractor, 84
Tyrone Canal, 17-18, 28

United States of America, 30, 146, *and see* Fulton, Robert
Upper Calder, *see* Calder & Hebble
Ure Nav, 13
Uxbridge, 110, 112, 114

Vallancey, Charles, engineer, 16
Varley, James, contractor, 144, 148
Varley, John, engineer, 24, 55, 262
Vaughan, William, author, 186, 191
Vaux, Daniel, engineer, 193, 199, 207, 217
Vauxhall, 188; bridge, 46, 238
Vermuyden, Sir Cornelius, 73, 77

Wakefield, 14, 134
Walker colliery rly, 172
Walker, James, engineer, 238
Walker, Ralph, engineer, 162, 188-90, 192, 198, 207-10, 212-14, 216-17, 267
Walton, estate, locks, 13, 134
Wandle River, 175, 178
Wandsworth, basin, 169, 175-9, 260
Wapping, 184, 186-91
Ward, James, contractor, 195
Warren, J. M., engineer, 197-8
Watchet harbour, 251
Watford, 110, 113, 212
Watt, James, engineer, 64-6, 153, 265
Watté, John, engineer, 66
Weel (Holderness), 69, 72
Welland River, Nav, 29, 247
Wendover, branch, feeder, 113-15, 124-5
West India docks, 98, 162, 170, 184, 191-2, 195-7, 200-22, 230, 239, 258-9, 267-8
Weston (Salop), 141, 148
Weston, Robert, lighthouse proprietor, 12
Weston, Samuel, William, engineers, 30
Whidbey, Joseph, engineer, 249
Whincop, Robert, clerk, 64
Whitchurch (Salop), branch, 139, 142, 144, 147-8
Whitchurch (Thames) lock, 31, 67
White, William, surveyor, 84-5, 227, 230-4, 241, 243, 248

Whitworth, Robert, sen, engineer, 13, 18, 24, 29-30, 44, 47-8, 55, 112, 119, 244, 246, 261-2, 267
Whitworth, Robert, jun, engineer, 55
Whixall Moss, 148
Wildgoose, George, surveyor, 175-6, 179
Wilkes, Joseph, industrialist, 121, 174
Wilkinson, John, ironmaster, 28, 148-9
Wilson, John, contractor, 156, 181
Wilson, John, surveyor, 181-2
Wilson, Thomas, engineer, 146, 238
Wilstone reservoir, 124
Windmills, for drainage pumping, 64
Wingerworth, 168, 173-4
Wirral, Canal, 141-2
Wisbech, 63
Witham River, Nav, 13, 56-61, 247, 257
Wollaton, 52
Wolverton, 112, 122, 125
Wood, George, contractor, 82
Woodhouse, engine mfgrs, 44, 113, 124

Woodlesford, cut, locks, 14, 20
Woolwich, 185, 211
Worcester, 27-8
Worcester & Birmingham Canal, 246
Workington harbour, 22, 251
Wreake River, 29, 49, 51
Wrexham, 139, 141
Wright, Elias, engineer, 134
Wright, John, Butterley partner, 45
Wyatt, Samuel, engineer-architect, 188
Wye River, Nav, 246

Yarmouth bridge, 251; harbour, 231, 247, 251, 268
Yeoman, Thomas, engineer, 13, 18, 261
York, 244, 252
Yorkshire Ouse, see Ouse
Young, George, surveyor, 28
Young, Joseph, surveyor, 75

Zonca, Vittorio, author, 18